HP Prime Guide
ALGEBRA FUNDAMENTALS

by Larry Schroeder

Computer Learning Service

HP Prime Guide Algebra Fundamentals
HP Prime Innovation in Education Series
HP Prime Guide Algebra Fundamentals: HP Prime Revealed and Extended

Published by
Computer Learning Service
1013 Woodbine Circle
Galesburg, IL 61401-2358
ComputerLearningService.com

Version 1.0.1

ISBN: 978-0-915573-02-8

Cover Photograph: Ray Mendez
Chalkboard, Haw Creek Township High School
Established 1903

About the Author

Brooks/Cole Math Tools Guide
LARRY SCHROEDER
Using TI™ Calculators and Excel™ Spreadsheets ▯ search
Brooks/Cole Math Tools Guide is © 2002-2007 by Cengage Learning/Thomson/Brooks/Cole

Larry Schroeder is the author of calculator tutorials found in Cengage Learning/ Thomson/ Brooks/Cole Math Tools Guide and WebTutor™ Advantage on WebCT or Blackboard for Tan's series of Finite Math and Applied Calculus texts.

Larry also authored *TI-Nspire Guide Algebra Fundamentals: TI-Nspire and TI-Nspire CAS Revealed and Extended* published by Computer Learning Service.

The *Brooks/Cole Math Tools Guide* for TI™-83/86/89/92 calculators and Microsoft Excel™ spreadsheets can be found on the Interactive Video Skillbuilder CD that accompanies various editions of College Algebra, College Algebra and Trigonometry, Precalculus textbooks, and Tan series of *Finite Mathematics, Calculus, College Mathematics*, and *Applied Mathematics* texts *For the Managerial, Life, and Social Sciences* published by Cengage Learning/Thomson/Brooks/Cole (*Interactive Video Skillbuilder CD-ROM*).

Larry authored the WebTutor™ Advantage for WebCT & Blackboard supplements for Thomson/Brooks/Cole Tan's *Finite Math, Calculus, College Mathematics*, and *Applied Mathematics* series of textbooks For *the Managerial, Life, and Social Sciences* (Schroeder and Tan).

From *College Mathematics* 6th edition preface's Learning Aids, "WebTutor Advantage for WebCT & Blackboard by Larry Schroeder, Carl Sandburg College, is the most extensive WebCT or Blackboard cartridge available and contains expanded online study tools including: step-by-step lecture notes; student study guide with step-by-step TI-83/86/89/92 and Microsoft Excel explanations; a quick check interactive problem for each online example with accompanying step-by-step solution and step-by-step TI-83/86/89/92 solution; practice quizzes by chapter sections that can be used as electronically graded online exercises, and much more (Schroeder and Tan)."

Education - Background

Larry holds a Master of Science and Bachelor of Science in mathematics from Western Illinois University. His electronic training and experience from the military plus having taught at the elementary, secondary, and college level helped motivate his passion for incorporating educational technology so that all students, young or old, can meet their dreams and goals.

For 27 years Larry taught math and computer science at Carl Sandburg College. In addition to instruction, he coordinated the faculty technology efforts and oversaw the school's online courses. He was the chief designer of a faculty WebCT course that won international recognition as one of the top ten exemplary courses in the world. He is also proud of his involvement with the University of Illinois higher education's extending technology efforts and Carl Sandburg College's secondary and elementary outreach initiatives that assist other educators with their student use of technology in the learning process.

Now retired, he enjoys riding his bike, coaching his granddaughter's basketball team, and spending time in general with his family, especially his wife, children and grandchildren.

Dedication

To my wife and children for their love and support.

Table of Contents

Welcome and What We're All About

Welcome to *HP Prime Guide Algebra Fundamentals, HP Prime Innovation in Education Series.*

There is no one road to the learning of mathematics. Different approaches for different learners are needed to take learners to where they want to go. The goal of this guide is to give you the flexibility of various approaches aided by the use of the HP Prime to reach your goals.

Manual explanations of math concepts in the guide are accompanied by HP Prime illustrations that can be used with the handheld, computer software, and iOS/ Android/ Windows app. Techniques, examples, and exercises can be done using any of the platforms with special instructions for the differences in their interfaces.

The *HP Prime Guide Algebra Fundamentals* emphasis is its attention on math standards that work. Significant time is spent on learning math by using methods that have shown to be successful in the classroom. There is additional emphasis given to building blocks topics.

HP Prime/Pro and HP Prime Free Revealed and Extended feature of the guide is used to show how the HP Prime/Pro and HP Prime Free commands and functions can be used to work individual problems as well as how they can be extended to help us understand complex math concepts or create a set of tools that can help with problem solving.

Upon mastery of the manual techniques apply the HP Prime/Pro and HP Prime Free solutions to increase your efficiency and problem solving power. Concentrate on the solution without being bogged down with traditional labor-intense steps. Embrace failure; use your additional time, to attempt more word and real world problems.

The *HP Prime Guide Algebra Fundamentals* is also available as a digital learning environment. Every example is followed by an interactive reinforcement exercise. Hyperlinks are used to references earlier discussions of a topic, future discussions of a topic, websites, Table of Contents entries, and Detailed Index entries. The hyperlinks are shown here to allow us to see the eBook's links.

The guide is also available on various eBook readers and eBook applications, be it a stand-alone reader, on a phone, tablet, pc, or through a web-browser. The content uses mathematical notation, text, graphics, and HP Prime screenshots that takes advantage of the resolution of the display. The real-time access, anytime, anyplace nature of the electronic allows a new way for you to gain the math knowledge and skills necessary to succeed in the classroom, at your job, and in your personal pursuit of learning.

An innovative approach is to use HP Prime/Pro and HP Prime Free Computer Algebra Solutions (CAS) as an aide in moving forward. In lessons requiring a concept that you have not yet mastered, use the HP Prime/Pro and HP Prime Free CAS solutions to assist with class assignments, allowing you to keep current. You keep moving forward with the new material, giving you additional time to master the concept causing problems.

Larry Schroeder

Understanding the HP Prime Family of Graphing Calculator

HP Family

The HP Prime family includes HP Prime handheld, Mac and pc Virtual computer software, a Pro and Free versions of iOS/ Android/ Windows apps plus accessories and classroom tools. Mac and pc software will be referred to as Virtual computer software.

HP Prime handheld, Virtual computer software, and HP Prime Pro versions of iOS/ Android/ Windows apps have a programming component plus additional HP Prime Library Apps. The HP Prime Free versions of iOS/ Android/ Windows apps lack the programming component 67

and have fewer of HP Library Apps. The good part is that the HP Prime Graphing calculator interface and its two major views, Home and CAS, are the same across all of the family of HP Graphing Calculators. This makes it easy to use any member of the HP Graphing Calculator family.

In *HP Prime Guide to Algebra Fundamentals*, we illustrate how the HP Prime handheld, Virtual computer software, and iOS/ Android/ Windows apps can be used to solve math problems. Our references to the HP Prime Family in this guide will include everything except the accessories and classroom tools. Thus, a HP Prime Family label will mean any version of the HP Prime Graphing Calculator, be it handheld, Virtual computer software, or iOS/ Android/ Windows app.

The HP Prime/ Pro/ Virtual label will be used when the iOS/ Android/ Windows HP Prime Free version does not support a feature being illustrated. You will not be able to use the HP Prime Free here but any of the Prime handheld, Virtual computer software, and Pro versions of iOS/ Android/ Windows apps will work.

In our illustrations if it only works for the Prime handheld, Virtual computer software, and Pro versions of iOS/ Android/ Windows apps, the heading will be labeled as HP Prime/ Pro/ Virtual. If some or all parts of the illustration will work for the iOS/ Android/ Windows HP Prime Free version as well, then heading will say HP Prime Family.

Currently, with the handhelds there have been two generations with three variations. The second generation has two variations of the keyboard with the second variation having an easier to read keyboard. For this guide any of the HP Prime handhelds will work. The same should be true for any future generations.

Note: We will use the Window app screens for our illustrations of math concepts. However, the handheld, Virtual computer software, and iOS/ Android/ Windows apps functionality are identical with the exceptions for the HP Prime Free app that we previously mentioned.

For all problems and solutions presented in this guide, the math input, solutions and are identical in content but because of the settings, options selected, and difference in screen sizes effect the format of how the solutions are displayed. Please refer to documentation provided by HP and/or second party sources for complete details about the differences in user interface, display format, and step-by-step procedures for how to use the handheld, Virtual computer software and the iOS/ Android/ Windows apps.

HP Prime Handheld Essentials

This guide is based on Version 2017 07 10 (12066). We recommend that you upgrade, to the highest version allowed.

The ACT™ college entrance exam does not allow the HP Prime handheld. SAT™ and advance placement exams allow the HP Prime handheld.

Recommending the CAS used in the HP Prime handheld is probably controversial but remember we earlier recommended that you manually do or show all your work.

See HP and/or second party sources for details about interface and use.

HP Prime Virtual Computer Software Essentials

This guide is based on Virtual computer software version 2016 08 29 (11226). Again the same details apply as we mentioned for the handheld. We recommend that you use the most current version. We recommend that you keep all your platforms, handheld, Virtual computer software, and iOS/ Android/ Windows apps with the most current allowed operating system.

There are two versions of the Virtual computer software, a Mac and pc.

Figure 1 HP Prime's pc version of Virtual computer software

For classroom demonstrations, the Virtual PC software be used to project on an interactive whiteboard or with a digital projector. This way your students can follow along using the same keystrokes on their handheld. We would use all the options and features of the Virtual calculator.

See HP and/or second party sources for details about interface and use.

HP Prime iOS/ Android/ Windows Apps Essentials

This guide is based on HP Prime Pro and HP Prime Free iOS/ Android/ Windows apps version 2017 02 14 (11455). We recommend that you upgrade, to the highest version allowed.

As stated earlier, the HP Prime Pro and HP Prime Free major differences is the lack of the Program option for the HP Prime Free and presence of only nine apps in the HP Application Library.

As with the Virtual computer software, the on HP Prime Pro and HP Prime Free iOS/ Android/ Windows apps be used to project on an interactive whiteboard or with a digital projector. Because of its clarity, we prefer this layout over the Virtual computer software layout. The HP Prime Free is shown next.

Notice the presence of the smaller number of Library Application Apps. The Program key is labeled but does not perform any function.

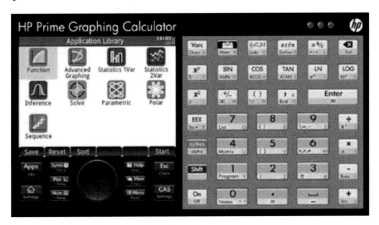

Figure 2 HP Prime Free version of HP Prime iOS/ Android/ Window app

See HP and/or second party sources for details about interface and use.

Explanation 1.1 - Real Numbers

In this section we introduce exponential notation and look at order of operations. We then introduce the real numbers; look at subsets of the real numbers, and the real numbers on a number line.

Exponential Notation

What is a billion divided by a thousand? Doing math with exponents is easier because you can subtract to do division and add to do multiplication.

The zeros in a problem can be used for its significant figures in measured numbers. For the trailing zeros in a billion and a thousand to be considered significant in measured numbers, they would have to be indicated. Various methods are used to identify significant figures in a number without a decimal point containing trailing zeros. Two common methods are bar above or under the last significant zero.

For multiplication or division the results number of significant figures is the least of its significant figures in the original measured numbers used in the calculation. Significant figures in arithmetic will be explained in section 1.3 discussion of Scientific Notation.

Note: When we are using a measuring tool to determine a quantity we will use measured numbers. Exact numbers are another important type of number used in measurement problems. Exact numbers result from a count or are defined numbers. We will assume in our discussion, examples, and exercises unless measurement or exact numbers are involved that we are dealing with numbers in general and no reference will be made to significant figure or decimal places in our solutions.

HP Prime Family Using Exponents

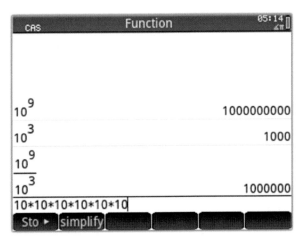

Begin by selecting the **CAS** key on the HP Prime. Key in as shown. Use the **exponent** key and **fraction template**. The **fraction template** is found by pressing the **fraction/ square root/ absolute value** key. For the last entry, press **Enter** to verify that there are six factors of ten in the answer of a million. If the **CAS** view has computations, clear the **history** first. To clear the **history**, press the **Clear** key.

The **fraction template** or **fraction icon** is found using **fraction/ square root/ absolute value** key. We will at times in the tutorial refer to this key as the **symbol template** key.

Before moving on with the tutorial we will take a moment to discuss the HP Prime features.

The HP Prime has two separate systems for performing calculation. The systems are referred to as the **CAS** view, Computer Algebra System view, and **HOME** view. Notice in the previous screen the **CAS** in the window's title. We will now press the **HOME** key and look at the second system.

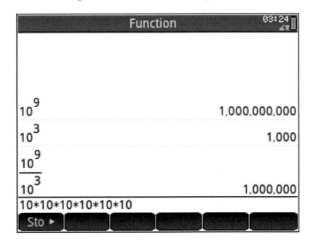

Begin by selecting the **HOME** key on the HP Prime. We can Key in as shown or use the **Menu** key to **Get from CAS** the entries from the previous **CAS** view screen. We will do the latter.

Press the **Menu** key and select the **Get from CAS** option. Highlight the 10^9 and press the soft **OK** key to transfer the 10^9 entry to the **HOME** view's command line. Press **Enter** to see the results. Repeat for entry two and three. For the command line entry, press **Enter** to verify that there are six factors of ten in the answer of a million. If the **HOME** view has computations, clear the **history** first. To clear the **history**, press the Clear key.

Notice the previous screen does not contain the word **CAS** in the window's title. This indicates we are using **HOME** view for our calculations. A nice feature of the **HOME** view is the use of commas in the "Digit Grouping:" of the **HOME** view Settings.

Primary and Secondary Keys;

- We will use **Black**, Blue, and Orange key names. Blue keys require the Shift key first and Orange keys requires the upper case ALPHA key first.

- We will use **Black** to refer to keys with a **Black** label, keys with a **Black** background and white label, or soft keys **generated** on the screen. For the **Black** key label and **Black** background the **Black** key name will be the key's primary function.

- **Black** keys are entered directly.

- In situations such as above, where the **command line** has a Textbook style or number entry, we will need to use the **Esc** key to clear the **command line** before clearing the **history** with the Clear key.

- On black and white eBook readers we need to use the key's name to determine if the Shift key or ALPHA key is needed.

Remark: The task of deciding when to use the HP Prime **HOME** view or **CAS** view is best understood after working with lots of HP Prime illustrations. For now, do not attempt to understand each part of the following overview of what each view can do. Instead use the view instruction that is include with each screenshot.

The screenshot's directions will instruct you to use the **HOME** or **CAS** view. After you start becoming comfortable with the **HOME** and **CAS** view come back, re-read this discussion of **HOME** and **CAS** views, and use the included hyperlinks to give you a good understanding of why and what each view can do.

HP Prime **HOME** and **CAS** views:

· Use the **CAS** key to select **CAS** view.

· Use the **HOME** key to select **HOME** view.

· **HOME** view allows Entry in Textbook, Algebraic, and RPN form.

· **CAS** view is automatically set to Textbook Entry.

· **HOME** view default output is numeric (decimals).

· For command line expression entry we use **CAS** view. The **CAS** view's Textbook Entry and exact nature of its Textbook Output better fit the needs of an algebraic tutorial.

· For numerical calculations such as the above two screen, we will use both the **HOME** view and the **CAS** view. If we prefer decimals and commas in the result, we use the **HOME** view.

· To parallel the tutorial's use of manual explanations of math concepts, **CAS** view is generally used. If the **HOME** view produces results that differ, other than decimals and commas, we will show both the **CAS** view and **HOME** view screens.

· For **CAS** command line programs and for programs that we evaluate its functions as numbers as well as lower case letters we will use the **CAS** view.

· For numerical **nonCAS** command line programs, programs that can run from the Program Catalog, programs that use an input or choose statement, or quick Define functions, we can use the **HOME** or **CAS** view's command line to run the program.

· Reference to **nonCAS** does not mean no **CAS** statements, but means that any **CAS** statements are qualified **CAS** statements in the program.

Uppercase and Lowercase Letters:

· **HOME** view – both uppercase and lowercase letters can be entered. Default entry is uppercase. Pressing ALPHA twice lock us into uppercase. **Shift ALPHA** i.e. (**alpha**) switches entry to lowercase. Pressing ALPHA again lock us into lowercase. Pressing ALPHA following key entry switches lock or shift mode back to default entry.

· **CAS** view – both uppercase and lowercase letters can be entered. Default entry is lowercase. Pressing ALPHA twice lock us into lowercase. **Shift ALPHA** i.e. (**alpha**) switches entry to uppercase. Pressing ALPHA again lock us into uppercase. Pressing ALPHA following key entry switches lock or shift mode back to default entry.

· Pay attention to our comments about case throughout this eBook. As in some cases a specific case is required. The entry's case may not be the default for that view.

There are three level of how users can use this tutorial to learn algebra. The system level, where we use the built-in features, will get us through 99% of the material found in Algebra I, Algebra II, College Algebra, and PreCalculus. Any HP Prime device including the HP Prime Free works great for the system level.

The extended level is next. It is easy to learn and works great for the HP Prime handheld, Pro, and virtual pc or mac software. It is not available for the HP Prime Free. It could be considered optional but adding just the one-line calculator entries is recommended. We introduce it at end of this chapter.

The advance level is where we add/create program libraries and Library Applications to the HP Prime handheld, Pro, and virtual pc or mac software. It is not available for the HP Prime Free. We consider this level optional for learning Algebra. However if we are just adding but not creating there are benefits. Added program libraries and/or added Library Applications can help with our algebra learning process. Creating program libraries is introduced at the end of this chapter and covered more in chapter 3 and 7. Creating Library Applications is covered in chapter 7.

We now look at Library Applications. They come in three forms, built-in, third party, and ones we create. The next screen entries comes from using <u>Library Applications that we created</u> and built-in Function Library Application. It shows how the HP Prime's current Library Application is critical to evaluation of a function.

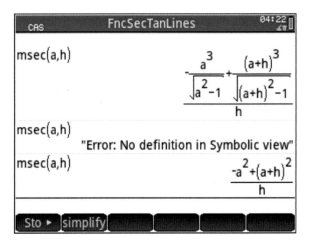

In Explanation 1.7 – Compound Fractions we create Library Applications based on the built-in Function Library Application. The created Library Application help with the algebra of calculus. We also created global libraries of functions to help us verify algebraic steps used in calculus calculations plus some of the global library functions are used in our Library Applications. The above function **msec** is the slope of the secant line at two points on our function F1. The function **msec** is from our global library CalcSecTan, <u>Calc</u>ulus version of <u>Sec</u>ant and <u>Tan</u>gent topics.

The above screen entry one, the Library Application was set to our Library Application GraphPlus. Function F1 was $x^3/\sqrt{(x^2 - 1)}$. We then keyed in **msec(a,h)**. The second entry, the Library Application was switched to the default Library Application Function. We returned back to the CAS view. We again keyed in **msec(a,h)**. In the Library Application Function, F1 was empty. Since F1 was empty it produced the "Error: No definition in Symbolic view". The third entry, the Library Application was switched to the Library Application FncSecTanLines. We returned back to the CAS view. We again keyed in **msec(a,h)**. Function F1 was x^2.

Remark: As stated above, there are three level of how users can use this tutorial to learn algebra. The system level, where we take advantage of all of the common features found in every HP Prime device. The extended level, where with the HP Prime handheld, Pro, and virtual pc or mac software we extend the capabilities by adding one-line global functions. The advance level is where we add/create functions, program libraries, and Library Applications for the HP Prime handheld, Pro, and virtual pc or mac software. The above screen program library function msec(a,h), slope of secant line at $P_1(a, f(a))$ and $P_2(a+h, f(a+h))$, illustrates the power of generalizing that occurs at the advanced level.

Library Applications:

· The calculator's Library Application in the above screenshot is currently set to **FncSecTanLines**.

· The current Library Application's name appears in the screen's title.

· The Library's Application shown in the screen's title is critical if the **CAS** view or **HOME** view uses it variables. See the above screenshot different results for msec(a,h) caused by our switching of the Library Application without clearing the history area. Switching the Library Application was done to demonstrate the fact that the Library Application variables F1 are critical as seen by the different Library Application results for msec(a,h).

· When a Library Application is appropriate we will use it. The main built-in Library Application that we will use in this tutorial is the Function Library. The built-in and third party HP Prime's Library Applications can be used in learning and solving math concept in general or for specific topics. We will discuss each use of an appropriate Application Libraries as we use them. In Explanation 1.7 – Compound Fractions we create our own Library Applications. Third party and creating Library Application is not available with the HP Prime Free.

Returning back to our tutorial. We start by using exponents to write the product where the factors are the same. **Factors** are numbers or expressions that when multiplied represent a number or a product. In general, we have the following definition of Exponential Notation. Later, in this section discussion of The Set of Real Numbers, we will explain what is meant by a being real and n being a natural number. We will expand upon the role of exponents in section 1.3 – Integer Exponents and section 1.4 Radicals and Rational Exponents of the tutorial.

Exponential Notation

For any real number a and natural number n

$$a^n = a \cdot a \cdot \ldots \cdot a \qquad n \text{ factors}$$

The number a is called the base and n is the exponent.

Example 1 Simplify Expressions

(a) $2 \cdot 2 \cdot 2 \cdot 2 \cdot 2 = 32$

(b) $4^3 = 4 \cdot 4 \cdot 4 = 64$

HP Prime Family Using Exponents

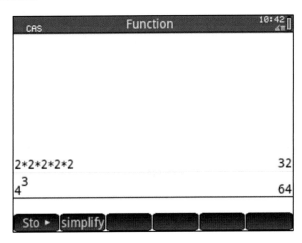

Use the **CAS** view on the HP Prime. Key in the expressions as shown followed by **Enter**. If the **CAS** view has computations, clear the **history** first. To clear the **history**, press the **Clear** key.

Exercise 1 Exponential Notation

Evaluate:

$$-2^4$$

<u>Solution</u> >>

Order of Operations

What order would we do 3 + 4 x 2? If we add 3 and 4 and multiply by 2, we get 14. If we add 3 to the product of 4 and 2, we get 11. As we can see, the order makes a difference. Calculate in the wrong order and we will get the wrong result. Long ago, people agreed to follow rules when doing calculations.

If we put in grouping symbols, (3 + 4) x 2 would give us 14 and 3 + (4 x 2) would give us 11. We do all the calculations within the grouping symbols first. The calculation 3 + (4 x 2) is displayed in the history as 3 + 4 x 2 with result of 11. The ()'s are not necessary. Pressing **Enter** to the last command in the following screen will illustrates this.

Note: If in doubt about the order, use ()'s in the command line and let the calculator drop them.

HP Prime Family Order of Operations

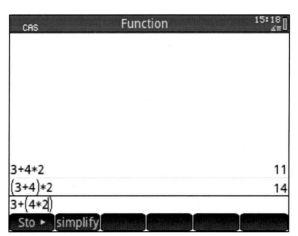

Use the **CAS** view on the HP Prime. Key in the expressions as shown followed by **Enter**. If the **CAS** view has computations, clear the **history** first. To clear the **history**, press the **Clear** key.

For grouping symbols we use parenthesis (), brackets [], or braces {}. Generally we will use them in that order. The HP Prime will use only nested parentheses, not brackets and braces.

Sometimes the following rule minus the unary step is referred to by the acronym *PEMDAS* (Parenthesis, Exponent, multiplication, division, addition, subtraction).

Order of Operations

1. Simplify all operations within any grouping symbols.

   Simplify all operations above and below fraction symbol.

   Start with intermost grouping symbol.

2. Simplify all exponential expressions.

3. Perform all multiplications and divisions in the order they appear.

4. Perform all addition and subtraction in the order they appear.

5. Simplify any unary operations.

Example 2 Order of Operations

Work inside parenthesis
$$\frac{2\cdot(4+3)-1\cdot3}{7^2+1^4}$$

Work above and multiply
$$=\frac{2\cdot(7)-1\cdot3}{7^2+1^4}$$

Work above and subtract
$$=\frac{14-3}{7^2+1^4}$$

Work below and exponents
$$=\frac{11}{7^2+1^4}$$

Work below and add
$$=\frac{11}{49+1}$$
$$=\frac{11}{50}$$

HP Prime Family Order of Operations

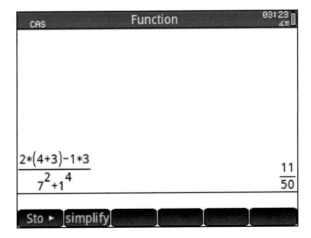

Use the **CAS** view on the HP Prime. Key in the expression as shown followed by **Enter**. Use the **fraction template** and **exponent** key. The **fraction template** is found by pressing the **fraction/ square root/ absolute value** key. If the **CAS** view has computations, clear the **history** first. To clear the **history**, press the **Clear** key.

Exercise 2 Order of Operations

Evaluate:

$$4+3\cdot(x-1)^2 \text{ for } x=5$$

<u>Solution</u> >>

The Set of Real Numbers

Real numbers will be the basis for most of this tutorial. Much of our everyday life math experiences can be modeled with real numbers.

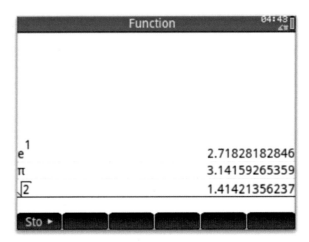

Figure 1 The real number system

We next look at how the HP Prime displays irrational numbers. The first screen is the **HOME** view and second screen is the **CAS** view.

HP Prime Family Irrational Numbers

Use the **HOME** view on the HP Prime. Key in the expressions as shown followed by **Enter**. Use the e^x key, **pi** key **fraction/ square root/ absolute value** key. If the **HOME** view has computations, clear the **history** first. To clear the **history**, press the **Clear** key. Notice the window's title does not have a CAS label.

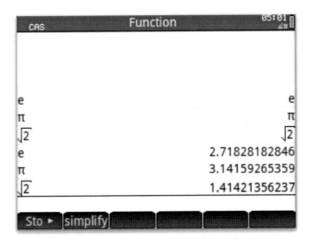

Use the **CAS** view on the HP Prime. Key in the expressions as shown followed by **Enter**. Use the e^x key, **pi** key, and **fraction/ square root/ absolute value** key. For the first three entries we pressed **Enter**. For the last three entries we used the **approx** (the wavy equal sign) key. If the **CAS** view has computations, clear the **history** first. To clear the **history**, press the **Clear** key. Notice the CAS label in the window's title.

To parallel the tutorial's use of manual explanations of math concepts, HP Prime's **CAS**, Computer Assisted Algebra, view is generally used. The **CAS** view gives up the ability to easily display a result in exact form using **Enter.** We can also use the **CAS** view to display as a decimal using the **approx** (the wavy equal sign) key.

The **mixed numeral key** can also be used to display the **CAS** view exact result as a decimal. The **mixed numeral** key works differently in the two above views.

Remark: The **mixed numeral** key used in the above **HOME** view toggles the last decimal result between decimal, fraction, and mixed numeral. With the irrational numbers shown in the first screen, all three results, decimal, fraction, and mixed numeral, will only be approximate. The **mixed numeral** key used in **CAS** view toggle the last exact result between decimal and fraction. With irrational numbers shown in the second screen, the decimal and fraction representation will only be approximate.

Decimal Representation for the Real Numbers

Every real number can be represented as a decimal. The decimal for the Real number can either be terminating, repeating, nonterminating, or non-repeating.

The set of Real Numbers is made up of the following:

· The Natural numbers are the counting numbers and are represented by terminating decimals.

· The Whole numbers are the Counting numbers plus 0 and are represented by terminating decimals.

· The Integers are the Natural numbers, their negatives plus 0, and are represented by terminating decimals.

· The Rational numbers are numbers that can be written in the form a/b, where a and b are integers and b is not equal to 0 and are represented by terminating or repeating decimals.

· The Irrational numbers are numbers that cannot be written in the form a/b, where a and b are integers and b is not equal to 0 and are represented by nonterminating, nonrepeating decimals

· The Real numbers are all of the above. They are all types of decimals.

The following are the basic properties of equalities.

Properties of Equality

If $a = b$ and c is any real number, then

1. $a + c = b + c$
2. $a \cdot c = b \cdot c$

Property 1 states that we can add the same number to both sides of an equality. In the next section we introduce the sign rules for real numbers. We show that adding a negative is the equivalent to subtracting. Thus, if c is negative we could think of this as subtracting the same number from both sides.

Property 2 states that we can multiply the same number to both sides of an equality. If the number we multiply is the reciprocal, we can think of this as dividing both sides by the same number.

Since we have real numbers, subtraction and division are not necessary but practically subtraction and division are easier to use as we see in the next example.

Example 3 Rational Representation for repeating decimal

Write $x = 1.2373737\ldots$ as a rational number.

Multiply by 10 to get repeating to right of decimal.
$10x = 12.373737\ldots$

Multiply by 100 because 2 repeating digits
$1000x = 1237.373737\ldots$

Subtract 10x from 1000x

$$1000x = 1237.373737\ldots$$
$$-10x = -12.373737\ldots$$
$$990x = 1225$$

Dividing by 990

$$\frac{990x}{990} = \frac{1225}{990} \qquad x = \frac{1225}{990} = \frac{245}{198}$$

To come up with a rational number we used the Property of Equality for multiplication and addition for real numbers. First we used multiplication twice. Subtraction was next. It is easier to think subtraction rather than addition of negative numbers. Then we used division. Likewise, division is easier to do then multiplication of the reciprocal. Final step is to reduce to simplest form.

HP Prime Family Repeating Decimal Calculations

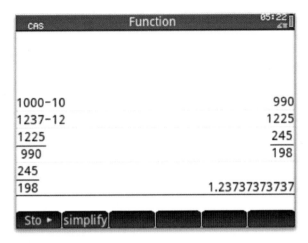

Use the **CAS** view on the HP Prime. If the **CAS** view has computations, clear the **history** first. To clear the **history**, press the **Clear** key.

Key in the first two expressions as shown followed by **Enter**.

For the third entry, enter the numerator divided by the denominator or use the **fraction template** from the **fraction/ square root/ absolute value** key. For the fourth entry, use the **arrow pad** to select the reduced fraction and press **Enter** to copy it to the command line. Use the **approx** (the wavy equal sign) key.

The **soft** key **Copy** could have been used to transfer the history item to the command line. **Soft** keys are ones on the screen that we touch.

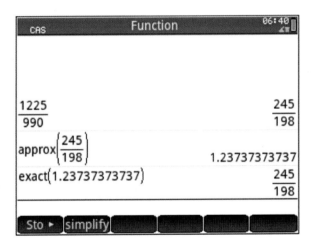

Use the **CAS** view on the HP Prime. Clear the **history** by pressing the **Clear** key.

Key in the first expressions as shown followed by **Enter**. Enter the numerator divided by the denominator or use the **fraction template** from the **fraction/ square root/ absolute value** key.

Instead of the **approx** (the wavy equal sign) key, we use the **mixed numeral key** to convert between fractions and the format given in our "HOME settings". The screen here is based on the format being Standard. Press the **mixed numeral key** and it converts the previous result to a decimal, *approx* entry. Press the **mixed numeral key** again and it will convert back to a fraction, *exact* entry.

Note: In **CAS** view the *approx* and *exact* functions were produced by us pressing the mixed numeral key. As we see in the next screen, the **HOME** view toggles the result rather than produce an entry in the history area.

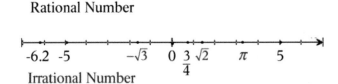

Use the **HOME** view on the HP Prime. If the **HOME** view has computations, clear the **history** first. To clear the **history**, press the **Clear** key

Use the **Menu** key to "Get from CAS". Use the **arrow pad** to select 1225/990 and press **Enter** or the **soft** key **OK**. An alternative is to enter the fraction shown in the history area. Do not use the commas when inputting the numerator.

We use the **mixed numeral key** to convert between improper fractions, mixed numerals, and the format given in our "HOME settings".

Press the **mixed numeral key** to see the mixed numeral representation of the fraction. Press the **mixed numeral key** again and it will convert back to an improper fraction. Press the **mixed numeral key** a third time it will convert to the format given in our "HOME settings". The screen here is based on the format being Standard.

Exercise 3 Repeating Decimal as a Rational Number

Write $x = 0.666\ldots$ as a rational number.

Solution >>

Representing Real Numbers on a Number Line

We will use the one-to-one correspondence between the set of real numbers and the points on a straight line to create a one-dimensional space.

Rational Number

Irrational Number

Figure 2 The real numbers

Next we use the Cartesian Coordinate system and Pythagorean theorem to locate the square root of 5 on the x-axis.

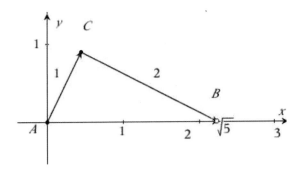

Figure 3 Square Root of 5 (Education.ti.com, The Number System)

Introduction to Absolute Value

We represent a number's distance from zero on a number line with notation $|a|$, read "the absolute value of a". The distance is always a nonnegative number. To find absolute value, if the number is zero or positive we leave it alone, if the number is negative, we make it positive. See the HP Prime entries that follow. The first two entries are the same as the formal definition of absolute value.

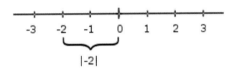

Figure 4 The absolute value of a number is its distance from zero.

Definition of Absolute Value

If a is real number, then the absolute value of a is

$$|a| = \begin{cases} a \text{ if } a \geq 0 \\ -a \text{ if } a < 0 \end{cases}$$

HP Prime Family Absolute Value

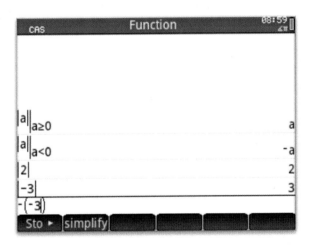

Use the **CAS** view on the HP Prime. Key in the expression as shown followed by **Enter**. The **absolute value template** is found by pressing the **fraction/ square root/ absolute value** key. Use the a key for the lowercase **a**'s. The **with template** (|) is found by pressing the **fraction/ square root/ absolute value** key. The **inequality templates** are found by pressing the **inequality** key. The command line entry –(-3) will be display as 3 with a result of 3 in the history area. If the **CAS** view has computations, clear the **history** first. To clear the **history**, press the Clear key.

The **Enter** or **soft** key **Copy** could be used to transfer the history item 1 to the command line for entry item 2. Then we would change the greater than or equality to inequality to a less than inequality. We would use the **arrow pad** to select the expression in the history. In the command line there will be extra parenthesis around the expression but will disappear when we press **Enter**.

The first two entries illustrate a nice feature of the **CAS** view. Many times we can use unassigned variables to display definitions. This is not possible on the **HOME** view since variables must be assigned a value. We will get a "Red and White **X** Error: Syntax Error" when no value has been assigned.

With the second entry on the **CAS** view, we need to make one note. "-*a*" result is not a negative number, but the opposite of the number inside the absolute value notation. Since $a < 0$, the number inside the notation must be negative and the opposite of the negative would be a positive. "-*a*" result therefore represents a positive number.

With either the **HOME** view or **CAS** view we can use the **absolute value template** with numbers. For the final entry, press **enter** to verify the absolute value technique of making a negative number positive by taking its opposite. The parentheses were added to emphasize that we were taking the opposite of negative 3. With the HP Prime the parentheses and opposite signs are gone when we press **Enter** since they are not necessary. We will need to get use to the difference between how we normally write expressions manually and how the HP Prime like to display those expressions. The HP Prime input and results are often displayed differently than the way we entered them or would manually display the results.

Absolute Value and Distance

What is distance between two points, -2 and 5, on the real number line? Our intuition say the distance is 7. We can calculate this by finding either $|5 - (-2)| = 7$ or $|(-2) - 5| = 7$. This leads us to the following definition.

> **Distance between Points on the Real Line**
>
> For any real numbers, *a* and *b*, then the distance between the points *a* and *b* on the real line is
>
> $$d(a,b) = |b - a|$$

HP Prime Family Using the Solve Library Application

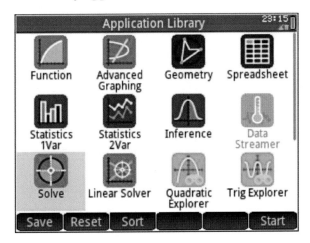

Press the **Apps** key on the HP Prime. From the Application Library select the **Solve** icon. The HP Prime Free will not have as many apps. On the HP Prime handheld Data Streamer will be enabled.

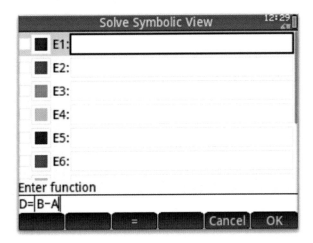

Select **E1:**. Key in the equation as shown followed by **Enter**. Use the letter keys for the uppercase D, B, and A. Use the = key. The **absolute value template** is found by pressing the **fraction/ square root/ absolute value** key.

If necessary Clear E1:. Select it and use the **backspace** key. To Clear all equations press Clear and press **Enter** to accept message "Clear all expressions?".

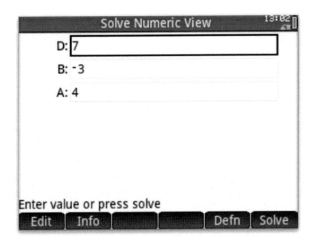

Press the **Num** key on the HP Prime. Key in values for two of three textboxes. Select the remaining textbox and press the **Solve** soft key. In the above screen we solved for **D**.

Note: Solving for **D** would always give us the correct answer. If we let **D** =7 and **B**=-3 and solved for **A** we would get 4. However, -10 would also be a solution. For variables with multiple answers we need to put in a seed value if we want to see additional solutions. See next two screens.

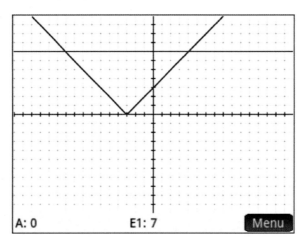

Press the **Plot** key on the HP Prime. With keyed in values of **D**=7, **B**=-3, and **A**=0 and the edit field being **A**, we see from the plot solutions of -10 and 4. Since the second solution is -10, to see this solution in the **NUM** view we pick a seed value close to -10 such as -9.

How the plot works. It takes our equation left and right expressions and makes them into two equations, Y=D and Y=|B-A|. Using our values and solving for A, we have Y=7 and Y=|-3-X|. With A being the solved variable it becomes X in the absolute value plot. We need A to be selected and its current value set to zero then we see the above Y=7 and Y=|-3-X| plots. The x-values 0f -10 and 4 in the intersections of the two plots are the solutions.

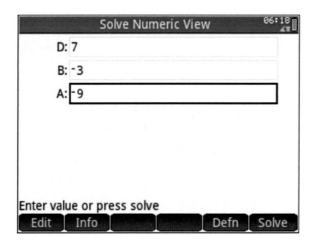

To get a second solution for **A**, we seed **A** with -9 and press **Enter**. Select entry **A** again and press the soft **Solve** key and we will see the second solution of -10.

See next screen for alternate technique that gives both solutions directly when solving for **A**. If solving for **B**, we would also use the alternate technique to directly solve for both **B** solutions.

HP Prime Family Using the CAS "solve" function

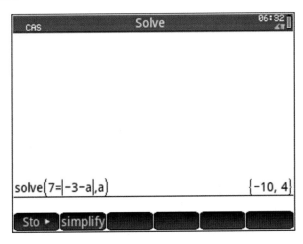

Use the **CAS** view on the HP Prime. Key in the command as shown followed by **Enter**. The **solve()** command is found by pressing the **Toolbox** key and using the **Toolbox > CAS > Solve > Solve** menu. The **absolute value template** is found by pressing the **fraction/ square root/ absolute value** key. Use the **a** key for the lowercase **a**. Solutions of -10 and 4 are shown.

If the **CAS** view has computations, clear the **history** first. To clear the **history**, press the Clear key

Since we have added a formula to the Solve Application Library, it would be a good time to backup our HP Prime.

There are two kinds of backups. An external file backup that we can use to restore following factory reset, quick factory reset, or firmware updates and an internal backup where we can restore to the internals' backup previous state of the calculator.

HP Prime/ Pro/ Virtual Creating an External Backup File

HP Connectivity Kit – External Backup Screenshot

The backup allowing us to restore following factory reset, quick factory reset, or firmware updates uses the HP Connectivity Kit software. The HP Prime Free is not recognized by the HP Connectivity Kit software. The backup allowing us to restore to a previous internal state uses the HP Prime calculator.

The HP Prime calculator internal backup allows us to restore to a previous internal state has two techniques that can be used.

See HP Connectivity Kit Guide and/or forums for instructions on backing up to an external file that can be used to restore following a factory reset, quick factory reset, or firmware updates. The HP Connectivity Kit Guide or the second post in the above forum link gives us the details for backing up and restoring.

Remark: The HP Connectivity Kit external backup file is a must as we add data to our HP Prime's Program Libraries Apps; add functions and programming libraries of functions; and/or add additional Program Library Apps. The two internal state backup techniques illustrated next do not help if we lose everything including the internal previous state backups. Remember the HP Connectivity Kit is not available to the HP Prime Free.

We now show the two HP Prime calculator techniques for backing up so that we can restore to the backup's internal previous state. Choose the technique that you prefer.

HP Prime Family Internal Backup

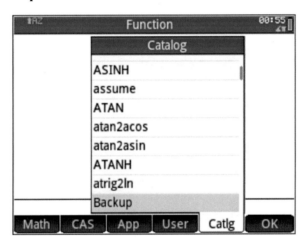

Press the **ToolBox**, press the **Catlg** soft key, letter **B**, and press the **OK** soft key.

Notice the **Function** label in the title bar. Backup can be done within the other HP Apps but for clarity purposes we switched to **Function**.

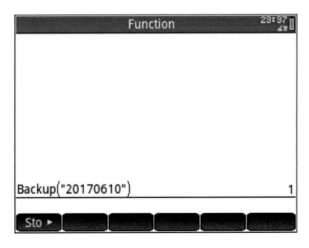

To the command line entry Backup(), add the date by pressing the double quotes, and typing a date, **yyyymmdd**. Press **Enter**.

Sometimes something goes wrong and we have to reset our HP Prime. At this point our loss would be small but as we add more formulas or our own programs the loss becomes larger.

We next look at an alternate backup technique.

HP Prime Family Internal Backup Alternate Technique

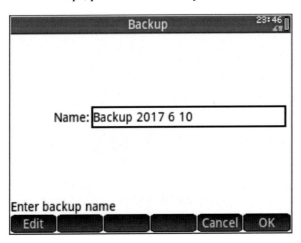

Press **Mem**, use the **arrow Pad** to select Backups, press **View** soft key or **Enter** on the keypad.

From the list of backups, press the **NEW** soft key to see the screen above. Press the **OK** soft key to accept default name.

If we use the alternate techniques default name, it will have Backup as part of the backup name plus use a space between fields in the date. Our first technique we only used the date with **mm** and **dd** having leading zeroes if necessary. Within the " "'s in our first technique or soft **Edit** key in the alternate, we could use any form for date or any name we liked.

Programming Related Information

We will now create our own program to solve for the distance between **a** and **b** on the real number line. For programming we have to use the handheld, HP Prime Pro app, or pc or Mac virtual computer software.

HP Prime Free users can skip the programming instructions. However, there is one section, HP Prime Family – Delete all user variables that HP Prime Free users should look at. Be sure to look at the **Note** in that section discussing difference between Delete all user variables and purge(variable).

HP Prime handheld, Pro, Virtual pc and mac users can go to computerlearningservice.com/html/ products.html to download all the program files.

Program functions are more flexible then the built-in Solve Library Application and not restricted to 10 stored formulas. Edward Shore made the eqnlib Library Application from the Solve Library Application. His enhanced Solve Library Application is capable of running 47 included formulas. After installing, it is run by selecting it from **Toolbox** > **App** > **eqnlib** > **eqnlib** and pressing **Enter** from the **HOME** view or **CAS** view command line. After looking at how we create our Library Applications in chapter 7 you could modify the built-in Solve Library Application using Shore's technique to make your own Library Application's collection of formulas.

Program's function can be standalone file or part of a program library file. The actual program can be single function or a collection of functions. Adding a single function would be the first step for an extended level user. Adding a collection of functions would be the last step.

HP Prime/ Pro/ Virtual Creating the "distrnl" Function

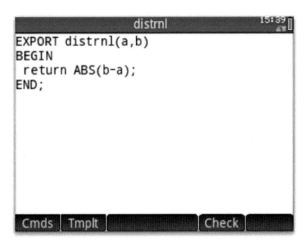

Press the **Program** key on the HP Prime. Press the **New** soft key. Type in **distrnl** to the **Name**: field. Leave the **CAS**: field unchecked. Press the **OK** soft key. Add the line **return ABS(b-a)**;. Press the **Check** soft key. Press **OK** soft key to message "No errors in the program".

Remember the HP Prime Free does not have the programming function.

Go to computerlearningservice.com/html/products.html to download the file.

We refer to function of this type as one-line global functions. Technically there are more than one-line in the program but the key line is only one-line. By the nature of HP Prime programming sometimes this one-line will also be more lines due to how the one-line needs to be constructed to meet the syntax requirements of the HP Prime programming.

There are two similar but different programming languages – **CAS** and **nonCAS**. Programs that have a #cas - #end declaration use the CAS programming language. The above **distrnl** program is an example of the **nonCAS** programming language since it has no such declaration. An interesting side note is that we can use CAS functions in the **nonCAS** environment by qualifying them.

We first run the **distrnl** program from the Program Catalog.

HP Prime/ Pro/ Virtual Running "distrnl" from the Program Catalog

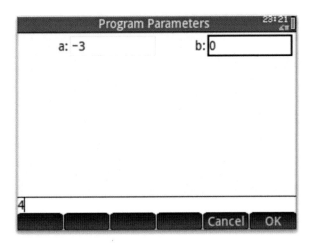

If necessary press the Program key and select **distrnl**. From the Program Catalog screen (not shown) press the **Run** soft key. Enter values for the **a; field** and **b: field**. Press **OK** soft key following the value entries.

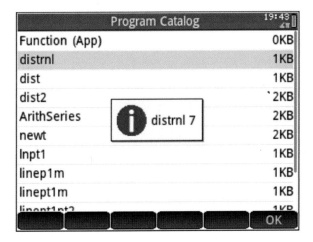

The message box will appear following the variables entry and pressing the **OK** soft key. Read the solution "distrnl solution" message box.

We can also run our program's function **distrnl** from the **HOME** view or the **CAS** view. The **HOME** view must be set to Textbook or Algebraic Entry. The **CAS** view is automatically set to Textbook entry.

Remark: Programs that use the <u>#cas - #end</u> declaration or programs where we want to evaluate function parameters with numbers as well as lower case letters need to be run from the **CAS** view command line.

Programs that can be run from the **HOME** view command line will have function parameters that only use numbers, use qualified CAS commands following the Export declaration of the function, or any combination of these. The quick Define function can also use the **HOME** view command line. Running from the **CAS** view will work for these categories as well.

HP Prime/ Pro/ Virtual Running "distrnl" from the HOME view

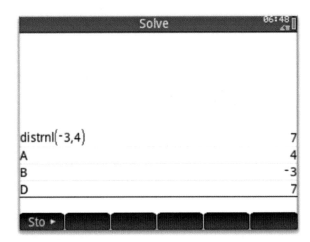

Using the **HOME** view on the HP Prime, press the **toolbox** key. Press the **User** soft key to locate the Program Function **distrnl**. Press the **OK** soft key. Key in the values shown and press **Enter**. An alternate method would be to type in the whole command, **distrnl(-3,4)**.

Next we enter uppercase A, B, and D. These are not necessary but are displayed to help with the understanding of how various variables in the HP Prime work. If we running from the CAS view to enter uppercase letters we would need to press the Shift key before the ALPHA key.

The function **distrnl**, dist̲ance r̲eal n̲umber l̲ine, works equally as well from the Program Catalog's **Run** soft key or directly from the **HOME** or **CAS** view command line. The **Run** soft key produced by using the **Program** key prompts us for the variables. Using **distrnl** from the **HOME** or **CAS** command line returns the output in the history area where we can manipulate it.

Notice the title bar has **Solve**. As we mentioned earlier the Library Application is important when using the **HOME** view or **CAS** view command line if our **distrnl** function needs to use some of the Library Application's variables. Since the Solve Library Application is active variable E0-E9 are available in a program as an unqualified name. In all of our other screen shots we were using the **CAS** view and the **Function** Library Application. With the **Function** Library Application, variable F0-F9 would be available in a program as an unqualified name.

Using an app as a prefix (Solve.E1 or Function.F1) is referred to as fully qualified name or app specifier. If we look at our program code we can find examples where our programs make use of the Function Library Application variable F0-F9 unqualified names. The current Library Application is what is important for unqualified names not the current view.

Do not confuse the HP Prime Library Applications (app screen icons) with our program library applications (the functions and programs we wrote that use the **Run** soft key or **HOME** and **CAS** command line to execute).

Note: Real upper case variables A-Z plus Theta are always available. A=4, B=-3, and D=7 because we used E1 to be D=|B-A| in our **Solve** Library Application. If we use E1 to be the formula D1=|X2-X1| then our Real variables for A, B, and D would be A=0, B=0, and D=0 as would be all A-Z and theta as zero is there default value.

Very important for us to recognize the **name** of the variable and the **value** stored in the variable are different. Without taking this into consideration our HP Prime can produce what look to be very strange incorrect results. If we execute the **HOME** view qualified command Solve.E1 with the Function app being current, we get D=|B-A|. If we copy D=|B-A| from the history we get '1' since with the current values 7=|-3-4| it is true.

HP Prime Family Delete all user variables

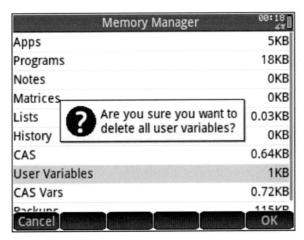

To delete all Real upper Case variables, press the **Mem** key, select the **User Variables**, press the **Backspace** key, and press **OK** to the message "Are you sure you wish to delete all user variables?". This also pertains to the HP Prime Free.

After deleting all variables, if we execute the **HOME** view command Solve.E1 with the function app current we still get D=|B-A|. Clearing a Library App variable such as E1 must be done manually from the Solve application. If we copy D=|B-A| from the history we still get '1' since with the current values 0=|0-0| it is true. A,B and D have been deleted. The default value for A-Z and theta is zero.

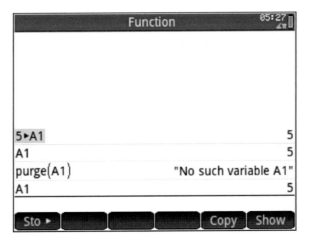

A screenshot illustrating the peculiarity when using purge with the HOME *variable* **A1**. The *variable* A1 could be either a HOME or CAS variable depending on which screen was used to create it. This screen pertains to the HP Prime Free as well.

Note: The purge(*variable*) command is for CAS variables. We get purge from the **Toolbox > Catlg > purge** menu item. It does not work with the HOME *variable* A1. The next screen shows the CAS *variable* **A1** cleared with purge.

HOME variables can be entered two ways from the command line. We can use *value* soft key **Sto->** *variable* or *variable* := *value*. The **Delete all user variables** method is used to clear a specified HOME variable plus all other current HOME user variables. HOME variables can be individually cleared using **Mem** or **Vars > User** and backspacing the variable. Use one of these methods to delete the HOME variable **A1**.

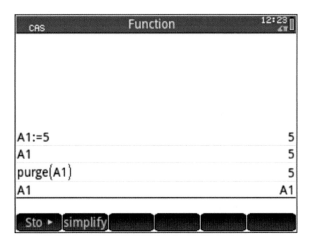

The CAS screenshot illustrating deleting the CAS variable **A1**. This also pertains to the HP Prime Free.

From **CAS** view the purge command clears the CAS *variable* A1. As with HOME variables, CAS variables can be entered using *value* soft key **Sto->** *variable* or *variable* := *value*. The **5 STO-> A1** was translated in history area to **A1:=-5**.

Remark: Adding a Global one-line function is one of the most powerful features of the HP Prime/ Pro/ Virtual. We can add any command or function that is missing, nest it, and use it in an expression with existing and other new commands or functions. We show how to use these techniques in the compound fraction section of this tutorial. Later we will add Input commands to our programs. The input command gives us prompts plus having the solution available in the history area. The input command works in **HOME** view or **CAS** view.

A **#cas** program is shown next. The **#cas** program must use the **CAS** view. As mentioned earlier we will only use the **CAS** view for **#cas** programs. The **Home** view cannot be used for programs with the **#cas** - **#end** declaration. The **#cas** one-line program shown next is a second example of the first step for an extended level user.

HP Prime/ Pro/ Virtual – "dist": #cas one-line "solve" function

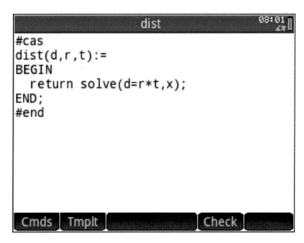

Press the **Program** key on the HP Prime. Press the **New** soft key. Type in **dist** into the **Name**: field. Check the **CAS**: field. Press the **OK** soft key. Add the line **return solve(d=r*t,x);**. Press the **Check** soft key. Press **OK** soft key to message "No errors in the program".

Remember the HP Prime Free does not have programming.

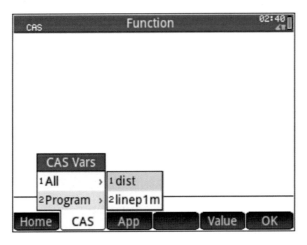

Using the **CAS** view on the HP Prime, press the **VAR** key. Press the **CAS** soft key to locate the CAS Var **dist**. Press the **OK** soft key. We also could of typed **dist** in the **CAS** view command line.

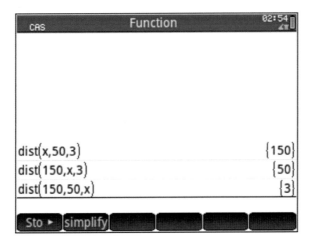

Key in the **( )**'s and parameters shown for the first entry. Press **Enter**. Use the **arrow pad** to copy the previous CAS var from the **history area**. Edit the previous CAS var and press **Enter**. Repeat for third entry.

Go to computerlearningservice.com/html/products.html to download the file.

The **HOME** view cannot be used for the above #**cas** Program. The **CAS** view must be used. See this comment about the similarities and difference of these two programming languages, CAS and nonCAS.

We next show the advanced program, **dist2**.

The Home view program **dist2** is an advanced program that uses a comprehensive input routine plus allows for CAS.Solve operation from the **HOME** view command line. This is the first example of an advanced level user program.

Remark: Because of these advanced feature you can use the #CAS **dist** program or similar #CAS programs as alternatives until you feel the need to use comprehensive input or qualified CAS operations in **HOME** view programs. Note that the text editor and HP Connectivity Kit details that follow are useful even if you will not be using the advanced program's comprehensive input or **CAS** operations.

The program **dist2**, takes advantage of prompts, has variable sensitive help message, and uses the CAS Solve function from **HOME** view. The support code necessary for these features makes it better to create the program using a text editor. Then we copy and paste the code from the text editor to the HP

Prime program editor. The HP Connectivity Kit has this capability as well. Plus the HP Connectivity Kit lets us transfer its programs to the handheld HP Prime.

There is one other option than using the text editor or HP Connectivity Kit. We can use the HP Prime Virtual computer Software or the HP Prime Virtual/ Windows/ Android/ iPad app built-in keyboards, USB keyboards, or Bluetooth keyboards to make program entry easier. However, the text editor or HP Connectivity kit is probably the better option for any program of 10 lines or more.

For windows we like Notepad++ with the HP PPL plug-in. Using this on the same windows machine allows us to copy and paste between Notepad++ and HP Prime Pro or HP Prime virtual software.

Note: In its current version, the HP Connectivity Kit sometimes loses wifi connection and is unable to work with HP Prime Pro running on the same windows machine. This is why we prefer to use Notepad++ or a text editor. Having a backup of our code in Notepad++ or a text editor is also a plus.

On Android using the Chromebook the HP Connectivity Kit and the current version of Android on the Chromebook platform does not find the HP Connectivity Kit. We can create directly on a text editor on the Chromebook or use Google Drive to copy the text file from a text editor where the file was created to a text file on the Chromebook. Then use copy and paste between the text editor and the HP Prime Pro on the Chromebook.

Google Drive or other cloud based system could be used in other HP Prime situations as well. On the iPad Google's app is called **Drive**.

HP Prime/ Pro/ Virtual "dist2": CAS "solve" function using input – Notepad++

```
1   EXPORT dist2()
2   BEGIN
3    local a,b,c,d,r,t;
4    if input(
5     {{d,[2]},{r,[2]},{t,[2]}},
6     "Distance Formula",
7     {"d=", "r=", "t="},
8     {
9      "Enter distance or capital X to calculate",
10     "Enter rate or capital X to calculate",
11     "Enter time or capital X to calculate"
12    },
13    {d,r,t}
14   ) then
15    a:=d+"="+r+"*"+t;
16    MSGBOX(a);
17    b:="X";
18    c:=CAS.solve(EVAL(a),EVAL(b));
19   end;
20   END;
```

The dist 2 version is shown using Notepad ++ with the HP prime plug-in. Any text editor could be used. Notepad ++ can be set to PASCAL if the HP Prime plug-in is not installed. The actual technique of adding a text file code to a HP Prime is given in the HP Prime ArithSeries program's screenshot that follows.

Remember the HP Prime Free does not have programming.

Go to computerlearningservice.com/html/products.html to download the file.

Shown next is the screen that follows when we execute the **dist2()** command from the **HOME** view command line. The parenthesis are optional since there are no parameters for the function. We also could have executed the program from the **CAS** view.

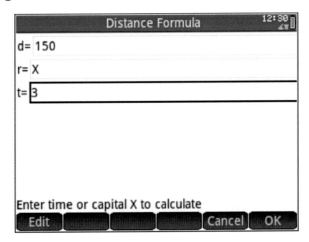

Using the **HOME** view on the HP Prime, press the **Toolbox** key. Press the **User** soft key to locate the Program Function **dist2**. Press the **OK** soft key to see the above screen. Key in the values as shown. Use the capital X key for the second entry. Press the **OK** soft key.

Notice the title, variable prompts, and specific help message for the variable being input. The entry {{d,[2]}, {r,[2]}, {t,[2]}} with a value of [2] allowed the variables to be input as strings.

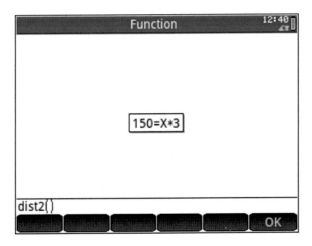

We next see our selection echoed back in a Message Box. Press the **OK** soft key to see the solution dist2 with {50} on the right side in the history area (not shown).

Notice that the original parameter list in **dist2()** is empty since we are using input in this program. In the Notepad++ listing above notice the use of **CAS.solve** command. Local values of **a**, **b**, and **c** with 2 uses of the **Eval** function are necessary for **CAS.solve** to work when the function **dist2()** is being run from the **HOME** view. Coded this way, it will also run from the **CAS** view.

We next look at the arithmetic series program for arithmetic sequences. This program allows us to add more than one function to a program's application library. Program application libraries will also be referred to as projects. This is the first example of the last step for an extended level user.

As math content is added to this volume and the series, we will utilize Global functions and Global programs to extend the HP Prime's power and facilitate our understanding. We will use Global functions and Global programs to add some very powerful and useful commands, functions, and programs to the built-in commands, functions, and capabilities of the HP Prime handheld/ HP Prime Pro app/ and Virtual computer software.

HP Prime/ Pro/ Virtual Arithmetic Series – Notepad++

```
1     ArithSeries;
2
3     EXPORT arithn(d,f,n)
4     BEGIN
5      return f+(n-1)*d;
6     END;
7
8     EXPORT arithsum(f,l,n)
9     BEGIN
10     return n/2*(f+l);
11    END;
12
13    EXPORT arithsum1(d,f,n)
14    BEGIN
15     return n/2*(f+arithn(d,f,n));
16    END;
```

The complete ArithSeries Library listing in Notepad++ with the HP prime plug-in is shown

To further illustrate Global one-line functions, we take a look at arithmetic sequences. We add a Library of one-line arithmetic sequence formulas to our ArithSeries Library.

The actual technique of adding this text file to a HP Prime is given in the HP Prime ArithSeries program's screenshot that follows.

Go to computerlearningservice.com/html/products.html to download the file.

Note: The return in line 15 uses line 3 function **arithn**. This will work since the function **arithn** was coded before **arithsum1**. The function **arithn** is a subroutine of **arithsum1**. To make the order of the function **arithn** irrelevant we would declare function **arithn();**, no parameters - ending in a semicolon, as the first entry after the program project name, **ArithSeries**.

Technically only the last two formulas are arithmetic series, but the function arithn is used in the last formula. This Library gives us a model for adding Global one-line functions for formulas. Use this Library's model to build and add formulas to your own Libraries. Beside math Libraries build your own Libraries of formulas from any subject area.

We next show a project for grouping our miscellaneous functions together. This is a second example of the last step for an extended level user.

HP Prime/ Pro/ Virtual A Collection of Miscellaneous Programs – Notepad++

```
1   CLSvol1;
2   // functions programs - 1
3   // Date: 2017-06-04
4   // © Larry Schroeder 2018
5   // All rights reserved
6
7   distrnl();
8
9   EXPORT distrnl(x1,x2)
10  BEGIN
11    return ABS(x2-x1);
12  END;
13
```

Here we add a project to group our miscellaneous programs in a single project. The double forward //s are comments. Listing all the functions before they occur allows us to use that function as a subroutine in any other miscellaneous function that we later add to the project.

We would delete standalone program **distrnl**.

Give the project a meaningful name. CLS is our publisher name, Computer Learning Service. The vol1 suffix representing volume 1.

Go to computerlearningservice.com/html/products.html to download the file.

Add other miscellaneous function as they occur to this project. Be sure to list it at the beginning following the program declaration **distrnl()**. Listing it here without the parameters helps document all the functions in the project plus makes the function available as a subroutine. This allows it to act as a subroutine without having to have its code declared before other functions in this project that call it.

Later in the compound fraction section of this tutorial we will add a program Library dealing with slope of a secant line, equation of a line, equation of a secant line, slope of a tangent line, and equation of a tangent line. Its Library functions demonstrate how Global one-line functions can help with the understanding of complex math concepts. We discuss in the Library's creation how enhancements such as using Private functions and providing Global function of one Library to another Library can be made.

We then add another group of functions to this Library. The additional functions include *x*-intercepts, minimums and maximums, inflection points, places where a graph is increasing or decreasing, and the concavity of a graph. The additional functions generate a set of tools that can be used to help with graphing and in solving optimization problems.

The HP Prime Innovation in Education Series' primary goal is giving us a path to learn math. Revealing the commands and functions of the HP Prime and learning how to create and use Libraries that extend the HP Prime power and usefulness is the other major goal of the HP Prime Innovation in Education Series.

HP Prime/ Pro/ Virtual Arithmetic Sequences – HP Prime Screen

```
                    ArithSeries                04:47
ArithSeries;

EXPORT arithn(d,f,n)
BEGIN
 return f+(n-1)*d;
END;

EXPORT arithsum(f,l,n)
BEGIN
 return n/2*(f+l);
END;

EXPORT arithsum1(d f n)
   Cmds    Tmplt     Page       Check
```

Here we show the three functions from ArithSeries. To see the third function refer to the earlier Notepad ++ listing. The functions are used for Arithmetic Sequences or also known as Arithmetic Progressions.

Press the **Program** key on the HP Prime. Press the **New** soft key. Type in **ArithSeries** to the **Name**: field. Leave the CAS: field unchecked. Press the **OK** soft key.

Use the following instructions to copy and paste the listing from Notepad++ or your text editor. In Notepad++ select all and copy. With the **ArithSeries** template showing, press the **Copy** key on the HP Prime. Press the soft key **All**, followed by pressing the soft key **Cut**. Use the paste function of the HP Prime Pro or HP Prime Virtual Calculator to paste from the system clipboard the listing from Notepad++. At this point, we will see the above screen. Press the **Check** soft key. Press **OK** soft key to message "No errors in the program".

Remember the HP Prime Free does not have the programming function

Go to computerlearningservice.com/html/products.html to download the file.

The last entry is an example of how a new function can be added that uses an existing function. We could of used $2 \cdot f + (n - 1) \cdot d$ instead of $f +$ **arithn**(d,f,n) expression but we wanted to demonstrate how new functions can be made up of built-in and/or user created functions.

Note: We choose to list the parameters in alphabetical order, d is the common difference, f is the first term, l is the last term, and n is the number of terms. The order of the parameters is up to us. We will use a logical order if that makes sense for the function or alphabetical order in functions where no logical order exists. This order is important when we run a function from the command line. If we choose to run from the Program Catalog, it will prompt us with the variable name.

Next we apply this to Gauss's famous example. Our function "arithsum(f,l,n)" formalizes the technique that Gauss used.

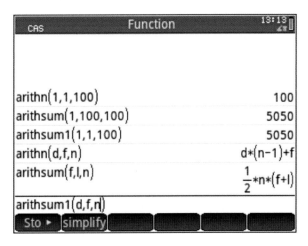

Using the **CAS** view on the HP Prime, press the **Toolbox** key. Press the **User** soft key to locate the Program Function **arithn**. Press the **OK** soft key. Key in the values shown and press **Enter**. Repeat the procedure for **arithsum** and **arithsum1**.

Use the history and Soft key **Copy** or press **Enter** to move to command line. Key in parameters as shown. Press **Enter**.

Pressing **Enter** will display the result as the expression, $\{[\ f\ +d(n-1)+f]n\}/2$, not the original expression, $n/2(f+\textbf{arithn}(d,f,n))$, that we entered. Using **toolbox> Algebra > Collect** will display $\{[\ d(n-1)+2f]n\}/2.$.

For HP Prime Free user skipping programming and all the other HP Prime family we now look at how to find the arithmetic sum by using the quick function **Define** key. We use its result in the Gauss anecdote that follows.

HP Prime Family Arithmetic Sum using Define

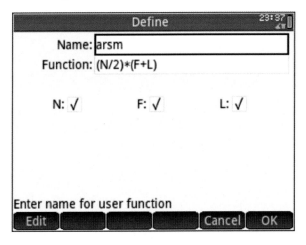

Begin by selecting the **Define** key on the HP Prime. Key in as shown. Be sure to use capital N, F, and L. Press the soft key **OK** or **Enter**.

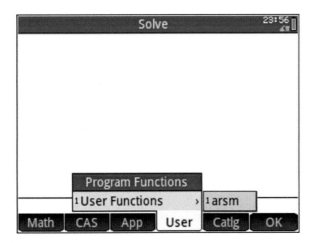

Using the **HOME** view on the HP Prime, press the **Toolbox** key. Press the **User** soft key to locate the User Functions **arsm**. Press the **OK** soft key. We also could of typed **arsm** in the **HOME** view command line. Screenshot is taken from HP Prime Free. Since we last used the Solve Library Application, Solve appears as the title.

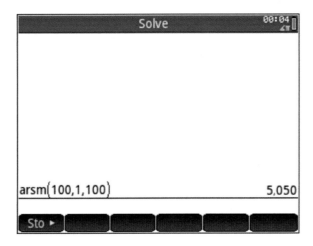

Key in the **( )**'s and parameters shown. Press **Enter**. The parameters values are entered in the order given by the definition: N, F, and L. The real variables N, F, and L are still set to zero. The parameters entry did not affect their value. To edit this function enter it as the **Name:** in the **Define** screen.

Gauss Anecdote

From Gauss's Wikipedia Anecdotes, "Another famous story has it that in primary school after the young Gauss misbehaved, his teacher, J.G. Büttner, gave him a task: add a list of integers in arithmetic progression; as the story is most often told, these were the numbers from 1 to 100. The young Gauss reputedly produced the correct answer within seconds, to the astonishment of his teacher and his assistant Martin Bartels.

Gauss's presumed method was to realize that pairwise addition of terms from opposite ends of the list yielded identical intermediate sums: 1 + 100 = 101, 2 + 99 = 101, 3 + 98 = 101, and so on, for a total sum of 50 × 101 = 5050. However, the details of the story are at best uncertain (see[30 in the article] for discussion of the original Wolfgang Sartorius von Waltershausen source and the changes in other versions); some authors, such as Joseph Rotman in his book A first course in Abstract Algebra, question whether it ever happened (*Carl Friedrich Gauss*)."

Investigation

A modern use for the number line would be the measuring wheel. Agriculture uses this tool to measure lengths and widths of fields in determining yields per acre. A commercial model found on the Internet had the specifications listed as a circumference of 5 feet and a diameter of 19 inches. Divide these two numbers. What is this number close to?

Figure 5 Measuring wheel

$$\pi = \text{ Circumference } \div \text{ diameter} \approx 3.14159$$

$$\pi \approx 5\cdot 12 \div 19 = 60 \div 19 = 60\cdot\frac{1}{19} = \frac{60}{19} = 3\frac{3}{19} \approx 3.15789$$

Unitary Analysis $\qquad \dfrac{5 \text{ ft}}{1}\cdot\dfrac{12 \text{ in}}{1 \text{ ft}}\cdot\dfrac{1}{19 \text{ in}} \approx 3.15789$

Identity for multiplication $a\cdot 1 = a \quad 5 \text{ ft}\cdot\dfrac{12 \text{ in}}{1 \text{ ft}} = 60 \text{ in}$

Invert and multiply $\qquad a \div b = a\cdot\dfrac{1}{b} \quad 60 \div 19 = 60\cdot\dfrac{1}{19}$

What does it mean to divide these two numbers?

We are looking at a mathematical constant *pi* that is the ratio of a circle's circumference to its diameter, which is approximately equal to 3.14159. When comparing numbers in the ratio, we recognize that they must be the same units. Thus, we change the circumference to inches, since it is the easier unit to change. Remember *pi* is an irrational number, which means we are unable to express it actually as the ratio of two integers. The more common approximate ratio that people use is 22/7 where the specification for our measuring wheel turns out to be 60/19.

To mechanically work this problem we take advantage of unitary analysis, the identity property for multiplication, and that division is the same as multiplying by the reciprocal.

Unitary analysis is where we setup the units to get the desired unit(s) or number needed in the outcome. We do not want to directly divide 5 by 19. But change the 5 feet to 60 inches and then divide by 19 inches.

In the next section we discuss the Operations and Properties of Real numbers. We will use two of these properties now.

First we use the identity property for multiplication, *a* x 1 = *a*. Here we multiply 5 feet by 1 to get 60 inches, the identical amount but using a different unit of measure. The 1 is 12in/1ft. To understand why this is 1, consider the number and unit of measure as a whole. Thus both 12in and 1ft are the same, and when we have the same over the same the result is 1. Keeping track of the units and canceling the units helps to perform the correct conversion. Common mistakes in conversions like this would be to divide by 12 rather then multiply by 12. Using units in the calculation prevents this kind of error.

Next, to divide we used the rule that we can <u>multiply by the reciprocal</u>. Commonly we think of this with fractions, "Invert and multiply". Historically math education has varied between various philosophies of how to accomplish skills and understanding. Hopefully rules such as "Invert and multiply" are preceded by a proper discussion that teaches learners the mathematics behind the rule not just a mechanical way to do it.

In learning mathematics, we need to understand that writing 60/19 as a fraction is just a way to specify division of 60 by 19. Pressing HP Prime divide key displays the problem as a fraction. Thus, the understanding between fraction notation and division is essential to working with the HP Prime.

Understanding and mechanical techniques both play essential roles in learning and using mathematics.

HP Prime Family Pi Approximation

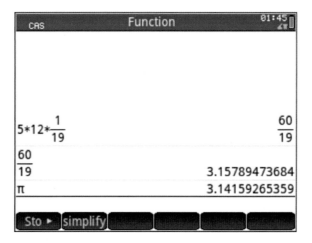

Begin by selecting the **CAS** key on the HP Prime. Key in as shown. Use the **pi** key plus **Enter** for a decimal approximation of the answer.

The Great Pyramid appears to have *pi* associated with a lot of its measurements and calculations. Use a search engine to investigate *pi* in general and the occurrence of *pi* in The Great Pyramid's measurements and calculations. It is theorized that using a wheel for measurements was what caused *pi* to be in many of the pyramid's results. It is generally considered that the existence of *pi* was unknown to the Egyptians at this time.

Astronaut photograph ISS007-E-12915 was taken August 18, 2003 by Cynthia A Evans, Great Pyramids as seen from the International Space Station.

Explanation 1.2 - Operations and Properties of Real Numbers

In this section we discuss the addition, subtraction, multiplication, and division of real numbers. To formalize the rules for addition of real numbers we use absolute value. We present an alternate approach to addition and subtraction of real numbers. Following our discussion of the other operations of real numbers, we look at some of the more important basic properties used in manipulating real numbers.

Addition and Subtraction of Real Numbers

To help with understanding we will introduce addition with a number line.

The a, represented by a solid red vector, and b, represented by dotted blue vector, are shown originating at zero. A **vector** in mathematics and physics is geometric entity that has both magnitude and direction. A second copy is shown above to represent the *actual* addition.

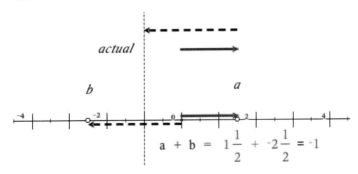

Figure 1 Addition of Real Numbers (Education.ti.com, The Number System)

In general, to use a number line to illustrate addition, we start by drawing vector a. If a is zero draw b starting at 0. If a is positive, draw to the right from zero. If a is negative, draw to the left from zero. From where a ends, draw vector b. If b is positive, we draw to the right. If b is negative, we draw to the left. If b is zero, we stay at a.

Drawing both vectors first on the number line as shown in the preceding drawing would be optional but does help to illustrate b's length and would be very useful for constructing the vector, $-b$, used in illustrating subtraction of $a - b$.

We now present a number line for doing subtraction. We show subtraction as "addition of the opposite". To illustrate what is meant by the opposite we draw vector $-b$. Vector $-b$ is vector b drawn in the opposite direction.

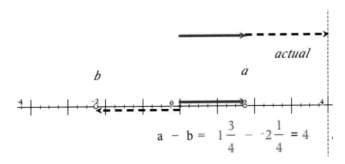

Figure 2 Subtraction of Real Numbers (Education.ti.com, The Number System)

Once we draw $-b$ the remaining steps would be the same as before, since we would be now solving the equivalent $a + (-b)$ addition problem. We are using the fact that $a - b = a + (-b)$, or to do subtraction of real numbers we do "addition of the opposite".

Rules for Addition of Two Real Numbers

We now present the following rule for Addition of Two Real Numbers.

Addition of Two Real Numbers

1. When both are positive, add the numbers, the result is positive.

2. When both are negative, add the absolute values, the result is negative.

3. When there is a negative and a positive, subtract the absolute values.

   a. If the positive number has a greater absolute value, the answer will be positive.

   b. If the negative number has a greater absolute value, the answer will be negative.

   c. If the positve number and negative number have the same absolute value, the answer is 0.

4. When one of the numbers is 0, the sum is the other number.

Rule for Subtraction of Two Real Numbers

We now look at subtraction of two real numbers.

Definition of Subtraction

The difference $a - b$ is the number that when added

to b gives a.

The definition of subtraction does not provide an efficient way to do subtraction. For example, $14 - 5 = 9$ since $5 + 9 = 14$ (9 is added to 5 giving us 14). Looking at a negative example, $4 - 6 = -2$, since $6 + -2 = 4$ (-2 is added to 6 giving us 4).

Changing the problem to addition and then use the addition rules is a better technique. Using the number line we found that $a - b = a + (-b)$, so to do subtraction of real numbers we do "addition of the opposite".

Subtraction of Two Real Numbers

For any real numbers a and b

$$a - b = a + (-b)$$

To subtract, do addition of the opposite.

The development of the addition and subtraction rules through the number line leads us to the following properties.

Inverse and Identity Addition Properties

1. $a + (-a) = 0$ **Inverse** property of addition

2. $a + 0 = a$ **Identity** property of addition

Inverse property of addition: $-a$ is the **additive inverse**, or **opposite** of a.

Identity property of addition: 0 is the **additive identity**.

HP Prime Family Graph of Function F1(x)

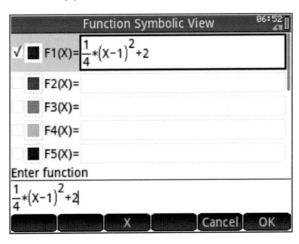

Press the **Apps** key. Highlight the **Function** icon on the Application Library screen. Press the soft **Start** key. Press the soft **Edit** key. The above screen will appear. Enter function as shown. Press the soft **OK** key.

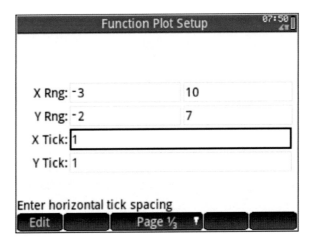

Press the Plot **Setup** key. Page 1/3, change these values X Rng: -3, 10; Y Rng: -2, 7. Page 2/3, check the Labels box.

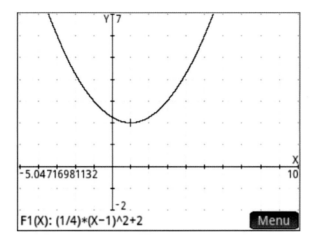

Figure 4 Parabola y = a(x – h)² + k

Press the **Plot** key to see a graph of the function. Press the soft **Menu** key. Use the **Fcn Extremum**. Press the soft **OK** key and then soft **Menu** key. Use the **Fcn Defintion** and soft **down arrow** key to display the function in algebraic form.

Inverse and Identity properties are frequently used together. In the Cartesian coordinate system to find the formula for the vertex (h, k) of a parabola expressed in three-terms, $y = ax^2 + bx + c$, we will add a number to make the first two-terms a multiple of a perfect square and then add the **opposite** of the multiple to the constant term. In essence what we are doing is adding 0, the **additive identity**. With the aid of factoring, **additive inverse**, and **additive identity** we turn our original three-term expression, $y = 1/4x^2 – 1/2x + 9/4$, into an equivalent expression of the form shown in figure 4, thus giving us formulas for the *h* and *k* components of the vertex.

Alternate Approach to Addition and Subtraction of Real Numbers

Before working out an example. Let us look at the "Gas Air Balloon". The "Gas Air Balloon" helps us understand why an alternate simpler approach to the traditional addition and subtraction approach is what most people eventually use and how an Alternate Approach is actually grounded in mathematical logic. With the "Gas Air Balloon" addition and subtraction we look at values for *a*, *b*, *c* and *d*. For *a*, *b* and *c*, we use a **positive** integer to **add** helium (raise the balloon) and/or a **negative** integer to **add** sand (lower the balloon). For *d*, we use a **positive** integer to **remove** helium (lower the balloon) or a **negative** integer to **remove** sand (raise the balloon).

The *d* in the "Gas Air Balloon" in used as the subtrahend, the number being subtracted or **removed**. The *a* in the "Gas Air Balloon" is the first addend and *c* is the minuend, the number from which another is to be subtracted. The *b* is the second addend. Thus *a*, *b*, and *c* are associated with **adding** helium or sand. The *d* is associated with removing helium or sand.

Technical notes: Most of us are more familiar with a "Hot Air Balloon". Let look at some information about the less familiar "Gas Air Balloon". A balloon filled with helium is an example of a gas balloon. Helium is expensive but non-flammable. Hydrogen can also be used, it is cheaper but it is very flammable. Helium and hydrogen gas balloons stay aloft because helium and hydrogen are lighter than air. Large blimps and rubber party balloons are familiar examples of helium gas balloons. Wikipedia show a picture of a free gas balloon that looks like a hot air balloon. Use a search engine to investigate the differences, advantages, and historical development and uses of hot air and gas balloons. Gas balloons can control height by either venting gas or dropping ballast. Modern designs use additional methods. In addition to venting helium or dropping sand, the "Gas Air Balloon" has us adding helium and sand to control height. For the ballast, the Wikipedia article mentioned using water.

Look at the following screenshot. Like the subtraction number line shown earlier, we find that $m - n = m + (-n)$ with m being -2 and n being -5. To do subtraction of real numbers we do "addition of the opposite." We are using m and n to avoid confusion with a and b in the illustrations.

For the balloon going down first, that is the minuend or first addend being negative, we could think of a balloon going into a canyon. The -2 in both the minuend and first addend would be **removing** helium, causing the balloon to go down. To go back up we **remove** sand, -5, or **add** helium, 5. Substituting in for m and n and putting the two equations together we have -2 – (-5) = -2 + 5 = 3. To do subtraction we can do the "addition of the opposite."

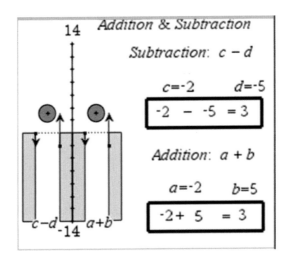

Figure 5 Gas Air Balloon – Balloon Going Down First (Education.ti.com, Classroom Activities)

Look at the next screenshot. We find that 5 + (-2) = 5 – 2, so we can do addition of real numbers by doing "subtraction of the opposite." Figure 5 showed that a subtraction expression with double signs is equivalent to a simpler addition expression and the next screenshot shows that an addition expression with double signs is equivalent to a simpler subtraction expression.

Figure 6 allows us to think of addition as "subtraction of the opposite." Thinking of addition as "subtraction of the opposite" is generally not found in textbooks or tutorials, however we use it and subtraction by "addition of the opposite" in developing an Alternate Approach for simplifying expressions with double signs. By double signs we mean subtraction of a negative number or addition of a negative number.

In figure 6, the 5 in both the minuend and first addend would be **adding** helium, causing the balloon to go up. Then **removing** helium, 2, or **adding** sand, -2, cause the balloon to go down. Substituting in and putting the two equations together we have 5 + (-2) = 5 – 2 = 3. To do addition we can do "subtraction of the opposite."

We recommend that you explore some more by setting up your own equivalent addition and subtraction problems. To do this you would parallel our first example, $m - n = m + (-n)$, subtraction by "addition of the opposite", with m and n being activity c and d and a being m and b being $-n$; and our second example, $m + n = m - (-n)$, addition by "subtraction of the opposite", with m and n being a and b and c being m and d being $-n$.

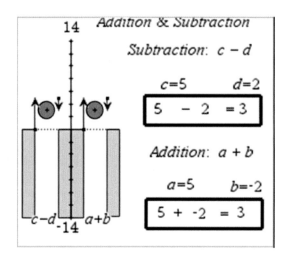

Figure 6 Gas Air Balloon – Balloon Going Up First (Education.ti.com, Classroom Activities)

To simplify problems with two like signs, $-2 - (-5)$, or unlike signs, $5 + (-2)$, the Alternate Approach changes the problem to an equivalent simpler problem, $-2 + 5$ or $5 - 2$. The complex subtraction gets changed to addition and the complex addition gets changed to subtraction. The two previous screen shots illustrate this. The 5.1 tab of the Hot Air Balloon activity was used to show the equivalent simpler addition and subtraction problem are equivalent to complex addition and subtraction problems.

When looking at the two screenshots we always look for the least complex equation. The Alternate Approach has us changing more complex equation to simpler equivalent equation by either changing subtraction to "addition of the opposite," first screenshot, or addition to "subtraction of the opposite," second screenshot. Shortly we will give a mnemonic that makes the process even easier.

The Alternate Approach to addition and subtraction of signed numbers leads us to create the Alternate Rule - Addition and Subtraction.

The Alternate Rule - Addition and Subtraction calculates the results of addition and subtraction expressions written without double signs. Any complex expressions are changed to a simpler form.

After their introduction to addition and subtraction of signed numbers textbooks and tutorials write future addition and subtraction problems in the simplest form. Finding a direct way to work the problems written in simpler form without double signs is why most people eventually develop their own similar Alternate Approach to use when solving addition and subtraction problems. The tutorial's Alternate Approach should help you with understanding why your personal approach works and give you an opportunity to see how the tutorial's Alternate Rule - Addition and Subtraction can help you work addition and subtraction problems.

In the TI-Nspire's Hot Air Balloon activity we simplified complex subtraction problems by changing them to "addition of the opposite" and complex addition problems by changing them to "subtraction of the opposite."

An easy way to accomplish this is to use the following mnemonic:

Two like signs become a positive sign (add). In our example: $-2 - (-5) = -2 + 5 = 3$

Two unlike signs become a negative sign (subtract). In our example: 5 + (-2) = 5 – 2 = 3

We will be studying multiplication and division of signed numbers shortly. This mnemonic is what we do when we multiply and divide signed numbers. Using this mnemonic to simplifying complex problems uses the same logic we use for multiplication and division of signed numbers. Therefore to simplify complex addition or complex subtraction we will use a rule that is already needed.

Some authors when introducing signed numbers like to use a positive sign instead of it being implied. Our same mnemonic holds. For example: -3 + (+4) = -3 + 4 = 1 and -3 – (+4) = -3 – 4 = -7. Positive signs on the first addend or the minuend can be dropped.

Changing addition and subtraction complex expressions to simpler expressions and addition and subtraction expressions stated as a simple expression results in the Alternate Rule – Addition and Subtraction having five types of problems to work, two addition and three subtraction problems.

For example: 3 + 4 = 7, -2 + 5 = 3, 5 – 2 = 3, 3 – 4 = -1, -3 - 4 = -7.

We find that an easy way to do these problems is to think money:

3 + 4 = 7 (have $3, get $4 more, net $7); -2 + 5 = 3 (owe $2, get $5, net $3); 5 – 2 = 3 (have $5, bill for $2, net $3); 3 – 4 = -1 (have $3, bill for $4, net owe $1); -3 - 4 = -7 (owe $3, bill for $4 more, net owe $7).

To formalize the Alternate Rule – Addition and Subtraction we see that it parallels the Addition of Two Real Numbers. For the two addition problems, we can think of the second addend being positive and for the three subtraction problems we can think of the subtrahend as being negative. We now have a sign for either the first addend or minuend and a sign for either the second addend or subtrahend. When the signs are the same for the first and second addends or minuend and subtrahend, we add the absolute values, when the signs are different for the first and second addends or minuend and subtrahend, we subtract the smaller absolute value from the larger absolute value. The last step for all five problems is to supply the result with the appropriate sign according to the Addition of Two Real Numbers rules.

For two of the five problems in our example, addition of two positives numbers and subtraction of a smaller positive from a larger positive number, we would use traditional addition and subtraction. In our example, 3 + 4 = 7 and 5 – 2 = 3 would be done traditionally.

For the three remaining, -2 + 5 = 3, 3 – 4 = -1, -3 - 4 = -7, thinking of addition as having the second addend being positive and subtraction as having the subtrahend being negative, we apply the Addition of Two Real Numbers rules. The first one, -2 + 5 = 3, we would subtract the absolute values of -2 from the absolute value of 5 and keep the sign of the greater absolute value. For 3 – 4 = -1, we subtract the absolute values of 3 from the absolute value of -4 and keep the sign of the greater absolute value. For the last one, -3 - 4 = -7, we add the absolute values of -3 and absolute value of -4 with the result being negative.

HP Prime Family Alternate Rule – Addition and Subtraction

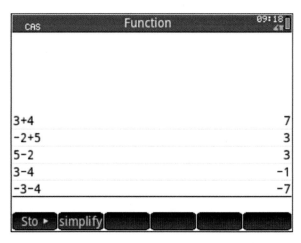

Begin by selecting the **CAS** key on the HP Prime. Key in as shown. If the **CAS** view has computations, clear the **history** first. To clear the **history**, press the **Clear** key.

The problems are the five examples we used for the Alternate Rule – Addition and Subtraction. We recommend that you do them mentally by the Alternate Rule – Addition and Subtraction "think money". They can also be done mentally by the traditional addition and subtractions rules. The traditional rules would mentally change entries four and five to "addition of the opposite" before simplifying.

Alternate Rule - Addition and Subtraction

For any real numbers a and non–negative b

$$a + (-b) = a - b$$
$$a - (-b) = a + b$$

Simplify
Two unlike signs, change to negative sign (subtract).
Two like signs, change to positive sign (add).

Calculate Results
Think money: a owe, have; $-b$ bill, $+b$ get

$a - b$	have, bill	$a \geq 0$	$4 - 7 = -3$
$a - b$	owe, bill	$a < 0$	$-4 - 7 = -11$
$a + b$	have, get	$a \geq 0$	$4 + 7 = 11$
$a + b$	owe, get	$a < 0$	$-4 + 7 = 3$

The Simplify is the mnemonic that allows us to easily accomplish the first two rules, $a + (-b) = a - b$ and $a - (-b) = a + b$. We are able to change complex expressions to a simpler form.

We now calculate the results for addition and subtraction expressions that are written without double signs. The Calculate Results, Think money: with money being something everyone already knows how to figure, allows us to know when to add and when to subtract and what sign to use for the results.

Example 1 Adding and Subtracting Real Numbers

(a) -11+(-5)=-16 Two negatives. Add absolute values, 11 and 5 getting 16. The result is negative, −16.

(b) -6-2
    = -6+(-2)=-8 Change subtraction to addition of the opposite. Work using addition rules. Add absolute values, 6 and 2 getting 8. The result is negative, −8.

Alternate Approach

(a) -11+(-5)
    = -11-5=-16 Two unlike signs become a negative sign. Think money: owe $11, bill for $5 more, owe $16.

(b) -6-2=-8 Think money: owe $6, bill for $2 more, owe $8.

HP Prime Family Adding and Subtracting

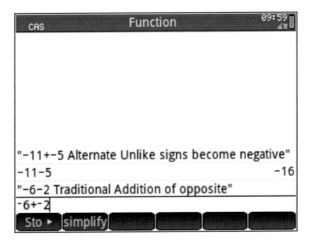

Begin by selecting the **CAS** key on the HP Prime. We used the double quotes " " for each comment line. Erased the second copy of the comment caused by pressing **Enter**. Key in first entry as shown in the first comment. Pressing **Enter** changed the entry, -11+-5, to -11-5 with a solution of -16.

When **Enter** is pressed to the entry, -6+-2, in the command line, the HP Prime will change the problem to "-6-2 with a result of -8" being given in the history area.

If the **CAS** view has computations, clear the **history** first. To clear the **history**, press the Clear key.

HP Prime is using the alternate approach of eliminating double signs of "addition followed by opposite" by changing it to "subtraction".

Exercise 1 Adding and Subtracting Real Numbers

Evaluate:

(a) -2.1-(-5.3)

(b) $1\frac{1}{2}+\left(-3\frac{1}{4}\right)$

Solution >>

Collecting Like Terms – Part 1

In Example 1's screen shot, entry one and comment two, -11 – 5 and -6 – 2, show how expressions using subtraction are written in textbooks and tutorials. Comment one and command line, entered as -11 + (-5) and 6 + (-2), show that expressions using addition of the opposite are equivalent to their subtraction expression, -11 – 5 and 6 - 2. By writing subtraction as addition we introduce the concept of terms. **Terms** are numbers, variables, products and quotients of numbers and/or variables. Here our terms are connected by addition. We can simplify expressions by **collecting** or **combining** expressions with **like terms**.

Remember our HP Prime displays entries such as -11 + (-5) and 6 + (-2) dropping the parenthesis that are entered. In textbooks and tutorials the parenthesis would be kept rather than dropped.

Thus using parenthesis and double signs, subtraction expressions such as -2x – 5 can be written as -2x + (-5). We change subtraction to "addition of the opposite" to rewrite our original expression as an equivalent addition expression. The equivalent expression allows us to see that the terms are -2x and -5.

For addition such as -4x + 7 the terms, -4x and 7, can be read directly.

The process of collecting like terms is based on the Distributive Property. The Distributive Property and other basic properties will be covered next. By using the Distributive Property to collect like terms we only need to add and subtract the real number coefficients and the real number constants.

When we work with collecting of like terms using the Distributive Property, textbooks and tutorials after the brief introduction of the topic, ask us, if we can, to just write the answer without showing the underlying distributive property.

The Distributive Property is replaced by having us mentally combine only like terms using the addition and subtraction rules of real numbers for the coefficients and constants. The textbooks and tutorials want us to mentally change subtraction of a term to "addition of the opposite" and then combine the like terms in our head. Remember the first term and addition terms can be determined directly.

Another option to the double signs created by "addition of the opposite" is to use the Alternate Rule - Addition and Subtraction approach for the addition and subtraction of real numbers to combine the coefficients and constants. We prefer the Alternate Rule - Addition and Subtraction approach for the combining of like terms, since it avoids the need to think of the double signs in our head and we only need to "think money" to combine like terms.

We will complete our explanation and give an example of Collecting Like Terms at the end of this section.

Basic Properties of Algebra

When learning our basic facts, we know that 5 + 8 = 8 + 5. Having learned the four fact for 7 x 4, learning the seven fact for 4 x 7 was easy, since the result was the same. Our experience with numbers lets us know that the following properties are true.

Properties of Real Numbers

1. $a + b = b + a$ **Commutative** addition
2. $(a + b) + c = a + (b + c)$ **Associative** addition
3. $a \cdot b = b \cdot a$ **Commutative** multiplication
4. $(a \cdot b) \cdot c = a \cdot (b \cdot c)$ **Associative** multiplication
5. $a \cdot (b + c) = a \cdot b + a \cdot c$ **Distributive**

The Commutative Property for addition and multiplication says that the order does not matter when adding or multiplying.

The Associative Property for addition and multiplication says that when there is three numbers, it does not matter which two we add or multiply first.

When we are adding 6 + 7 + 4 + 5 + 3, we can think 6 + 4 + 7 + 3 + 5 = 10 + 10 + 5 = 25. In other words when we add or multiply as we can do as we please and no parentheses are necessary. What we are doing is combining the Commutative and Associative Property for addition into the "Do As You Please Property" for addition. The same can be done for the Commutative and Associative Property for multiplication.

The Distributive Property of multiplication over addition allows us to add first and multiply next or multiply the first factor times each addend and then add these results. Since the Commutative Property for multiplication holds, the a, or the first factor in the Distributive Property, could be listed as the second factor, $a(b + c) = (b + c)a$. Some textbooks or tutorials refer to these two versions as the Left and Right Distributive Properties. The results for both are $ab + ac$.

The Distributive Property holds for subtraction as well, since subtraction can be thought of as "addition of the opposite". Therefore we have that $a(b - c) = ab - ac$.

Earlier, we stated the Inverse and Identity Addition Properties. To complete the Basic Properties of Algebra we now state the Inverse and Identity Multiplication Properties.

Inverse and Identity Multiplication Properties

1. $a \cdot \dfrac{1}{a} = 1$ **Inverse** property of multiplication
2. $a \cdot 1 = a$ **Identity** property of multiplication

Inverse property of multiplication: $1/a$ is the **multiplicative inverse**, or **reciprocal** of a.

Identity property of multiplication: 1 is **multiplicative identity**.

As with the Inverse and Identity Addition Properties, the Inverse and Identity Multiplication Properties are frequently used in problem solving.

In the last section, in the <u>measuring wheel</u> calculation of pi we multiplied by 1, 12in/1ft, to change 5 feet to 60 inches.

Multiplying by 1 would also be necessary in this section parabola example of changing the formula from terms to vertex form if the first and second term did not have a factor in common. The 1 would take the form of Inverse Property for Multiplication, using both the number and its reciprocal.

Multiplication and Division of Real Numbers

The results for this multiplication and division are the same as our Alternate Rule - Addition and Subtraction's mnemonic.

Like signs: result Positive

Unlike signs: result Negative

We begin by looking at the four possibilities: (+)(+); (+)(-); (-)(+); and (-)(-). We note that $a \times 0 = 0 \times a = 0$.

Multiplication as Repeated Addition

For positive number times a positive number, (+)(+), we can think of multiplication as repeated addition. Thus, "2 x 4" as "add two fours", or

$4 + 4 = 8$

and "3 x 8" as "add three eights", or

$8 + 8 + 8 = 24.$

In general, we have that "$a \times b$" means to "add a numbers of b's"

$a \times b = b + b + b + \ldots + b$ (a times).

Multiplication with Signed Numbers

Applying the same rule for a positive number times a negative number, (+)(-). Thus, "3 x (-5)" as "add three negative fives", or

$(-5) + (-5) + (-5) = -15.$

Reversing, the rule fails when we try to multiply a negative number times a positive number, (-)(+). For example, "(-6) x 2" the rule fails. However, by the Commutative Property

$(-6) \times 2 = 2 \times (-6) = (-6) + (-6) = -12.$

Next, we find that we are in trouble for negative number times a negative number, (-)(-). One approach is to make tables and look for a pattern. However, we will take a more formal approach. Let us look at -3(5 - 4), using subtraction as "addition of opposite" and the Distributive Property

$-3(5 - 4) = -3[5 + (-4)] = (-3)(5) + (-3)(-4).$

We evaluate the left side

$-3(5 - 4) = -3(1) = -3.$

Since the Distributive Property must be true, the right side must be equal to -3 as well

(-3)(5) + (-3)(-4) = -3.

For this to work we have

(-3)(5) + (-3)(-4) = -15+12 = -3.

The only way for this to be true was that (-3)(-4) = 12.

HP Prime Family **Multiplication of Two Real Numbers**

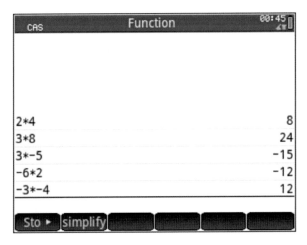

Begin by selecting the **CAS** key on the HP Prime. Key in as shown. If the **CAS** view has computations, clear the **history** first. To clear the **history**, press the **Clear** key.

Key in as shown. Calculation like this should be done mentally using the following rule.

We now present the rule for Multiplication of Two Real Numbers.

Multiplication of Two Real Numbers

1. Multiply the absolute values.

2. If the signs are alike, the result is positive.

3. If the signs are different, the result is negative.

4. If one number is zero, the product is zero.

To practice with multiplication, addition, and subtraction of real numbers and help with understanding of the Distributive Property, we look at the following figure.

The figure represents the left and right expressions in the Distributive Property. We look at the values for a, b, and c to see how both expressions are equivalent.

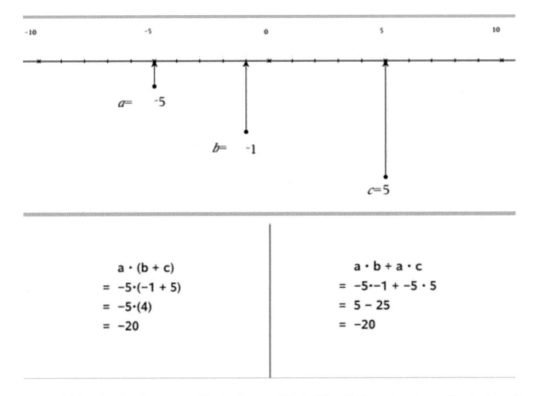

Figure 7 Distributive Property – Equivalence of Both Sides (Education.ti.com, Equivalence)

Substituting into the Distributive Property left and right expressions shows that both side are equal.

Note: Since the Distributive Property must hold, this would be another example that we can use showing that a (-)(-) must be (+), that is (-5)(-1) = 5.

To mentally verify the addition and subtraction operations in the figure we prefer to use the Alternate Rule – Addition and Subtraction. If the traditional approach for the additions and subtractions works better for you, it could be used as well.

Equivalent expressions are especially important when working problems manually and using the HP Prime CAS, Computer Algebra System, to work a problem.

Remark: Just because the answer came from our HP Prime does not necessarily mean that it is correct. Assuming the HP Prime answer is equivalent to textbooks, tutorials, and manual techniques is a big mistake. It is very easy to enter problems incorrectly, use incorrect operations or commands, or enter or leave out parentheses that create a problem different then what was given.

If everything was done correctly it is likely that the form of the answer that the HP Prime CAS gives us will differ from the form of the answer that ours textbooks, tutorials, and manual techniques ends up with. It is our job to show that they are equivalent. As in the next screenshot we may need to change the HP Prime CAS answer of -5(x + 4) to -5x + 20 by using the **expand** command or change its answer of -5x + 20 to -5(x + 4) by using the **factor** command.

Equivalent form of the answer is generally not a problem with the HP Prime **HOME** view since it does not have the Computer Algebra System. However, we still need to be aware of possible errors in our input and logic.

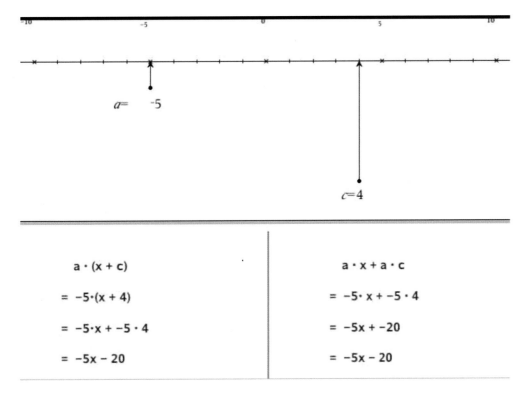

Figure 8 Distributive Property – Equivalence Using a Variable (Education.ti.com, Equivalence)

In figure 7 with numbers we showed that the left and right expressions are equal. We are trying to do the same thing here using the variable *x*.

The left work for line two to line three shows us using the expand of the Distributive Property

  -5(x + 4) = -5x + -5(4).

As before we can use Alternate Rule – Addition and Subtraction approach or traditional addition and subtraction with some mental reasoning to finish each side's simplification.

We can go from left side to right in the Distributive Property, $a(b + c) = ab + ac$, by multiplying (expand) and right side to left by factoring (factor). This is what the HP Prime CAS **expand** and **factor** do. The HP Prime CAS **expand** turns the left side into the right and the HP Prime CAS **factor** turns the right side into the left.

HP Prime Family Expand and Factor

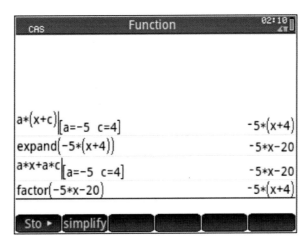

Begin by selecting the **CAS** key on the HP Prime. Key in as shown

Key in entry one. The **width** (|) operator, or **instantiation bar**, is located using the **Template** key. Type in "a=-5,c=4" following the **width** operator. The comma entry portion is changed to brackets. Use the **Toolbox > Algebra > Expand** and the **Toolbox > Algebra > Factor** commands for entry two and entry four. Use the **up arrow Enter** or soft **Copy** key combination to transfer the previous result to the command. Notice that **expand** changes the factors to terms. **Factor** does the opposite and changes terms to factors.

If the **CAS** view has computations, clear the **history** first. To clear the **history**, press the Clear key.

The above example shows us that without our intervention, the HP Prime CAS substitutes in but does not switch forms. It is up to us to use the **expand** and **factor** commands.

We now turn to division of real numbers.

> **Definition of Division**
>
> The quotient $\dfrac{a}{b}$ is the number, provided it exists,
>
> that when multiplied by b gives a.

We will use this definition to define integer division.

We begin by looking at the four possibilities: (+)/(+); (+)/(-); (-)/(+); and (-)/(-). We note that a / 0 is **undefined**, 0 / a = 0, and 0 / 0 is **indeterminate**.

Division of Positive Numbers

First we look at a positive number divided by a positive number, (+)/(+). For "20/5" we think what number when multiplied by 5 gives us 20? The number is 4 since (4)(5) = 20 thus

$20/5 = 4$.

Division of Signed Numbers

Next, we look at a positive number divided by a negative number, (+)/(-). For "35/(-7)" we think what number when multiplied by -7 gives us 35? The number is -5 since (-5)(-7) = 35 thus

$35/(-7) = -5$.

We now look at a negative number divided by a positive number, (-)/(+). For "(-24)/6" we think what number when multiplied by 6 gives us -24? The number is -4 since (-4)(6) = -24 thus

$(-24)/6 = -4$.

Lastly for signed numbers, we look at a negative number divided by a negative number, (-)/(-). For "(-12)/(-3)" we think what number when multiplied by -3 gives us -12? The number is 4 since (4)(-3) = -12 thus

$(-12)/(-3) = 4$.

Division of a non-zero number by zero

We now look at a non-zero divided by zero, $a/0$. For "11/0" we think what number when multiplied by 0 gives us 11? The question is for what value does $a \times 0 = 11$? There is no number since any number times zero equals zero, $a \times 0 = 0$. Thus we say that

11/0 is undefined.

Therefore, any non-zero real a, is **undefined** for $a/0$.

<u>Division of zero by a non-zero number</u>

Next, we look at zero divided by a non-zero number, $0/a$. For "0/3" we think what number when multiplied by 3 gives us 0? The number is 0 since 0 x 3 = 0 thus

  0/3 = 0.

Therefore, any non-zero real a, is **zero** for $0/a$.

<u>Division of zero by zero</u>

Finally, we look at zero by zero, 0/0. For "0/0" we think what number when multiplied by 0 gives us 0? Instead of a single number any number times zero, a x 0 = 0. Since it is impossible to determine any one number

  0/0 is indeterminate.

HP Prime Family Division of Two Real Numbers

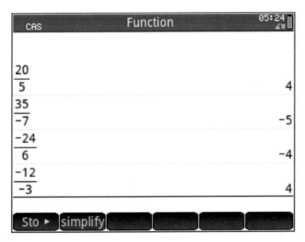

Begin by selecting the **CAS** key on the HP Prime. Key in as shown. . For division, we can use the **Fraction Template** using the **Template** key or **divide key**, "/". If the **CAS** view has computations, clear the **history** first. To clear the **history**, press the **Clear** key.

Calculation like this should be done mentally using the rule following the next screenshot.

.

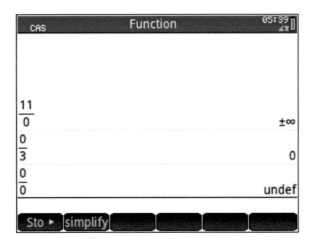

Continuing with the zero cases. Notice that the calculator displays the first answer as +- infinity and the last entry as undefined. From our earlier discussion it would have been better if the HP Prime used undefined for the first and indeterminate for the last.

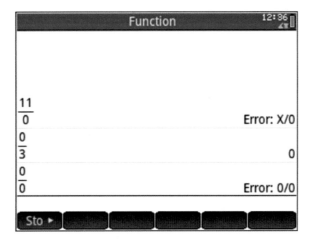

Press the **HOME** key. Enter as shown. Switching to **HOME** view notice the two error messages for division by zero. If the **HOME** view has computations, clear the **history** first. To clear the **history**, press the **Clear** key.

These answers should be done mentally with us using indeterminate for the 0/0 entry.

We now present the following rule for Division of Two Real Numbers.

Division of Two Real Numbers

For non–zero real numbers

1. Divide the absolute values.
2. If the signs are alike, the result is positive.
3. If the signs are different, the result is negative.

For problem involving zero, a non–zero

4. $\dfrac{a}{0}$ is undefined

5. $\dfrac{0}{a} = 0$

6. $\dfrac{0}{0}$ is indeterminate

Example 2 Multiplying and Dividing Real Numbers

(a) $-12 \cdot (-5) = 60$ Signs the same. Multiply absolute values, 12 and 5 getting 60. The result is positive.

(b) $16 \div (-2) = -8$ Signs different. Divide absolute values, 16 divided by 2 getting 8. The result is negative.

TI-Nspire Family /Multiplying and Dividing

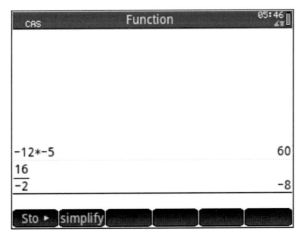

Begin by selecting the **CAS** key on the HP Prime. Key in as shown. . For division, we can use the **Fraction Template** using the **Template** key or **divide key**, "/". If the **CAS** view has computations, clear the **history** first. To clear the **history**, press the **Clear** key.

Exercise 2 Multiplying and Dividing Real Numbers

Evaluate:

(a) $21.1 \cdot (-4.2)$

(b) $-\dfrac{2}{7} \div (-5)$

Solution >>

Additional Properties

We have in some of our earlier discussions used fractions and fractional expressions. We now will take a look at their properties. We will refer to a/b as the quotient of a over b.

Remark: In the rest of our tutorials, all denominators are assumed to be nonzero real numbers. It should be noted that with the HP Prime CAS that variables in the input denominator can result in erroneous results. The domain of the equivalent expression is larger than the domain of the original. Usually this involves zero not allowed in original domain but allowed in the equivalent and thus showing a result of zero for the problem. This would be an error in the calculator's result. Some CAS systems produce warning for these situations.

Said in another way, an example of an erroneous result would be that division by zero restriction of the original input would not be present in the HP Prime CAS simplified result.

Thus, we will get an erroneous result if we work a problem with zero in the input denominator when the HP Prime CAS simplifies an expression first, and then allows the HP Prime CAS to substitute the zero in. The simplified HP Prime CAS result does not have a restriction of division by zero for its expression. Later we will see a HP Prime CAS example of where division by zero produces an erroneous result.

Properties of Fractions

1. $\dfrac{a}{b} = \dfrac{c}{d}$ if $ad = bc$

2. $-\dfrac{a}{b} = \dfrac{-a}{b} = \dfrac{a}{-b}$

3. $\dfrac{a \cdot d}{b \cdot d} = \dfrac{a}{b}$

4. $\dfrac{a}{b} + \dfrac{c}{b} = \dfrac{a+c}{b}$

5. $\dfrac{a}{b} + \dfrac{c}{d} = \dfrac{a \cdot d + b \cdot c}{b \cdot d}$

6. $\dfrac{a}{b} \cdot \dfrac{c}{d} = \dfrac{a \cdot c}{b \cdot d}$

7. $\dfrac{a}{b} \div \dfrac{c}{d} = \dfrac{a}{b} \cdot \dfrac{d}{c} = \dfrac{a \cdot d}{b \cdot c}$

HP Prime Family **Properties of Fractions**

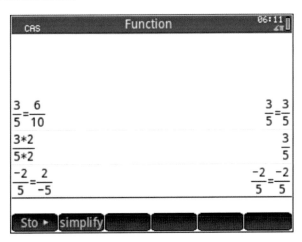

Begin by selecting the **CAS** key on the HP Prime. Key in as shown. . For the second entry use the **Fraction Template** using the **Template** key. For the others entries use **Fraction Template** or **divide key**, "/".

If the **CAS** view has computations, clear the **history** first. To clear the **history**, press the Clear key.

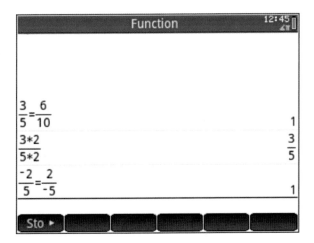

Press the **HOME** key. Enter as shown. Switching to **HOME** view notice the two uses of 1 for Boolean true. If the **HOME** view has computations, clear the **history** first. To clear the **history**, press the Clear key. The **mixed numeral** key was used with entry two.

We can see in the first entry that the two fractions are equivalent.

The second entry of first screenshot shows that when we would multiply 3/5's numerator and denominator by 2 in an attempt to make the equivalent fraction 6/10, the HP Prime displays the answer in lowest terms. So we cannot use fractions to display answers in higher terms. However this could be used to show how an answer in factored form is reduced to its lowest terms.

The third entry shows how the negative sign can be written in the numerator or denominator. If we attempt to put in in the front or denominator of the fraction the HP Prime will usually move it to the numerator. \

The next screenshot shows the negative sign with an expression being put in the front.

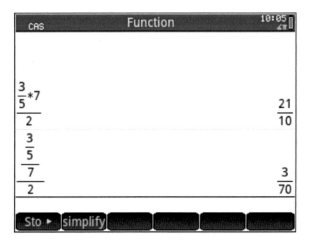

Continuing with the location of the negative sign. Begin by selecting the **CAS** key on the HP Prime. Key in as shown. If the **CAS** view has computations, clear the **history** first. To clear the **history**, press the **Clear** key.

Note: If we attempt to do lower case variables that are not defined from the **HOME** view the HP Prime we will get the error message "Error: Syntax Error". With HP Prime **CAS** view device HP Prime will display it back or an equivalent default view.

Begin by selecting the **CAS** key on the HP Prime.In the above screenshot we used the **Fraction Template** with **Parentheses, ( )s**. We were trying to get the multiplication product (3/5) x (7/2) and division product (3/5) / (7/2). Somehow we fouled up.

If the **CAS** view has computations, clear the **history** first. To clear the **history**, press the **Clear** key.

The HP Prime's precedence rules where followed for our crazy entry.. The multiplication example is equivalent but the division example produces an incorrect result. The input in the division example almost looks correct, but if we look closely we see the longer fraction sign is above the two and that problem is not mathematically equivalent to our original example.

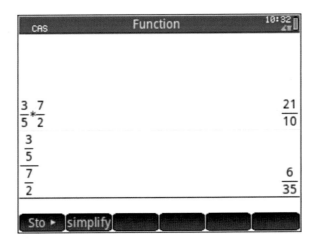

Begin by selecting the **CAS** key on the HP Prime. This screenshot shows what happens when we use the **Fraction Template** correctly. If the **CAS** view has computations, clear the **history** first. To clear the **history**, press the Clear key.

The answer for the multiplication example is 21/10 and division example is 6/35. Notice that on your screen that the division example is displayed as a complex fraction.

Complex Fraction or Compound Fraction

A **complex fraction** or **compound fraction** is a fraction which has in its numerator and/or denominator at least one other fraction.

Complex fractions are also referred to as compound fractions.

Switching to a TI-spire CAS device, we see in the next screen how it can be used to display the properties.

HP Prime Family **Properties of Fractions**

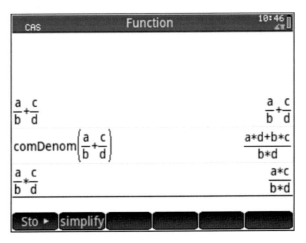

Begin by selecting the **CAS** key on the HP Prime. Key in as shown. . For the entries use **Fraction** icon from the **Symbol Template** or **divide key**, "**/**". Key in as shown. Use **Toolbox > Catlg > comDenom** to display the **comDenom** command. Use the **up arrow enter** combination to transfer the previous result to the command.

If the **CAS** view has computations, clear the **history** first. To clear the **history**, press the Clear key.

For the second entry we could of used **factor** to produce the same result. Using **comDenom** is a more logical choice. Remember with the distributive property **expand** shows the answer with terms, **factor** shows the answer as multiplication times terms. Remember that we have to use these types of commands, as they are not automatically applied. The **factor** command applied to fractional terms attempts to put the final answer in factored form, that is multiplication times terms. Multiplication turns out to be multiplication by the reciprocal, which would be shown in the result as division by the product of factors b and d. Using **factor** is not shown but as we mentioned the result would be the exact same result **comDenom** produced.

When we start working with fractions expressions many times the HP Prime CAS will leave the answer as terms. As in the previous screenshot, for us to see that its answer and our manual solution are the same we will need to use the **comDenom** command. Sometimes in very complex problems we will have to follow the **comDenom** result by applying the **factor** command. Using the **comDenom**, **factor**, and **expand** commands or a combination of the commands is often used to change the HP Prime CAS result into the alternate form given in textbooks, tutorials, or produced when manually working the problem.

The last entry on this screen is for multiplication. Our next screen is for division.

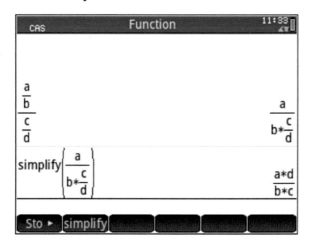

Begin by selecting the **CAS** key on the HP Prime. We keyed using the **Fraction** icon from the **Symbol Template**, and then using twice more, one for numerator and one for denominator. Used the soft **simplify** key to produce the final results. In the original problem b, c, and d cannot be zero.

In the final result b and c cannot be zero. The domain on the result lets d be zero where domain of the original problem does not let d be zero.

If the **CAS** view has computations, clear the **history** first. To clear the **history**, press the **Clear** key.

Remark: When we use the soft **simplify** key it calls the **simplify()** command, copies our last result as its input, and displays the simplified result. The **simplify()** command can be entered directly by using Use **Toolbox > CAS > Algebra > Simplify** to display the **simplify()** command. Then we need to type or copy a parameter for its use, followed by pressing **Enter**. The soft simplify key is easier but the direct method takes less screen space by typing the input directly. A helpful fact for our placing more information in our tutorial screens. Using either technique will work when we need to **simplify**.

The property was entered in complex fraction form. The domain of our original complex fraction restricts b, c, and d from being zero. The domain of our result only restricts b and c being zero. The domain of our output is larger than the domain of our input.

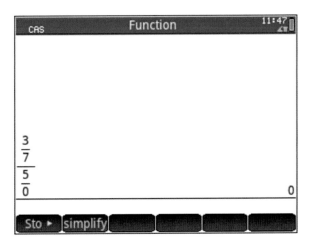

Begin by selecting the **CAS** key on the HP Prime. We keyed using **Fraction** icon form the **Symbol Template**, and then using twice more, one for numerator and one for denominator .Type in 3,7,5,0 for the values. If the **CAS** view has computations, clear the **history** first. To clear the **history**, press the Clear key.

Note: We are using 0 for *d*. It is not allowed in the original problem but allowed in the answer. See previous screenshot and discussion. The HP Prime CAS give the **erroneous** answer 0, thus the need for us to Pay Attention. Just because the problem is entered correctly and the calculator gives an answer does not mean that it is correct.

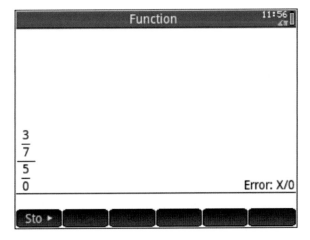

Begin by selecting the **HOME** key on the HP Prime. Select the **Menu** key. Select the **Get from CAS** entry. Select the previous entry using the soft **OK** key. Press **Enter**. With non-CAS, HOME view, it correctly displayed the answer as "Error:X/0".

If the **CAS** view has computations, clear the **history** first. To clear the **history**, press the Clear key.

Remark: There is no warning alerting us to potential problems with using the simplification. When we actually use the above values on the HP Prime **CAS** view we get an erroneous result of 0. It is up to us to always question the HP Prime results and see potential problems with the device's results. The HP Prime **HOME** view handles it correctly producing an error message.

We next turn to properties involving zero. In our rules for multiplication of two real numbers we covered the property that $a \times 0 = 0$ for every real number a. In our rules for division of two real numbers we covered the properties $a / 0$ is undefined, $0 / a = 0$, and $0 / 0$ is indeterminate with a being non-zero real number. The last property-involving zero, known as the zero product property, is given next.

Zero Product Property

If $a \cdot b = 0$, then either $a = 0$ or $b = 0$.

The word *or* in this property is in the inclusive or. This means that at least one of the factors a and b is 0. This property with factorization will later allow us to find the roots of a polynomial. We will be studying polynomials in a later section. Roots of a polynomial will be studied in a later tutorial.

The final properties we look at are the properties of negatives. Working with negatives we will use the following properties.

Properties of Negatives

1. $-(-a) = a$

2. $-a = -1(a)$

3. $(-a) \cdot b = a \cdot (-b) = -(a \cdot b)$

4. $(-a) \cdot (-b) = a \cdot b$

5. $-(a + b) = -1(a + b) = -a - b$

6. $-(a - b) = -1(a - b) = -a + b = b - a$

The opposite of the opposite of a is the number a, -(-5)=5.

A number opposite is the same as the product of -1 and the number, -6 = -1 x 6 .

Properties 3 and 4 are basically our sign rules for multiplication with the addition of negative times the product of a and b, (-3)(4)=(3)(-4)=-[(3)(4)] and (-3)(-4)=(3)(4).

Properties 5 and 6 allow us to use property 2 so we can use the distributive property to eliminate the parentheses.

HP Prime Family Properties of Negatives

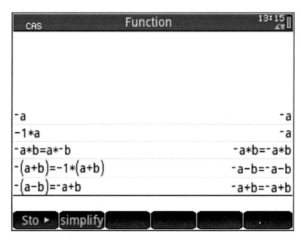

Begin by selecting the **CAS** key on the HP Prime. Key in as shown. If the **CAS** view has computations, clear the **history** first. To clear the **history**, press the **Clear** key.

For properties 4 and 5 we prefer to use the -1 in front and then use the Properties of Negatives to eliminate the parenthesis. On the screen shot we did property 4 with the -1 and property 5 without. We showed only the -1 but did show the final result for property 4. Use whichever form, the -1 or without, works best for you.

Use the next screen for **non-CAS**, HP Prime **HOME** view.

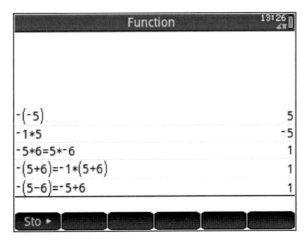

Begin by selecting the **HOME** key on the HP Prime. Key in as shown. Notice the last three entries are 1. **Boolean 1** means **true**. If the **CAS** view has computations, clear the **history** first. To clear the **history**, press the Clear key.

The same properties work on both. The difference is that on the **non-CAS**, HP Prime **HOME** view we use actual values.

For entry one of actual values being used for property illustrations, we choose to illustrate property 1 with double negative entry, $-(-5)$, rather than typing a plain -5 like the $-a$ in entry 1 of the HP Prime's previous **CAS** view screenshot.

Collecting Like Terms – Part 2

We now complete our earlier discussion of Collecting Like Terms.

Many texts and tutorials refer to Collecting Like Terms as Combining Like Terms.

First we show how to use the distributive property's expand to remove grouping symbols and then we use the distributive property's factor to allow us to add the constants that were originally written as coefficients.

Expand and factor is an example of a property that is being used two ways. Two ways means using a property forward and backward, or left to right and right to left. The forward or left to right would be the expand part of the distributive property. The backward or right to left would be the factor part of the distributive property.

Note: The HP Prime **CAS** menu has both the **expand** and **factor** commands. We will use these commands directly and also when we want to change the form of an answer. When we need an expanded expression or answer displayed as terms we will use the **expand** command. When we need a factored expression or answer displayed as products we will use the **factor** command. Exercise 3, shown shortly, illustrates the need to change our TI-Nspire CAS factor form answer to the expanded terms form.

Our mnemonic that was used in the Alternate Rule – Addition and Subtraction's <u>double signs elimination</u> and in <u>multiplication and division</u> of real numbers is now applied to removal of grouping symbols.

We use the properties shown by entries 4 and 5 from the two previous screenshots to aid us in grouping symbol removal.

For each grouping symbol removal we collect the like terms before proceeding with the next grouping symbol removal.

We use the distributive property to remove grouping symbols before collecting like terms. We next illustrate how we can use -1 and 1 to change non-distributive expressions to the distributive form.

The -1, that we inserted in entry 4, represents the a in the distributive property's $a(b + c)$. Entry 6 shows the result of parenthesis being removed without using a -1.

Entry 6 in general, says $-(a - b) = -a + b$. We could use entry's 4 insertion of -1 to prove this general rule. For parenthesis removal, we prefer entry 4's technique of -1 being added since it is less error prone then entry 5's technique where -1 is not used and the result it written directly.

In problems with adjacent grouping symbols like <u>exercise 3</u>, adding a 1 between the grouping symbols is useful. The other option to inserting a 1, would be to realize that when simplifying that pair of grouping symbols with no coefficient, we drop the group symbols since they are no longer needed.

We note that adding the -1 and 1 can be applied to all situations where a negative sign or no sign is used before the grouping symbol.

We now state our mnemonic for performing the **distributive property expand**.

Like signs: result Positive or Add

Unlike signs: result Negative or Subtract

When using the distributive property to remove grouping symbol, the first sign of the mnemonic, that is the a of $a(b + c)$, of the distributive property will be **positive**, if first factor is positive or expression $a(b + c)$ is being added; or **negative**, if first factor is negative or expression $a(b + c)$ is being subtracted. Examples of **positive** first sign: first factor positive as in **2**(x-4) or expression being added as in 6x**+3**(x-4). Examples of **negative** first sign: first factor negative as in **-5**(x-3) or expression being subtracted as in 4x**-3**(x-6).

We now look at the second signs used in our mnemonic. The first inside term inside grouping symbol, the b of $a(b + c)$, will **use its sign** as the second sign of the mnemonic. The second term inside the group symbol, that is the c of $a(b + c)$, will use a **positive** sign for addition and a **negative** sign for subtraction as the second sign in the mnemonic. If there are additional inside terms they follow the **same rule** as the second inside term.

Apply the mnemonic to remove the grouping symbols. Use the sign for the first factor with the sign of each term inside the grouping symbols. For a **positive** result use **addition** and a **negative** result **subtraction** except for the first term of the solution. For the first term of the solution, **no sign** is used for **positive** and a **negative sign** is used for a **negative** result.

The distributive property expand mnemonic is similar to the double sign elimination mnemonic and very close to the multiplication and division mnemonic. The **Add** and **Subtract** in the distributive property expand mnemonic are the only changes from our multiplication and division mnemonic.

Once the grouping symbol is removed we collect like terms if possible.

Note: We could use a full distributive property expand to remove the grouping symbol rather than our mnemonic. If we used the full distributive property expand we would need to remove the extra signs that it generates.

We use the factor side of the distributive property to combine coefficients of like terms. We factor out the variable or power of the variable. To do the factoring, we will use what some authors call the right distributive property.

Since the commutative property for multiplication holds for the $a(b + c)$ we can think of the right distributive property as $(b + c)a$. Thus with the variable or powers of variables factored to the right we can add the remaining constants, $b + c$, for each variable and power of variables.

The factoring shows us what the variable parts of the answer should be. The constants part of the answer, if any, is added directly.

We will now combine like terms mentally or by using the Alternate Rule - Addition and Subtraction technique we used when adding and subtracting real numbers. When trying to combine like terms mentally we need to think of subtraction as "addition of the opposite" and apply our traditional addition and subtraction rules to each term with the same power of the variables and to any constant terms. With the Alternate Rule - Addition and Subtraction technique we can combine each power of variables and constant without the need to think of subtraction as "addition of the opposite."

Note: Combining terms mentally or using Alternate Rule – Addition and Subtraction approach there is no need to write the power of variables in factored form but understand that the implied factoring is what allows us to combine the like powers of variables. The associative and commutative properties allow the traditional mental technique to directly combine like terms because the like terms could be moved so that they would be next to each other and grouped together. For the same reasons, the Alternate Rule – Addition and Subtraction approach also allows like terms to be moved and then directly combined. With both the mental and Alternate Rule – Addition and Subtraction approach there is no need to actually move and group terms but we visualize the move and grouping process mentally.

We now repeat this process for each grouping symbol. We now present the following rule for Removing Grouping Symbols.

Removing Grouping Symbols

1. If necessary, insert a 1 or −1 in front of grouping symbol.

2. Use expand mnemonic to remove grouping symbol.

3. If possible, combine like terms.

4. Repeat process for each grouping symbol.

We use entry 1's, -(-5) input, from the previous screenshot to illustrate double negative sign removal. Remember our HP Prime drops the parenthesis and writes the input as --5 rather than the traditional –(-5) notation used in textbooks and tutorials.

In general, double negative sign removal can be used to simplify expressions such as $-(-a)$. For removal, the double **like signs** of the $-(-a)$ would be thought of as **positive**, or as **unnecessary**, and thus the result would be a. Now, using the double sign removal for entry 1 we can directly simplify –(-5) to 5.

Example 3 Collecting Like Terms

(a) Collect like terms: $4x+x^2+3x+5x^2$

Use the commutative property	$4x+x^2+3x+5x^2$
Distributive property – factor	$=4x+3x+x^2+5x^2$
Add	$=(4+3)x+(1+5)x^2$
	$=7x+6x^2$

(b) Simplify: $2x-[3+4(x+5y)]$

Distributive property – expand	$2x-[3+4(x+5y)]$
Replacing with -1	$=2x-[3+4x+20y]$
Distributive property – expand	$=2x-1[3+4x+20y]$
Combine like terms	$=2x-3-4x-20y$
	$=-2x-20y-3$

We start by showing how the commutative, associative, and distributive property -factor are used to gave equivalent expressions that result in a final expression that combines like terms and constants. Part (a) of example 3 illustrates this. The associative property is not physically shown but visualized mentally. It is necessary to apply when we group two expressions so that we can then use the commutative property to change their order. A second mental use of the associative property allows us to group the like terms so that the factored result of the like terms can be used with the addition and subtraction real number rules to write a new combined coefficient for the like terms.

Part (b) of example 3, illustrates how we first need to use the distributive property - expand to remove a set of grouping symbols before looking to combine possible like terms. Combining like terms is not always possible, but when combining is possible we need to combine before going on. The combining is done after group symbol removal so as to keep the remaining steps as simple as possible.

In part (b), combining like terms was not possible after parenthesis removal but was possible for bracket removal.

Unlike part (a), in the last step of part (b), we went to combining the terms mentally. After the brief introduction in part (a) of showing how the commutative, associative, and distributive property - factor allow us to combine like terms, in part (b) we use the standard procedure of arranging and combining terms mentally. We like to use the Alternate Rule – Addition and Subtraction approach, which is simpler than the traditional approach, which needs us to mentally visualize "addition of the opposite" for any subtraction terms in order to combine the like terms.

Note that we wrote the answer for problem 2 in standard from, highest power of variables in alphabetical order followed by the constant if it exists. Problem 1 answer would not be in standard form since the highest power is written last.

During the introductions to collecting like terms most introductory algebra textbooks and tutorials show double signs for "addition of the opposite". This allows introductory algebra textbooks and tutorials to easily use the traditional approach to combine the terms. For grouping symbol removal their use of distributive expansion will result in all the signs being shown. They next will remove the extra signs to produce the final solution.

After the introduction, the introductory algebra textbooks and tutorials only show abbreviated problems and their answers. Using abbreviated problems is the reason why we like the Alternate Rule – Addition and Subtraction approach and the distributive expand mnemonic for collecting like terms and removing grouping symbols. The Alternate Rule – Addition and Subtraction approach and the distributive expand mnemonic allow us to directly work the problems and see the solutions using easy to follow and uncomplicated procedures and expressions. As we previous stated, use of the traditional approach for abbreviated problems requires that we mentally think of "addition of the opposite" for subtraction terms and using the full distributive expansion requires that we eliminate the extra signs it generates.

Summary: We use our Alternate Rule – Addition and Subtraction approach for addition and subtraction of real numbers and combining like terms. We use variations of the sign's mnemonic for multiplication and division of real numbers, elimination of grouping symbols, and double negative sign removal.

Another side benefit of the sign's mnemonic is that when textbooks and tutorials use double signs to introduce addition of real numbers and solve subtraction by changing to "addition of the opposite," we can use the sign's mnemonic to change these introductory forms to the traditional abbreviated form of the expression. Then we can use Alternate Rule – Addition and Subtraction approach to directly simplify the abbreviated form of the expression. This allows us to see how double signs are beneficial to understanding why while at the same time giving us an alternate and efficient method for simplifying the expression.

Remark: Thus for simplifying of basic expressions we only use two rules, Alternate Rule – Addition and Subtraction and variations of the sign's mnemonic.

HP Prime Family Collecting Like terms

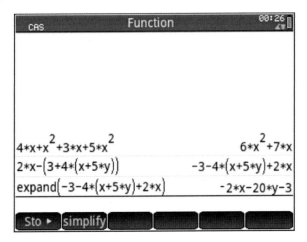

Begin by selecting the **CAS** key on the HP Prime. Key in as shown. Notice that the second entry we needed to use **Toolbox** > **CAS** > **Algebra** > **Expand**. Copy the previous solution. Press **Enter**. The soft **simplify** key would also have worked. If the **CAS** view has computations, clear the **history** first. To clear the **history**, press the **Clear** key.

The HP Prime second entry distributive "the subtract" (negative) first as well as applying the commutative property to the terms. When working manually, we find it better to consistently when work from the inside out.

 The HP Prime CAS displays the answer in standard form.

Exercise 3 Collecting Like Terms

Simplify: $2\{[5(x-3)+4]-[3(2x-4)+6]\}$

Solution >>

Explanation 1.3 - Integer Exponents

In Explanation 1.1 we introduced natural number exponents and briefly discussed their use. In this section we will extend the exponent notation to zero and negative numbers. We will go-over the properties that are used for working with exponents. In science we often work with numbers that are very large and very small. We will see how exponents can be used to represent these very large and very small numbers and perform calculations using this notation.

Integer Exponents

Explanation 1.1 dealt with natural numbers exponents. We will now look at zero and negative exponents and the properties that are useful for working with exponential notation.

We first look at expressions involving multiplication of two numbers with exponential notation.

HP Prime Family Multiplying Exponents

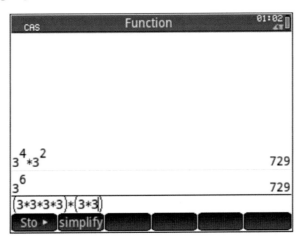

Begin by selecting the **CAS** key on the HP Prime. Key in as shown. If the **CAS** view has computations, clear the **history** first. To clear the **history**, press the **Clear** key.

For the final entry, press **Enter** to verify that to multiply the two powers of 3 we add the exponents. The parentheses were added to emphasis that the two powers of 3 were being multiplied. An implied multiplication could not be used between the two sets of parentheses. Implied multiplications are generally used between a number and a variable. With the HP Prime implied multiplication between a number and variable is the only place we use implied multiplication. The parentheses are dropped when we press **Enter**.

Remark: We cannot use implied multiplication between two letters as the HP Prime interprets this as a single variable. This is common mistake because in math normal usage of two joining letters implies multiplication. Thinking that two joining letters implies multiplication will lead to the HP Prime giving us an incorrect result. To fix use the multiplication operation between the two letters.

Equivalent Properties of Equalities

For any quantities a, b, and c

Reflexive: $a = a$
Symmetric: If $a = b$, then $b = a$.
Transitive: If $a = b$ and $b = c$, then $a = c$.

What we are doing in the screenshot is using the TI-Nspire and two of the properties of the **Equivalent Properties of Equalities**, if $a = b$ then $b = a$ and if $a = b$ and $b = c$, then $a = c$, is to illustrate that for positive integers, m and n, that to multiply two powers with the same base we add their exponents. The **Equivalent Properties of Equalities** we are using are the **Symmetric** and **Transitive** Properties. The **Symmetric** Property is when we want to flip the equation around. From our HP Prime screenshot, we use the **Symmetric** Property to flip entry two to

$729 = 3^6$

From our HP Prime screenshot we take entry one and the flipped entry two, and use the **Transitive** property to conclude that

$3^4 \times 3^2 = 3^6$

That is that when working with exponential notation, to multiply two powers with positive exponents and the same base we add the exponents.

The first property of the **Equivalent Properties of Equalities**, is the **Reflexive** Property: $a = a$. When using deductive reasoning for proofs, we can start with the **Reflexive** Property and apply definitions and other properties to the right side to reach a new property.

We can do the reverse as well. Start with the new property on the right, and through definitions and other properties conclude that it must be true because our last step is that the right side is equal to our original left side, that is the quantity $a = a$.

A less formal deductive proof is where we change both sides and conclude when both sides are the same, that the original statement must be true. For each statement in this and the reverse style a question mark above the equality is used until the last step.

To prove the property for integers, m and n, that to multiply two powers with the same base we add their exponents we divide the proof into cases. The property is listed here. The first case is for positive integers, m and n.

To prove the property for positive integers, m and n, that to multiply two powers with the same base we add their exponents, we start with the **Reflexive** Property, apply definitions and other properties to the right side to reach the new property.

Reflexive Property	$a^m \cdot a^n = a^m \cdot a^n$
m factors and n factors	$= (a \cdot a \cdot \ldots \cdot a) \cdot (a \cdot a \cdot \ldots \cdot a)$
$m+n$ factors	$= a \cdot a \cdot a \cdot \ldots \cdot a$
Exponential Notation	$= a^{m+n}$

Line two is using the definition of Exponential Notation twice. Line three is using the associative property for multiplication. Line four is where we use definition of Exponential Notation but in the reverse order of line two. Using something in the beginning and then in reverse order is a quite common technique for proofs.

HP Prime Family Zero and Negative Exponents

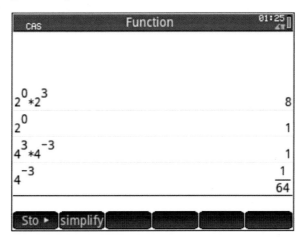

Begin by selecting the **CAS** key on the HP Prime. Key in as shown. If the **CAS** view has computations, clear the **history** first. To clear the **history**, press the **Clear** key.

We would like the property to hold when m and n are zero or negative integers.

We now look at entry one of the second screenshot, a base raised to a zero exponent. For a base raised to a zero exponent, we would like the property of multiply two powers with the same base of adding their exponents to be true. Extending the property to this situation, we add the exponents 0 and 3 to get 3. Since 2 raised to the third is 8, 2 to the zero power in entry one must be 1.

$$2^0 \times 2^3 = 2^{0+3} = 2^3 = 8$$

thus

$$2^0 \times 2^3 = 1 \times 2^3 = 2^3 = 8$$

Proceeding to the entry for 4 raised to powers. Here, we would like the property to be true for negative exponents as well. Extending the property for negative exponents, we add 3 and -3 to get 0. Since 4 raised to zero power is 1, 4 raised to a negative three power must be 1 divided by 4 raised to the third power.

$$4^3 \times 4^{-3} = 4^{3+(-3)} = 4^0 = 1$$

thus

$$4^3 \times 4^{-3} = 4^3 \times 1/\, 4^3 = 1$$

The preceding work leads us to the following definitions.

Definition of Zero and Negative Exponents

For any nonzero real number a and positive integer n

$$a^0 = 1 \qquad \text{and} \qquad a^{-n} = \frac{1}{a^n}$$

To help with positive, zero, and negative exponents, we look at figure 1, shown next. The figure represents 2 and 3 raised to the -3 power. Results are 1/8 and 1/27. The left dot on the number line represent -10 and the right dot 10.

If x was shown at 0, 2 and 3 raised to 0 power both results would be 1. If x was at 4, we would have 2and 3 raised to an exponent of 4, the results would be 16 and 81.

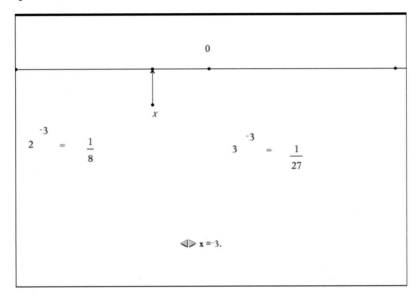

Figure 1 Exploring Exponents (Education.ti.com, Expressions and Equations)

By using the definitions of zero and negative exponents it can now be proved for the cases where the integer exponents are less than or equal to zero, that to multiply two powers with the same base we add their exponents.

Let us look as two of the cases. Similar arguments could be made for the other cases.

Beware of remarks in textbooks or tutorials such as by using definitions of zero and negative exponents that state that it can now be proved for the cases where the integer exponents are less than or equal to zero, that to multiply two powers with the same base we add their exponents but no proof is given.

If there are remarks like it can now be proved but none is offered or trivially this is true, it is good idea to actually prove the statement or prove some of the cases if there are multiple cases.

As an example, for our exponent rule, once we see how to verify some of cases there is probably no need to verify all of the cases, since similar techniques to the techniques that were used on the verified cases could be applied to the remaining cases.

Case $-m<0$ and $n>0$ (negative and positive)

Reflexive Property $a^{-m} \cdot a^n = a^{-m} \cdot a^n$

Definition of a^{-n} $= \dfrac{1}{a^m} \cdot a^n$

n factors over m factors $= \dfrac{a \cdot a \cdot a \cdot \dots \cdot a}{a \cdot a \cdot a \cdot \dots \cdot a}$

$n-m$ factors $= a \cdot a \cdot \dots \cdot a$

Exponential Notation $= a^{n-m} = a^{n+(-m)}$

Commutative for addition $= a^{-m+n}$

Case $m=0$ and $n>0$ (zero and positive)

Reflexive Property $a^0 \cdot a^n = a^0 \cdot a^n$

Definition of a^0 $= 1 \cdot a^n$

Identity for multiplication $= a^n$

Identity for addition $= a^{0+n}$

Line four in the case of a negative and a positive, the n-m could be either positive or negative depending whether the numerator or denominator has more factors. We assume that it uses our definition and the numerator has more factors. In line five we are using definition of Exponential Notation in reverse and subtraction as "addition of the opposite."

In line four, if $n - m$ is negative we have $m - n$ factors in the denominator. This is not shown. By using the definition of a to the negative n we can translate the denominator's a raised to the $m - n$ power to the standalone expression of a raised to the $n - m$ power. The rest of the proof would be the same as shown. Usually using words like we did here to explain additional possibilities is how proofs are handled.

HP Prime CAS Zero and Negative Exponents

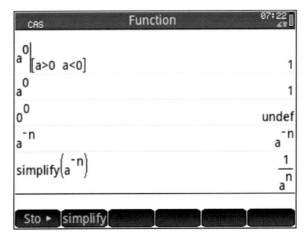

Begin by selecting the **CAS** key on the HP Prime. Key in as shown.

The **width** (|) operator is located using the **fraction / square root / absolute value** key. The > **and** < are with the **inequalities**. For entry one width use a>0, a<0. It will show in history area as [a>0 a<0]. Using comma separated is an easy way to enter a matrix. We also could use the [ ] key and **right arrow** on the **arrow pad**. The expression, [a>0 a<0], stands for "a not equal to 0".

If the **CAS** view has computations, clear the **history** first. To clear the **history**, press the Clear key.

The definition specifies that a cannot be zero. The HP Prime gives us an error message when the **width** operator used **not equal**, that is what we tried with entry one. We cleared the **history**, by pressing the **Clear** key. We changed entry one to the matrix [a>0 a<0] and got 1.

For entry two, a raised to the domain of the result cannot include zero. The HP Prime does not know automatically about this restriction, thus the need for us to know this fact. This is demonstrated by entry three result of **undef**.

Remark: Raising zero to the zero power is problematic. You can investigate zero to zero power on the Internet, but our current level of math is not sufficient for most of the discussions. In entry three our HP Prime CAS handles this by displaying that it is undefined. For now, this will be sufficient for us as well.

The fourth entry is a to the negative n power, gives back the entry unchanged. By using the soft **simplify** key we get the result we wanted.

Remark: To get a result using the HP Prime **CAS** view we may need to try the soft **simplify** key, alternate methods, or use equivalent form of the expressions.

HP Prime Family Negative Exponents

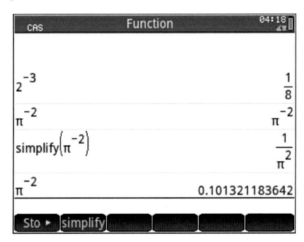

Begin by selecting the **CAS** key on the HP Prime. Key in as shown. Use the **pi** key for entry two, soft **simplify** key entry three, and **approx** key for entry four.

If the **CAS** view has computations, clear the **history** first. To clear the **history**, press the **Clear** key.

Thus 2 raised to the negative third is shown as a fraction with HP Prime **CAS** view and as a decimal with the HP Prime **HOME** view.

Using pi raised to the negative 2 results with the HP Prime **CAS** view the answer is unchanged until we apply **simplify**. On the HP Prime **HOME** view the answer is shown as the decimal 0.101321183642. The HP Prime **HOME** view calculates constants as a decimal.

Example 1 **Zero and Negative Exponents**

(a) $-x^0$ for $x = 4.1$ substituting for x $-4.1^0 = -1$

(b) $3^{-4} = \dfrac{1}{3^4} = \dfrac{1}{81}$

(c) $\dfrac{1}{2^{-3}} = 2^{-(-3)} = 2^3 = 8$ or $\dfrac{1}{2^{-3}} = \dfrac{1}{\frac{1}{2^3}} = 1 \cdot \dfrac{2^3}{1} = 8$

In part (a) simplifying exponents has a higher priority then the unary operation of opposite. The 4.1 raised to the zero power is 1, and then the opposite of 1 is -1.

In our definition of Negative Exponents we restricted n to be a positive integer. Therefore $-n$ would be a negative integer. This was done so that expression like (b) could be changed to a positive.

Some authors let n in the definition for a negative exponent be an integer. Then when we have a situation like (c), the $-n$ in the definition with n negative represent the opposite of a negative integer, or a positive integer. We can eliminate the denominator in part (c) by taking the opposite of it in the numerator. Their definition is not as eloquent but in actual use is easier to work with. With our definition we would need to use complex fractions to work part (c).

> **Properties of Negative Exponents**
>
> For any nonzero real numbers a and b and positive integers m and n
>
> 1. $\dfrac{a^{-n}}{b^{-m}} = \dfrac{b^m}{a^n}$
>
> 2. $\left(\dfrac{a}{b}\right)^{-n} = \left(\dfrac{b}{a}\right)^{n}$

Using the definition for a to negative n power and generalizing our complex fraction from part (c) of Example 1 for b to the negative m power, we now have a way to eliminate negative exponents. By generalizing, we now created property 1 of Properties of Negative Exponents and no longer need to use complex fractions for these kinds of problems.

Property 1: Factors with negative exponents when moved across the fraction bar become factors with positive exponents.

Property 2: To raise a quotient to a negative power, -n, invert the quotient keeping the signs of all of their current exponents but changing the external exponent to positive n. Our properties are shown with a single variables a and b, but in actual use a and b represent the entire numerator and denominator of the quotient. Inverting only changes the outside exponent sign, not the signs of the factors in the inverted numerator and denominator.

We said that to prove property 1 of Negative Exponents we could use the definition for a to negative n power and then use complex fraction for b to the negative n.

Another way to prove property 1 of Negative Exponents is shown next.

Reflexive Property
$$\frac{a^{-n}}{b^{-m}} = \frac{a^{-n}}{b^{-m}}$$

Definition Negative Exponents
$$= \frac{1/a^n}{1/b^m}$$

Invert and Multiply
$$= \frac{1}{a^n} \cdot \frac{b^m}{1}$$

Perform Multiplication
$$= \frac{b^m}{a^n}$$

When doing proofs or performing simplification there is no one right solution.

Proof of property 2 of Negative Exponents is shown next.

Reflexive Property
$$\left(\frac{a}{b}\right)^{-n} = \left(\frac{a}{b}\right)^{-n}$$

Definition Negative Exponents
$$= \frac{1}{\left(\frac{a}{b}\right)^n}$$

n factors
$$= \frac{1}{\frac{a}{b} \cdot \frac{a}{b} \cdot \ldots \cdot \frac{a}{b}}$$

Multiply $-$ Exponential Notation
$$= \frac{1}{\frac{a \cdot a \cdot \ldots \cdot a}{b \cdot b \cdot \ldots \cdot b}} = \frac{1}{\frac{a^n}{b^n}}$$

Invert Multiply
$$= 1 \cdot \frac{b^n}{a^n}$$

Exponential Notation
$$= \frac{b \cdot b \cdot \ldots \cdot b}{a \cdot a \cdot \ldots \cdot a}$$

Multiply $-$ Exponential Notation
$$= \frac{b}{a} \cdot \frac{b}{a} \cdot \ldots \cdot \frac{b}{a} = \left(\frac{b}{a}\right)^n$$

Line three is n factors of the Exponential Notation. Line six is Exponential Notation of n factors.

Line four and six of the proof are reverses of each other. Line four use factors of line three's denominator to come up with a product and then switches both the top and bottom of the product to Exponential Notation.

In line six we use the product of line five and break down into factors, from which we apply definition of Exponential Notation in reverse.

The multiply in line four is factors of line three to product and the multiply in line six is product of line five to factors. They are the reverse of each other. Just as Exponential Notation can mean break into factors or combine the factors to an exponent, multiply can mean either direction; factors to product or product to factors.

Note: Going both directions with a known equality is one of the keys to proofs. What we are doing with a known equality, is using it to change our expression in the proof by taking the expression on the left of the known equality to the expression of the right of the known equality; or the reverse, changing our expression in the proof by taking the expression on the right of the known equality to the expression on the left of the known equality.

HP Prime Family Equivalent Expressions

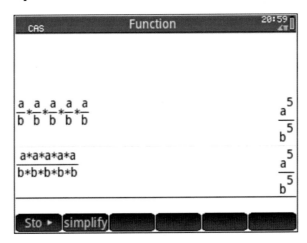

Begin by selecting the **CAS** key on the HP Prime. Key in as shown. The **fraction template** is located using the **fraction / square root / absolute value** key. If the **CAS** view has computations, clear the **history** first. To clear the **history**, press the Clear key.

The HP Prime CAS likes to put equivalent expressions in simplest form. For proofs, we would like a command to change entry one's answer to the form, (a/b) raised to the fifth power. This would help us with the form when we have n factors.

Therefore with proofs, the HP Prime CAS is of value only in situations where the HP Prime CAS's simplest form is what we need. This would be the case with entry two. The HP Prime **HOME** view does allow unassigned variable. So neither of these entries is allowed.

Most textbooks and tutorials leave out the Reflexive Property line and write a proof as one long string of equalities with or without all the reasons being given. Using the Reflexive Property is more formal. We like putting the reason or partial reasons by each line of the proof and following up with additional statements at the end of the proof for clarification of our reason or partial reasons of a line.

When writing proof we should mention that we mainly work from the top down but it is useful to work from the conclusion upward as well. If we hit a blockage in our thinking or we our totally on the wrong track working backwards can be an aid that allows to see the missing steps or suggest a different approach.

HP Prime Family Zero and Negative Exponents

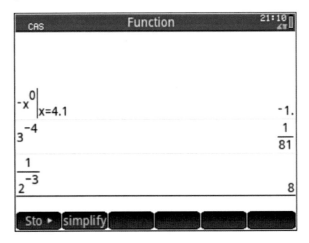

Begin by selecting the **CAS** key on the HP Prime. Key in as shown.

The **width (|)** operator and **fraction template** are located using the **fraction / square root / absolute value** key.

If the **CAS** view has computations, clear the **history** first. To clear the **history**, press the **Clear** key.

We next look at the **HOME** view version. **HOME** view uses uppercase letters as the variable names.

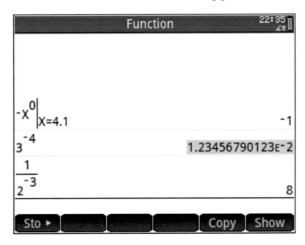

Begin by selecting the **HOME** key on the HP Prime. Key in as shown.

The **width (|)** operator and **fraction template** are located using the **fraction / square root / absolute value** key. We can use the **mixed numeral** key to convert the highlighted result of 3^{-4} to the fraction 1/81. In settings with Number Format set to Standard, the highlighted result is displayed in scientific notation. It switches to scientific mode to display more digits by removing zeros after the decimal point. Pressing the **mixed numeral** key repeatedly toggles the highlighted entry between scientific notation and fraction format.

If the **HOME** view has computations, clear the **history** first. To clear the **history**, press the **Clear** key

Remark: When we use the **HOME** view we needed to switch the lowercase x to capital X in entry one.

In entry one of the above screen, the HP Prime **HOME** view has no trouble with using a capital variable X since the **with (|)** operator is assigning the capital variable X a value. We remember the fact that **HOME** view likes working with numbers and not symbolic or literal form.

The first screen **CAS** view answer for entry one was displayed with a decimal since the variable in the entry is assigned the decimal value 4.1. Keying a capital X in the **CAS** view's command line will display 0 or its current value as its result. Keying a lowercase x in **CAS** view well display a lower case variable "x" or its current value if previously defined. The **width's (|)** variable's value only works for the statement and does not permanently assign the variable the 4.1 value.

The second screen **HOME** view answer for entry one was displayed without a decimal. Not sure why, but maybe it's possible since the fact that anything raised to zero power is 1. Keying a capital X in the command line will display 0 or its current value as its result. Keying a lowercase x in **CAS** view well display an error message, "Error: Syntax Error". As in the **CAS** view, the **width's (|)** variable's value only works for the statement and does not permanently assign the variable the 4.1 value.

Remember one of the major difference between **HOME** view and **CAS** View is that **HOME** view uses uppercase letters and **CAS** view uses lowercase letters.

Using the **xt(theta)n** key for the independent variable provides the proper case of the variable. In this case pressing the **xt(theta)n** key gives us a capital "X" for **HOME** view and lowercase "x" for **CAS** view.

We see in the title line that Function is our HP Prime App. The Function App has the uppercase "X" or lower case "x" as its independent variable. Thus, pressing the **xt(theta)n** key uses uppercase "X" or lower case "x" depending on the view.

Exercise 1 Zero and Negative Exponents

If possible, express using positive exponents and simplify.

(a) $-x^0$ for $x = -2.3$

(b) $\dfrac{2^{-4}}{3^{-2}}$

(c) $\dfrac{x^{-1}}{y^{-2}}$

<u>Solution</u> >>

Before presenting the rest of exponential properties, let's take a closer look at property 2 of Negative exponents.

(a) $\left(\dfrac{2^3}{5^{-1}}\right)^{-2} = \left(\dfrac{5^{-1}}{2^3}\right)^{2} = \left(\dfrac{1}{2^3 \cdot 5^1}\right)^{2} = \left(\dfrac{1}{40}\right)^{2} = \dfrac{1}{40} \cdot \dfrac{1}{40}$

$= \dfrac{1}{1600}$

(b) $\left(\dfrac{x^{-2}}{y^3}\right)^{-1} = \left(\dfrac{y^3}{x^{-2}}\right)^{1} = x^2 \cdot y^3$

In part (a) and (b) we eliminate the negative exponent of the expression by inverting the quotient and changing the sign of the outside exponent. We do not change the signs of the inverted quotient's exponents.

We next use property 1 of Negative exponents to eliminate factors with negative exponents by bring them across the bar and making them positive. To finish we perform the math in part (a) and drop the parenthesis and power of 1 in part (b).

Once we establish exponential properties for all integers, we can work directly with the negative exponents to come up with the correct solution as well. When working with exponential notation, the technique of eliminating negative exponents, working directly with negative exponents, or a combination of both can all be used.

HP Prime Family Quotient to a Negative Exponent

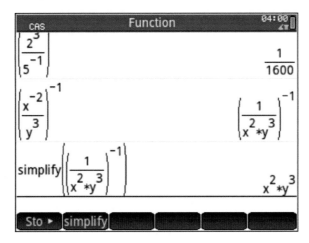

Begin by selecting the **CAS** key on the HP Prime. Key in as shown.

Key in as shown. The **fraction template** is located using the **fraction / square root / absolute value** key.

If the **CAS** view has computations, clear the **history** first. To clear the **history**, press the **Clear** key.

Entry two will not work on the HP Prime **HOME** view since the variables are not assigned values and well use zero as a default. Remember to use capital letters. Division by zero will result in an error message, "Error: infinity result". Notice the result for entry two, x and y cannot be zero. We then **simplify** which allows x and y to be zero, where in the original input they cause division by zero. The next screenshot shows the HP Prime CAS producing the incorrect answers of zero for these values.

HP Prime Family Quotient to Negative Exponent

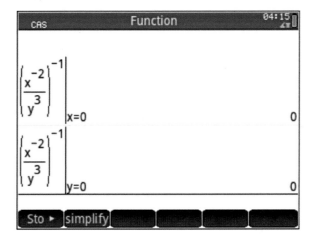

Using the **up arrow** to highlight our entry. Press **Enter** to copy to the command line. Add the **width** expressions. The **width** (|) operator and **fraction template** are located using the **fraction / square root / absolute value** key.

Key in as shown.

Note the incorrect answer for $x = 0$ and $y = 0$. This was the reason for HP Prime CAS's operation. The domain of the result includes $x = 0$ and $y = 0$ where the domain of the input does not. The value of 0 for x and y is substituted in the HP Prime CAS simplified form thus giving an answer of 0 in both entries even though 0 for x and y are not allowed in the input form.

Additional Exponential Properties

In this section we begin by listing the Properties of Exponents. The first property says that to multiply two powers with the same base we add their exponent. We began this section with a discussion of this property. We wrap up our discussions of exponential notation by looking at additional properties.

We will use Exponential Notation, the Definition of Zero and Negative Exponents, Properties of Negative Exponents along with the Properties of Exponents to simplify an expression involving powers of real numbers. An expression is simplified when each real number variable appears only once and all exponents are positive. We will assume that all denominators are nonzero real values.

In the Properties of Exponents the bases a and b are real numbers, and the exponents m and n are integers.

Properties of Exponents

1. $a^m \cdot a^n = a^{m+n}$

2. $(a^m)^n = a^{m \cdot n}$

3. $(a \cdot b)^n = a^n \cdot b^n$

4. $\left(\dfrac{a}{b}\right)^n = \dfrac{a^n}{b^n}$

5 a. $\dfrac{a^m}{a^n} = a^{m-n}$ use if $m > n$

   b. $\dfrac{a^m}{a^n} = \dfrac{1}{a^{n-m}}$ use if $n > m$

Property 5a and 5b state where to use. It should be noted that they hold for all integers m and n. Many authors will not have statement 5b and only have statement 5a with no use specification.

We proved property 1 of Exponents earlier for positive integer exponents. Following the Definition of Zero and Negative Exponents we comment that the Definition of Zero and Negative Exponents could be used to prove the cases where the integer exponents are less than or equal to zero.

To prove property 2 of Exponents, we write, for m and n positive,

Reflexive Property	$(a^m)^n = (a^m)^n$
n factors of a^m	$= (a^m \cdot a^m \cdot \ldots \cdot a^m)$
$m \cdot n$ factors	$= a \cdot a \cdot a \cdot \ldots \cdot a$
Exponential Notation	$= a^{m \cdot n}$

We start with the Reflexive Property. Line two is the definition of Exponential Notation for n power. Line three is the definition of Exponential Notation for m power used n times. Line four the definition of Exponential Notation for m x n in reverse. The Definition of Zero and Negative Exponents can be used to prove the cases where the integer exponents are less than or equal to zero.

To prove property 3 of Exponents, we write, for m and n positive,

Reflexive Property	$(a \cdot b)^n = (a \cdot b)^n$
n factors of $a \cdot b$	$= (a \cdot b) \cdot (a \cdot b) \cdot \ldots \cdot (a \cdot b)$
n factors of a and b	$= (a \cdot a \cdot \ldots \cdot a) \cdot (b \cdot b \cdot \ldots \cdot b)$
Exponential Notation	$= a^n \cdot b^n$

Again, we start with the Reflexive Property. Line two is the definition of Exponential Notation for n power. Line 3 is the Commutative and Associative Properties used repeatedly. Line four the definition of Exponential Notation for a and b in reverse. The Definition of Zero and Negative Exponents can be used to prove the cases where the integer exponents are less than or equal to zero

The remaining two properties could be proved in similar fashion.

Example 2 **Using the Properties of Exponents**

(a) $2^3 \cdot 2^4 = 2^{3+4} = 2^7 = 128$

(b) $3^4 \cdot 3^{-6} = 3^{4+(-6)} = 3^{4-6} = 3^{-2} = \dfrac{1}{3^2} = \dfrac{1}{9}$

(c) $(2^2)^{-3} = 2^{2 \cdot (-3)} = 2^{-6} = \dfrac{1}{2^6} = \dfrac{1}{64}$

(d) $\dfrac{4^7}{4^5} = 4^{7-5} = 4^2 = 16$

(e) $\dfrac{5^2}{5^6} = \dfrac{1}{5^{6-2}} = \dfrac{1}{5^4} = \dfrac{1}{625}$

(f) $\left(\dfrac{3^2}{4^{-1}} \right)^{-2} = \dfrac{(3^2)^{-2}}{(4^{-1})^{-2}} = \dfrac{3^{2 \cdot (-2)}}{4^{-1 \cdot (-2)}} = \dfrac{3^{-4}}{4^2} = \dfrac{1}{16 \cdot 3^4}$

$= \dfrac{1}{16 \cdot 81} = \dfrac{1}{1296}$

(g) $(3x^{-2})^3 = 3^3 \cdot (x^{-2})^3 = 27x^{-2 \cdot 3} = 27x^{-6} = \dfrac{27}{x^6}$

HP Prime Family Using the Properties of Exponents

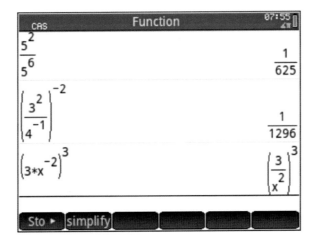

Begin by selecting the **CAS** key on the HP Prime. Key in as shown. The **fraction template** is located using the **fraction / square root / absolute value** key.

If the **CAS** view of the first screenshot has computations, clear the **history** first. To clear the **history**, press the **Clear** key.

Entry three on second screen shot will not work on the HP Prime **HOME** view since the variables are not assigned values and well use zero as a default. Remember to use capital letters. Division by zero will result in an error message, "Error: infinity result".

Exercise 2 Using the Properties of Exponents

Simplify:

(a) $\left(\dfrac{2^3 \cdot 3}{4^2}\right)^3$

(b) $\left(\dfrac{3 \cdot s^{-2}}{t}\right)^2 \cdot \left(\dfrac{t^{-1}}{s^2}\right)^{-3}$

Solution >>

Scientific Notation

We start by defining Scientific Notation for a positive number. Using the definition Scientific Notation allows us to write in compact form a very large positive number by using a positive power of 10 or very small positive number by using a negative power of 10 times a number greater than or equal to 1 and less than 10.

> ### Scientific Notation
>
> A positvie number c is written in scientific notation
>
> $$c = a \times 10^b$$
>
> where $1 \le a < 10$ and b is an integer.

A negative number c written in scientific notation would have $c = a \times 10^b$ where $-10 < a \le -1$ and b is an integer. We could change the definition to a number c by using absolute value where $1 \le |a| < 10$ and b is an integer.

Do not confuse a negative number and a negative b. Negative b means a c where $-1 < c < 1$. Negative number in scientific notation just has a negative sign in front of it.

From The Cosmic Distance Scale, "Proxima Centauri, the closest star to our own, is still 39,900,000,000,000 km away. (Or 271,000 AU.) When we talk about the distances to the stars, we no longer use the AU, or Astronomical Unit; commonly, the light year is used. A light year is the distance light travels in one year - it is equal 9.46×10^{12} km. Alpha Centauri A & B are roughly 4.35 light years away from us. Proxima Centauri is slightly closer at 4.22 light years (Masetti)."

Our Universe, enormous and spectacular, intergalactic space, matter and energy, planets, stars, galaxies, black holes, and supernovas, many celestial objects to arouse our curiosity, mysterious concepts, and unlimited far away places for our mind to explore. Use a search engine to investigate our Universe and discover the wonders for yourself.

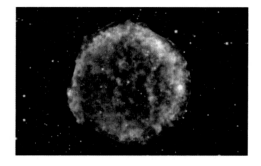

Tycho's Supernova Remnant. Credit: NASA/MPIA/Calar Alto Observatory, Oliver Krause et al.

Let us take a closer look at the numbers in our nearest star example.

HP Prime Family Light Year Calculation

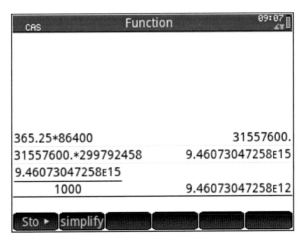

Begin by selecting the **CAS** key on the HP Prime. Key in as shown. The **fraction template** is located using the **fraction / square root / absolute value** key.

If the **CAS** view has computations, clear the **history** first. To clear the **history**, press the Clear key.

For entry two we used the **up arrow Enter** to transfer the seconds from entry one and multiply by meters per second, using unitary analysis to get meters. We use unitary analysis again to arrive at the number of kilometers in a light year. Change the meters entry to kilometers by multiplying by one kilometer / 1000 meters, or dividing by 1000. When working the decimals the HP Prime uses a precision of twelve digits.

All entries will work on the HP Prime **HOME** view as well. The **CAS** view will automatically show decimals in the result since decimals are involved in the input. Both views will switch to scientific notation when the number of digits is too large to display.

The HP Prime use "E" notation, "E" representing times ten raised to the power, for scientific notation.

The figures above are based on a Julian year, 365.25 days, 24 hrs/day or 86 400 s/day, defined speed of light as 299 792 458 m/s. Entry one is 3.15576E7 or 31 557 600 seconds. We like using the notation where a space is used to display groups of three in very large and very small numbers. However, use of this notation is not common. The HP Prime has the space setting for large numbers but not small numbers. Therefore, since there is no advantage, we will use the traditional comma notation.

Since a decimal was used in the input and HP Prime's default is to display twelve significant figures the twelve digit result was displayed in scientific notation with twelve significant figures.

Note: Do not confuse HP Prime precision with arithmetic precision, which is defined to be the fixed number of decimal places when adding and subtracting. When number are multiplied or divided, the precision is the number of significant digits in the answer. It is found by setting the number of significant digits in the answer to the smallest number of significant digits used in the multiplication or division problem. Exact numbers have infinite precision. When adding, subtracting, multiplying, and dividing problems that contain approximate numbers we will use arithmetic precision.

We next work the problem again, this time using units. When working physics and chemistry problems students are required to show the units in their calculations.

HP Prime Light Year Calculation

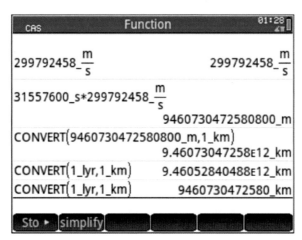

Begin by selecting the **CAS** key on the HP Prime. Key in as shown. If the **CAS** view of the first screenshot has computations, clear the **history** first. To clear the **history**, press the Clear key.

Entry one was used to show the constant and its units. We could have just started with entry two.

For entry one press the Units key and select the menu item, **Units > Const > Physics > c:**. Press **Enter**. Next add the units by pressing the Units key and select the menu item, **Units > Units > Speed > m/s**. Press **Enter**.

For entry two type 31557600. Next add the time by pressing the Units key and select the menu item, **Units > Units > Time > s**. Press **x** for times. Use the **up arrow Enter** to transfer entry one and multiply its meters per second value times second, using unitary analysis to get meters. Since we are using the **CAS** view we get an "exact" answer of 16 digits. In the previous screenshot we calculated the number of seconds with result being a decimal. However, we entered the seconds here without a decimal. This allowed us to calculate an "exact" result for the number of meters.

We pressed the **Toolbox** key and selected the **Toolbox > Catlg > CONVERT** command. Use the **up arrow Enter** to transfer entry two. Added a **comma** and "1_(km)". Press **Enter**. Entering "1_(lyr)", the soft **Sto->** key, _"1_(km)" for the fourth entry we got the 12 digit incorrect result. Repeating with the **CONVERT** process from the Toolbox and parameters "1_(km), 1_(lyr)" we got the correct answer.

The **CONVERT** command can also be found under **Units > Tools > CONVERT**.

The conversions done using the soft **Sto->** key, however gave us the fifth significant digit as a different answer than the other calculations. The the soft **Sto->** key is the fourth entry. When we press **Enter** it switches in the history to the **CONVERT** form. Something strange going on with its answer.

HP Prime Family HP Prime's Precision

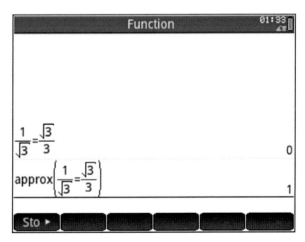

Begin by selecting the **CAS** key on the HP Prime. Key in as shown. The **fraction template** is located using the **fraction / square root / absolute value** key. Use the approx() command for the first two entries. The **shift** key function of **Enter**.

If the **HOME** view of the first screenshot has computations, clear the **history** first. To clear the **history**, press the **Clear** key.

HP Prime precision illustration inspired by Google Group thread's Post referencing a slide rule use and discussion about precision in that thread.

Entry's one and two approx()'s have the same answer. Entry three and four differ at the end. We now want to investigate the command line entry plus the **approx()** version of the command line entry.

This illustration about effect of precision is from what we will be learning in the next section, Radicals and Rational Exponents.

Continuity on with the investigation in the next screenshot, it looks like there is an Operating System error. The second entry in the next screenshot uses the **approx(~)** operator located below the **equal (=)** key.

Begin by selecting the **HOME** key on the HP Prime. The **fraction template** is located using the **fraction / square root / absolute value** key Key in as shown. Use the approx() command for the last entry. The **shift** key function of **Enter**.

If the **HOME** view has computations, clear the **history** first. To clear the **history**, press the **Clear** key.

Pressing **Enter** gives us a solution of 0 for entry one. Entry two solution for approx() of the same identity is 1. Remember Boolean 0 is false and Boolean 1 is true. Precision of HP Prime causes entry one's command line identity to be false. From the previous screenshot the left and right expression's values are different.

Since the **approx**(identity)'s left and right expressions are the same value, the command line entry's solution would be 1 or true.

The HP Prime **HOME** view in approximate mode have different last digits, thus the statement in our previous screenshot was false. HP Prime's precision came into play.

Remark: As we mentioned before, just because the calculator gives us an answer do not automatically assume that it is correct. Precision comes into play with the HP Prime **HOME** view's approximate answers. Generally precision for calculations is not a problem, as about the only area we are aware of using twelve or more digits is frequency measurements in elaborate lab situations. As we see from the radical example testing equality of approximate number could lead to what looks like an error if the least significant digit or digits are calculated different ways for each side of the equality. Something that would appear to be true shows as false because of the internal decimal representation.

We now turn to looking at an exact solution using calculation for the distance that light travels in one year. This calculation can be exact because we are using the defined speed of light, 299 792 458 m/s, a defined calculation of 86 400 s/d, and a defined Julian year 365 1/4 d/yr, all rational numbers in the calculation. The Julian year of 365 1/4 days is used in astronomy. Multiplying the rational versions together by unitary analysis we end up with m/yr or meters per year.

Remark: <u>Earlier</u> we enter the Julian year as 365.25 the HP Prime used approximate values so the large decimal answer was written in scientific notation. If we enter the Julian year as (365+1/4) then the HP Prime well display an exact result.

Exact numbers or exact results can be thought of as having an infinite number of significant digits. As explained in the remark, for the HP Prime to work the problem exactly we need to use the fractional form rather than the decimal form for the Julian year or reenter any decimal calculation without its decimal.

HP Prime Family Exact Mode and Approximate Mode

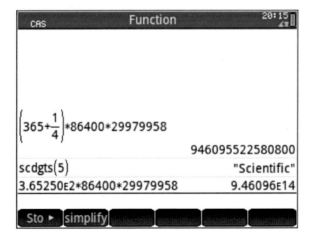

Begin by selecting the **CAS** key on the HP Prime. Key in the first entry as shown. The **fraction template** is located using the **fraction / square root / absolute value** key.

If the **Cas** view has computations, clear the **history** first. To clear the **history**, press the **Clear** key.

On the HP Prime Free we skip entry two, **scdgts(5)**. Remember, the HP Prime Free cannot create program functions such as entry two's **scdgts**.

For the HP Free we manually change **Number Format** for the next entry. In the "Home Settings" change **Number Format** to Scientific with 5 digits. The current history and future entries in the history area will show approximate numbers in Scientific Notation with 5 digits. Everything we have so far is exact so nothing in the history area changed.

HP Prime handheld, Pro, or Virtual Software calculators users cannot do entry two until we add the application library Key_user to our calculator. The Key_user library is explained next. The application library Key_user contains the function, **scdgts**. The function, **scdgts**, with a parameter of 5 digits, upon first use, remembers the current settings, and then sets our calculator to convert all numbers in the history except exact results and all future calculation to 5 decimal place scientific notation.

Remark: If you have a HP Prime handheld, Pro, or Virtual Software you can opt to manually change the "Home Settings" to Scientific with 5 digits and add the Key_user application later. Creating the Key_user program would be considered to be at the advanced user level. Downloading and using it would be at the extended level.

Returning to the above screenshot. We notice that in entry one the result has sixteen digits. When working with rational numbers, a HP Prime exact result can be calculated and displayed using a large numbers of digits.

An extremely large exact rational number can cause an "Overflow" error. The HP Prime CAS view will display an "Overflow" result as "undef". Remember for our calculations integers are rational numbers.

Try to get the "Overflow" condition by raising a rational number, such as 7/2 to an exponent power. Start with seventy-five as your power. You will have to scroll sideways to see all of the number. Use the **up arrow** and then the **right arrow** and **left arrow** to view the entire number. Then try a much larger exponent. If necessary, keep making the exponent bigger by a larger magnitude until you see the "Overflow" error answer of "undef".

Now for the last step in our screenshot. Copy our first entry to the command line. Change the date to 365.25. Press **Enter**. The edited entry, displayed the 365.25 and result in the history area as scientific notation with five decimal places. It used our manual setting of Scientific or for those that added the library, it used the function **scdgts(5)**.

Remark: HP Prime Free or those using the manual Scientific setting can skip the "Scientific Notation" programming instructions.

The HP Prime's "Home Settings" **Number Format** determines how decimal results are displayed. Next, we will create a program to store and temporarily change the "Home Settings" **Number Format**. When done we will use our program's "K_Apps" user_key function to set the **Number Format** back to its original setting.

We now create the program to temporarily display results in scientific notation. This allows us to leave our "**HOME** Settings" at their default values. Credit to user Wipf for the program Key Eex whose concept inspired program **Key_user**.

The amount of code makes it better to create the program using a text editor. We use the windows text editor Notepad++ with the HP PPl plug-in. Using Notepad++ on the same windows machine allows us to copy and paste between Notepad++ and HP Prime Pro or HP Prime virtual software. The

HP Connectivity Kit can be used as well although as we mentioned before, in its current version its communication can drop out plus it is not able to work with the HP Prime Pro on the same windows computer.

On Android using the Chromebook the HP Connectivity Kit and the current version of Android on the Chromebook platform does not find the HP Connectivity Kit. We can create directly on a text editor on the Chromebook or use Google Drive to copy the text file from a text editor where the file was created on a different computer to a text file on the Chromebook. Then use copy and paste between the text editor and the HP Prime Pro on the Chromebook.

Google Drive or other cloud based system could be used in other HP Prime situations as well. On the iPad Google's app is called **Drive**.

The following program, Key_user, is © Larry Schroeder 2018. All rights reserved.

HP Prime/ Pro/ Virtual Scientific Notation Program

```
Export gclsdigits, gclscount, gclshformat, gclshdigits;

K_Eex();
K_Apps();
first();

EXPORT scdgts(digits)
BEGIN
 LOCAL message;
 first( );
 IF (digits >= 0 AND digits <= 11) THEN
  gclsdigits := digits;
  HFormat := 2;
  HDigits := gclsdigits;
  message := "Scientific";
 ELSE
  message := "Error: Range 0-11";
 END;
 RETURN message;
END;

KEY K_Eex()
BEGIN
  first();
  IF HFormat <> 2 THEN
    HFormat := 2;
    HDigits := gclsdigits;
  ELSE
    HFormat := 0;
  END;
  STARTVIEW(-1,1);
  RETURN 10;
END;
```

We start by creating the Key_user application library. The code is shown using two Notepad++ listing. The first listing is shown above. The second part is shown following the HP Prime initial instructions.

Go to computerlearningservice.com/html/products.html to download.

Notice in the above listing use of prefix gcls with our global variable names. Computer Learning Service is our publisher's name. So the global variable names will be unique.

We next declare three functions, this allows the three functions to be called anywhere in the code. The "first()" subroutine is called twice in our code.

Notice also the mixing of Export and Key functions in the same application library. The **K_Eex()** has a Return of 10. The value of 10 is needed for the **CAS** view. If using the **HOME** view change the value to 5. The original code used the STARTVIEW and 5 to redraw the **HOME** view's screen. On the web, we found a reference to 10 for the redraw of the **CAS** view's screen.

The return 5 references a **HOME** key press according to the original author and STARTVIEW(-1,1) updates the history and command line. A return 10 would be used to reference a **CAS** key press.

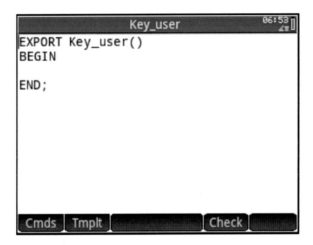

On our HP Prime/ Pro/ Virtual press the **Program** key. Remember the HP Prime Free does not have the programming function. Next, press the **New** soft key. Type in **Key_user** to the **Name**: field. Leave the **CAS:** field unchecked. Press the **OK** soft key twice. Leave the template **Key_user** program blank.

```
KEY K_Apps()
BEGIN
LOCAL message;
 message := "Unknown";
 IF gclscount <> 0 THEN
  HFormat := gclshformat;
  HDigits := gclshdigits;
  gclscount := 0;
  gclsdigits := 0;
  CASE
   IF gclshformat == 0 THEN message := "Standard"; END;
   IF gclshformat == 1 THEN message := "Fixed"; END;
   IF gclshformat == 2 THEN message := "Scientific"; END;
   IF gclshformat == 3 THEN message := "Engineering"; END;
   IF gclshformat == 4 THEN message := "Floating"; END;
   IF gclshformat == 5 THEN message := "Rounded"; END;
  END;
 END;
 STARTVIEW(-1,1);
 RETURN "Restored Number Format " + message + " - Press Es
END;

first()
BEGIN
 gclscount := gclscount + 1;
 IF gclscount == 1 THEN
   gclsdigits := 6;
   gclshformat := HFormat;
   gclshdigits := HDigits;
 END;
END;
```

From the Notepad++ select all and copy. This will copy both parts of the listing into the windows clipboard.

The **K_Apps()** code should only be executed follow any combinations of **K Eex()** and **scdgts(digits)** executions. Following the **K_Apps()** execution we need to use the **Esc** key to clear the command line.

The **fist()** subroutine sets the Scientific Notation default to 6 digits. Subsequent use of **scdgts(digits)** will override this.

The program when executed as instructed seems to be fairly robust. Unusual operations may require switches to **HOME** view and back to **CAS** view. Pay attention to the upper left icons in the Title line to see what state we are in.

With the Key_user template showing, press the **Copy** key on the HP Prime. Press the soft key **All**, followed by pressing the soft key **Cut**. Use the paste function of the HP Prime Pro or HP Prime Virtual Calculator to paste from the system clipboard the listing from Notepad++. Scroll to the top. At this point, we will see the above screen. Press the **Check** soft key. Press **OK** soft key to message "No errors in the program".

Our main goal in developing Key_user was to expand on Wipf K_Eex user key concept so that the current HP Prime "Home Setting" could be preserved and restored after toggling between Scientific and Standard Number Format. In addition we wanted to have our results displayed in any of the allowed Scientific Number Format 0-11decimal place range.

This process of creating Key_user is more involved than our earlier programs in first section of the book. But once we get our update/ debugged code into the template, the execution is no different than the one-line functions such as distrnl and our program library one-line functions as found in ArithSeries program library. With one-line functions such as distrnl, the program has one essential line in the Export template. The one-line functions did not need us to use a text editor. In either one-line functions such as distrnl or the longer multi functions libraries such as ArithSeries or Key_user returning to the **HOME** view or **CAS** view command line meant that the function or the program library syntax was correct. That the functions were ready to be executed/ tested.

HP Prime/ Pro/ Virtual Key_user library users can now use the Key_user program with the nearest star calculations. HP Prime Free or those using the manual Scientific setting will use the Home Settings.

HP Prime Family Constants and Units in Calculations

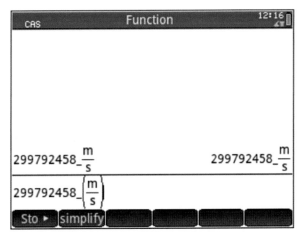

Begin by selecting the **CAS** key on the HP Prime. For entry one press the **Units** key and select the menu item, **Units > Const > Physics > c:**. Press **Enter**. Next add the units by pressing the **Units** key and select the menu item, **Units > Units > Speed > m/s**. Press **Enter**.

If the **CAS** view of the screenshot has computations, clear the **history** first. To clear the **history**, press the **Clear** key

We re-entered the command line constant and units. We see that when we press **Enter**, the results in the history area drop the parenthesis used in the command line. Press **Esc** to clear the re-entered entry out.

Let us look at keeping the correct number of digits. In our opening illustration the distance to our nearest star Proxima Centauri was given to be 39,900,000,000,000 km away at 4.22 light years. Another source has Proxima Centauri at 4.2421 light years. What would be the distance using their light year value?

HP Prime Family Distance to Proxima Centauri using 4.2421 Light years

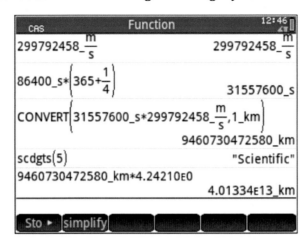

Continuing with the previous screen. For entry two type 86400. Next, add the time by pressing the Units key and select the menu item, **Units** > **Units** > **Time** > **s**. Press **x** for times. Press the **( )'s** key. Type 365+1/4. Press **Enter**. Press the Units key and select **CONVERT**. Use the **up arrow Enter** to transfer entry two. Press **x** for times. Use the **up arrow Enter** to transfer entry one. Press **Enter**.

For the HP Prime/ Pro/ Virtual Key_user library users, press the **Toobox** key to enter our function **scdgts**. Select **Toolbox** > **User** > **Key_user** > **scdgts** and press **Enter**. We set the number of digits by typing 5 as the parameter to our **scdgts** function. Since all calculation in the history area are exact, none of the values change.

HP Prime Free users or those using manual Scientific Notation, press the Home Settings. Switch the **Number Format:** to Scientifc with 5 digits. Press the **Esc** key. Since all calculation in the history area are exact, none of the values change.

Use the **up arrow Enter** to transfer entry three result to the command line. Press **x** for times. Type the light value of 4.2421 and press **Enter**. Notice the 4,2421 was changed to 4.24210E0 and result of this final calculation is 4.01333E13_km. Both of these are using 5 digit decimal place scientific notation we setup with our **scdgts(5)** command or manual setting if using the HP Prime Free or manual Scientific Notation option.

By looking at the last result and knowing the distance 4.2421 has 5 significant figures, with all other values being exact we round our answer to 5 significant figures, that is 4.0133E13 kilometers away. When we are multiplying, dividing, or using power we round the answer to the lowest significant figures occurring in the calculations. For addition and subtraction we round the result to the fewest number of decimal places used in any of the additions or subtractions.

HP Prime Free users or those using manual Scientific Notation can <u>skip the next screen and its instructions</u>.

HP Prime/ Pro/ Virtual Key_user Library Distance to Proxima Centauri using 4.2421 Light years

For the HP Prime/ Pro/ Virtual Key_user library users. Notice the bold Uparrow U displayed in orange next to our CAS in the Function title line. By pressing **User** twice we have locked the HP Prime into the alternate key mode. Remember we need to use the **Blue** Shift key for keys labeled in **blue**. Then when we press the EEX key the non-exact values toggle between Standard and Scientific.

In Standard mode small numbers such as the 4.2421 in the above screenshot will be shown using decimal notation. Very large numbers such as 4.01333647377E13_km will stay in Scientific Notation since the precision of the HP Prime cannot display them as a decimal. Scientific Notation would also be used for very small numbers that the HP Prime could not display as a decimal.

Notice that 4.2421 and 4.01333647377E13_km are the only two that change as all other numbers in the history area are exact. Since we set Scientific Notation to 5 digit with our function scdgts(5), we see 4.24210E0 and 4.01334E13 as the scientific values when we toggle the EEX key.

Pressing the **Apps** key while it is locked will restore the "Home Setting" to its original state. A message stating this will appear in the command line. Press **Esc** to clear this message out. A third press of **User** will be necessary to turn the lock off.

A single press of **User** will run the alternate functions as well. Our function **scdgts** with a parameter of 0-11 can be used as well. The scientific notation number of decimals will then show the new number of decimal places. Pressing the **App** key is also used to restore "Home Settings" following the use of the **scdgts** function.

HP Prime/ Pro/ Virtual Key_user library users should use the above fourth and fifth paragraphs **User** and **Apps** keys directions for restoring their calculator to its original settings.

Note: HP Prime Free users or those using manual Scientific Notation should manually restore their original Home Setting. Press the Home **Settings** Key. Switch the **Number Format:** back to original settings and number of decimal place. Press the **Esc** key.

The answer to our question is 40,133,000,000,000 km at 4.2421 light years compared to the 39,900,000,000,000 km away at 4.22 light years. Here we used the more traditional commas for the result and our original value rather than spacing. Notation can cause problems. A comma in some parts of the world is used for a decimal point. To a student living there the comma form of the result would appear as having multiple decimal places, totally confusing the student.

We now look at the other use of scientific notation, very small numbers. What happens when there is an imbalance between negative and positive charges in objects? To understand that static electricity is occurring from this imbalance of negative and positive charges, we need to understand the basics of atoms and magnetism.

What is this basic electric charge, 1.602 176 565 x 10⁻¹⁹ coulombs? It is the charge carried by a single proton, or the opposite of it, the charge carried by an electron. Here we see very small numbers being used. Use a search engine to investigate static electricity and its imbalance of electronic charge.

Example 3 Scientific to Decimal Notation – Decimal to Scientific Notation

Change to decimal notation.

(a) $7.351 \times 10^{-6} = 0.000\ 007\ 351$

(b) $9.780 \times 10^{5} = 978\ \overline{0}00$

Change to scientific notation.

(c) $4\ 35\overline{0} = 4.350 \times 10^{3}$

(d) $0.000\ 072\ 10 = 7.210 \times 10^{-5}$

In decimal notation to indicate that a trailing zero is significant we put a bar above it. In scientific notation any trailing zero is significant.

HP Prime Family Scientific to Decimal Notation – Decimal to Scientific Notation

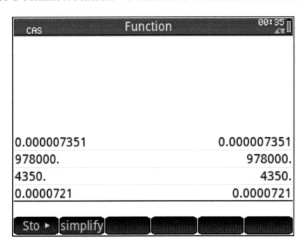

Begin by selecting the **CAS** key on the HP Prime. If the **CAS** view of the screenshot has computations, clear the **history** first. To clear the **history**, press the **Clear** key.

Key in **7.351E-6** followed by **Enter**. The first entry is displayed with 9 decimal places.

For the second entry key in **9.780E5** followed by **Enter**. Upon pressing **enter** the problem was changed to the default notation. There is no way to tell that we have four significant figures.

For the third entry key in **4350.0**. Note the decimal entry. Exact are not converted to scientific notation in the next screenshot without adding the decimal.

Key in entry four, **0.00007210**. The HP Prime default notation again dropped the significant zero.

Note: The default HP Prime "Home Settings" handles scientific notation to decimal correctly except significant zeros for all the HP Prime Family.

For the HP Prime Free we need to do the conversion from decimal to scientific notation manually or set the "Home Settings" Number Format: to Scientific with 3 decimal places to display the results in Scientific Notation. HP Prime Free would not see the **scdgts(3)** line.

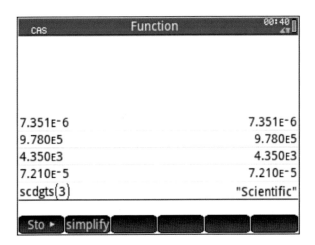

Continuing from previous screen. For the HP Prime/ Pro/ Virtual use the **Toobox** key to enter our function **scdgts**. Select **Toolbox > User > Key_user > scdgts** and press **Enter**. We set the number of digits in Scientific by typing 3 as the parameter to our **scdgts** function. Since all calculation in the history area are decimal, all of the values change. As mentioned above the, HP Prime Free would use the "Home Settings" to set the Number Format to Scientific and decimal digits to 3.

It just happens that all value in the screenshot used 3 decimal places. In scientific notation any trailing zero is significant. This would be true for the last two entries.

Note: HP Prime/ Pro/ Virtual user need to restore the HP Prime "Home Settings" by pressing the **Apps** key when the HP Prime is in **User** key mode. HP Prime Free user should manually set the "Home Settings" Number Format back to its original settings.

Exercise 3 **Scientific to Decimal Notation – Decimal to Scientific Notation**

Change to decimal notation.

(a) 8.21×10^{6}

(b) 4.30×10^{-5}

Change to scientific notation.

(c) 0.006 25

(d) $81\bar{0}\ 000$

<u>Solution</u> **>>**

Explanation 1.4 – Radicals and Rational Exponents

In this section we introduce radicals and rational exponents. We start by going over the difference between the square root of a number and the *principal square root.* We expand this to the *n*th root and the *principal nth root.*

We then use the radicals to define rational exponents. The rational exponents are also referred to as fractional exponents. It can be shown from the Definition of Rational Exponents that the *Properties of Exponents* hold as well.

We conclude this section with eliminating radicals in the denominator. This process is referred to as rationalizing the denominator.

Radicals and Their Properties

A number is squared when it is raised to the second power. Many times we need to know what number was squared to produce a value of *a*. If this value exist we refer to that number as a *square root of a.*

> **Definition of Square Root**
>
> The number b is a **square root** of a if $b^2 = a$.

Thus

25 has -5 and 5 as square roots since $(-5)^2 = 25$ and $(5)^2 = 25$,

49 has -7 and 7 as square roots since $(-7)^2 = 49$ and $(7)^2 = 49$,

-16 has no real number square root since no real number b where $b^2 = -16$.

Zero only has itself as a *square root.* We will later add the complex number system where *square roots* exist for negative numbers.

HP Prime Family Square Root - solve

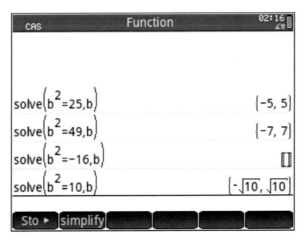

Begin by selecting the **CAS** key on the HP Prime. If the **CAS** view of the screenshot has computations, clear the **history** first. To clear the **history**, press the **Clear** key.

Key in as shown. Use the **Toobox** key to enter **solve()**. Select **Toolbox > CAS > Solve > Solve** and press **Enter**. Keying in a negative value for entry three gives us an empty matrix. The empty matrix means that there is no solution. With the solve command there are three possibilities, identity, no solution, and unique answers. The letter we are solving for would be given inside braces when we have an identity, that is, all real values for the letter work as the solution. Empty matrix is given when no real values work as a solution.

Try adding an entry for the square roots of zero to see that there is only one solution.

We need to be careful when using **approx** key followed by the **mixed numeral** key.

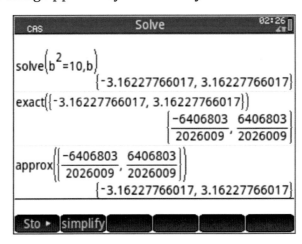

Begin by selecting the **CAS** key on the HP Prime. If the **CAS** view of the screenshot has computations, clear the **history** first. To clear the **history**, press the **Clear** key.

Key in the first entry in the command line. Use the **Toobox** key to enter **solve()**. Select **Toolbox > CAS > Solve > Solve** and press **Enter**. Press the **approx** key. Press the **mixed numeral** key twice.

Note: Since our answer was a terminating decimal the **mixed numerical** key converted it back to a rational number, not the square roots we were looking for. The same problem occurs if we use the **mixed numerical** key to convert the $-\sqrt{10}$ and $\sqrt{10}$ to a decimal and then use it again. We end with rational numbers for the decimal and not the square roots.

We next look at the HP Prime command **fsolve** that directly displays the solution numerically.

HP Prime Family Square Root - fsolve

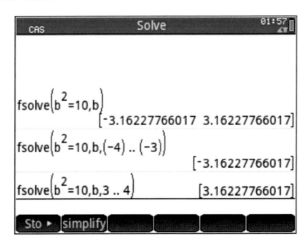

Begin by selecting the **CAS** key on the HP Prime. If the **CAS** view of the screenshot has computations, clear the **history** first. To clear the **history**, press the **Clear** key.

Key in entry one and three as shown. Entry two for the range use -4..3. Use the **Toobox** key to enter **fsolve()**. Select **Toolbox > CAS > Solve > Numerical Solve** and press **Enter**.

The HP Prime's fsolve command has an optional lower and upper bounds. It will show all the solutions in the range. From the screenshot the first entry has no boundaries. The second entry has a boundary where only the negative solution is shown. The third entry has a boundary where only the positive solution is shown.

We could also use the Solve Application Library to display numerical results.

HP Prime Family Square Root – Solve Application Library

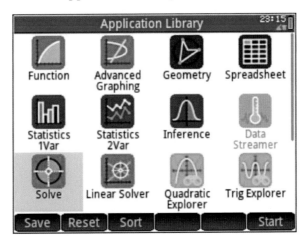

Press the **Apps** key on the HP Prime. From the Application Library select the **Solve** icon. The HP Prime Free will not have as many apps. On the HP Prime handheld Data Streamer will be enabled.

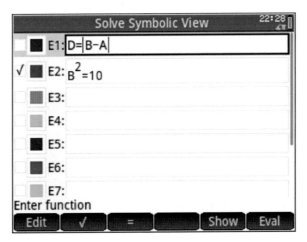

Select **E2:**. Key in the equation as shown followed by **Enter**. Use the letter keys for the uppercase B. Use the = key. Key in 19.

If necessary Clear E2:. Select it and use the **backspace** key. To Clear all equations press Clear and press **Enter** to accept message "Clear all expressions?".

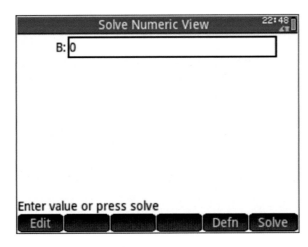

Press the **Num** key on the HP Prime. Key in 0 for **B**.

Note: For variables with multiple answers we need to put in a seed value if we want to see additional solutions. See next two screens.

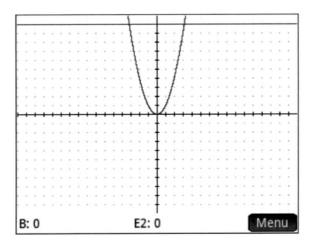

Press the **Plot** key on the HP Prime. With keyed in value of **B** =0 and the edit field being **B**, we see from the plot solutions of -√10 and √10. To see the solutions in the **NUM** view we pick as seed values -3 and 3.

How the plot works. It takes our equation left and right expressions and makes them into two equations, $Y=B^2$ and $Y=10$. Using our values and solving for B, we have $Y=X^2$ and $Y=10$. With A being the solved variable it becomes X in the parabola plot. We need A to be selected and its current value set to zero then we see the above $Y=X^2$ and $Y=10$ plots. The x-values of -√10 and √10 in the intersections of the two plots are the solutions.

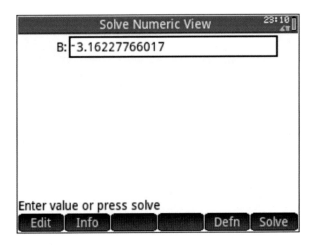

To get the first solution for **B**, we seed **B** with -3 and press **Enter**. Select entry **B** again and press the soft **Solve** key and we will see the solution of -3.16227766017. To get the second solution for **B**, we seed **B** with 3 and press **Enter**. Select entry **B** again and press the soft **Solve** key and we will see the solution of 3.16227766017.

Square roots are specialized case of *nth roots*. The *nth root* of *x*, would be the number that when raised to the *n*th power gives *x*.

We now turn to the *principal square root* of a number. This is the one that uses the *radical sign*.

Definition of Principal Square Root

The **principal square root** of *a*, $a \geq 0$, is its nonnegative square root:

$$\sqrt{a} = b \quad \text{means} \quad b^2 = a$$

Thus

25 has 5 as its principal square root since $5^2 = 25$,

49 has 7 as its principal square roots since $7^2 = 49$,

-16 has no real principal square root since no real number b where $b^2 = -16$.

Let's take a look at how the HP Prime handles the *principal square root*.

HP Prime Family Principal Square Root

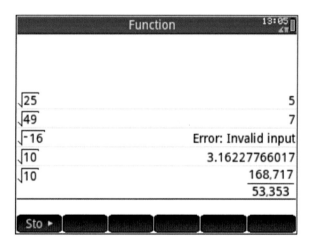

Begin by selecting the **CAS** key on the HP Prime. If the **CAS** view of the screenshot has computations, clear the **history** first. To clear the **history**, press the **Clear** key.

Key in as shown. Keying in a negative value for entry three gives non-real result. The HP prime's Standard "Home Settings" allows a complex result. The HP Prime show the principal root solution. The radical sign, or principal root, only has one root. For the two square roots of -16 there would be two solutions. To get both solutions both solutions for square roots, see entry four with **cSolve**. Press the **Toolbox** key and select **Toolbox > CAS > Solve > Complex Solve**. Enter the equation and use **z** as second parameter. There are two square roots of -16. To check raise list of solutions to the second power. A warning appears. Press **Enter** to continue. To work two square roots of -16 manually we use cos(angle)+i*sin(angle).

For entry seven press the **approx** key.

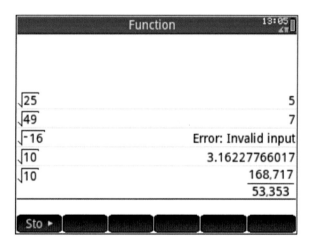

Begin by selecting the **HOME** key on the HP Prime. If the **HOME** view of the screenshot has computations, clear the **history** first. To clear the **history**, press the **Clear** key.

Key in as shown. Keying in a negative value for entry three gives an error message. Pressing the HP prime's **mixed numeral** key gives an approximate rational representation of square root of 10.

The "$\sqrt{}$" is referred to as a *radical sign* and is used to indicate the *principal square root*.

In addition to being referred to as the "*principal square root* of *a*", it also referred to as the "*square root* of *a*" or "*root a*".

Generalizing the *principal square root* of *a* we have the following definition for *principal nth root*. The entire expression is the *radical*, the number *a* is the *radicand*, and *n* is the *index* of the *radical*.

Definition of Principal nth Root

Let a be a real number and n a positive integer greater than 1, the **principal nth root** of a is

(1) If $a = 0$, then $\sqrt[n]{a} = 0$

(2) If $a > 0$, then $\sqrt[n]{a} = b$ a positive real number such that $b^n = a$

(3) If $a < 0$,

    (i) n is odd, then $\sqrt[n]{a} = b$ a negative real number such that $b^n = a$

    (ii) n is even, the $\sqrt[n]{a}$ is not a real number

To visually see the relationship we look at a drawing of an even and odd nth root. In the following drawing, the square root is shown as the blue or heavier graph. The seventh root is shown as blue as well. On gray scale it will appear as the graph that goes through A'.

As in the definition the nth root of zero in square root and seventh root is zero. When a is greater than zero all the values for the square root and seventh root are positive real numbers. When a is less than zero, the square root does not exist, and the seventh root is a negative real number.

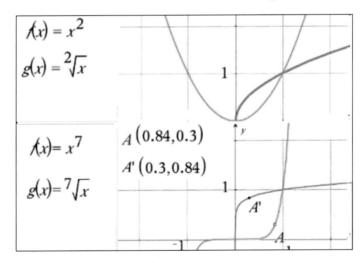

Figure 1 Power Function Inverses (Education.ti.com, Power Function Inverses)

Notice in the drawing that the x and y coordinate is reversed for the function and its inverse. In a later tutorial we will cover functions and their inverses. The parabola needs to be restricted to greater than or equal to zero.

The drawing, as mentioned, highlights the relationship between the power and the roots of variables for even and odd numbers. The same relationship we see in the definition. We recommend additional exploration using HP Primes <u>Advanced Graphing Application Library App</u> with other even and odd relations. It follows the Function Application Library App shown next.

We could use the graphs function of our HP Prime to display the roots as well.

HP Prime Family Graph Square Root and Seventh Root

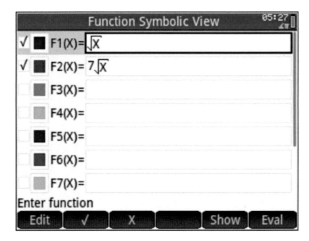

Press the **Apps** key. Highlight the **Function** icon on the Application Library screen. Press the soft **Start** key. Press the soft **Edit** key. The above screen will appear. Enter function as shown. Press the soft **OK** key.

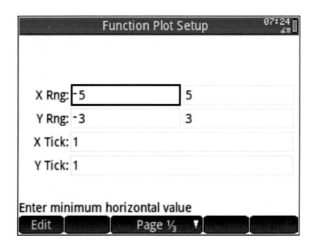

Press the Plot **Setup** key. Page 1/3, change these values X Rng: -5, 5; Y Rng: -3, 3. Page 2/3, check the Labels box.

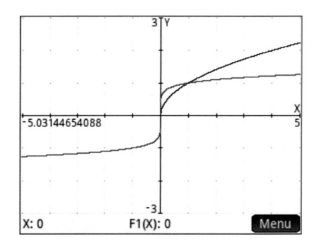

Press the **Plot** key to see a graph of the function. Press the soft **Menu** key. Use the **Fcn Extremum**. Press the soft **OK** key and then soft **Menu** key. Use the **Fcn Defintion** and soft **down arrow** key to display the screen.

If viewing in gray scale the square root function only exist in the first quadrant. The flatter graph in the first and third quadrant is the seventh root.

HP Prime Family Advance Graphing App - Graph Y=X² and X=Y²

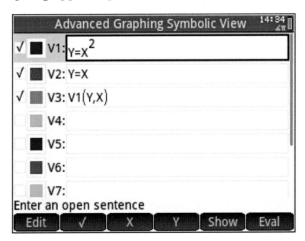

Press the **Apps** key. Highlight the **Advanced Graphing** icon on the Application Library screen. Press the soft **Start** key. Press the soft **Edit** key. The above screen will appear. Enter functions as shown. Press the soft **OK** key.

Notice in entry three that the x and y coordinate is reversed for the relation and its inverse. Using this technique all we would have to do is change V1 to graph a different relation and its inverse. We could make an Inverse Relation Library App. HP Prime/ Pro/ Virtual see our GraphPlus Library Application for a model. For dealing with the syntax for the relations it might be helpful to look at the code of Graph3D Library Application dealing with variables V0-V9.

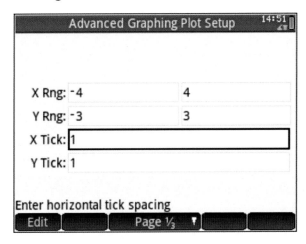

Press the Plot Setup key. Change if necessary. Page 1/3, values X Rng: -4, 4; Y Rng: -3, 3. Page 2/3, the Labels box is checked.

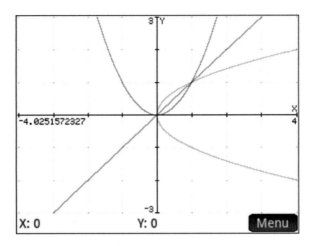

Press the **Plot** key to see a graph of the relations.

Inverse functions would have to be given as two pairs of functions. One pair is the blue and green graphs in the first quadrant. The second pair would be the blue graph in the second quadrant and the green graph in the fourth quadrant. The red line of reflections helps identify the inverse functions. For functions the blue graphs would need restrictions and the green graphs would need to be written with radicals.

Let's now look at HP Prime illustrations of *principal nth roots*.

HP Prime Family Principal nth Root

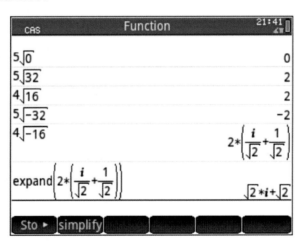

Begin by selecting the **CAS** key on the HP Prime. If the **CAS** view of the screenshot has computations, clear the **history** first. To clear the **history**, press the **Clear** key.

Key in as shown. Keying in a negative value for entry five gives a non-real result. The HP prime's Standard "Home Settings" allows a complex result. Press the **Toolbox** key and select **Toolbox > CAS > Algebra > Expand**. Use the **Up Arrow** to copy the previous result from the history area. Press Enter.

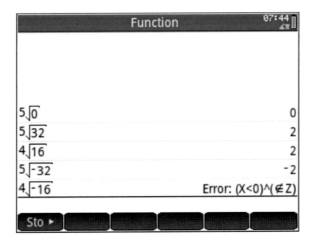

Continuing with the previous screen. The HP Prime **CAS** shows the principal solution. The radical sign, or principal root, only has one root. To get the four fourth roots of -16 see entry three of this screen with the **cSolve** command.

The HP prime's Standard "Home Settings" allows a complex result. The HP Prime **CAS** show the principal solutions. Press the **Toolbox** key and select **Toolbox > CAS > Solve > Complex Solve**. Enter the equation and use z as second parameter. There are four fourth roots of -16. We see entry two of this screen and the first item in the simplify result list are equivalent. All of these items raised to the fourth power would produce -16. To work four solutions manually we use cos(angle)+i*sin(angle).

Begin by selecting the **HOME** key on the HP Prime. If the **HOME** view of the screenshot has computations, clear the **history** first. To clear the **history**, press the **Clear** key.

Key in as shown. Keying in a negative value for entry five with an even index gives an error message.

The entries in the **HOME** screenshot illustrate the *Definition of Principal nth Root.* First we illustrate for an *index* greater than zero that root of zero is zero. Entries two and three show that an odd and even *index* for *a* greater than zero that *a* raised to the index power of *a* results in *a*. The definition only specifies odd and even *index* case when *a* raised to the index power is less than zero. This illustrates that it is not necessary to have both odd and even case where *a* is greater than zero. Entry four with *a* raised to an odd index power greater than zero and *a* raised to an index power that is less than zero results in *a*. The above **HOME** view screen entry five with *a* raised to an even index power greater than zero and *a* raised to an index power that is less than zero results in an error message. In the earlier **CAS** view screen this results in a complex solution. However, we had to use **cSolve** to get all four complex solutions.

Next we notice some observations that lead us to the *Properties of Radicals.*

HP Prime Family Square Root Observations

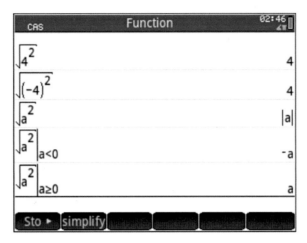

Begin by selecting the **CAS** key on the HP Prime. If the **CAS** view of the screenshot has computations, clear the **history** first. To clear the **history**, press the **Clear** key.

Key in as shown.

The first interesting thing to note about entry four is that $-a$ is a positive number. This is true since it was specified that a was less than zero. Therefore $-a$, or the opposite of a negative number, is a positive number. This is what is shown in entry two, where the answer is the $-(-4)$ or positive 4.

Entry five is entry four changed to a greater than or equal results in a as the solution. Therefore, the only way to always have the result be true is entry three with absolute value for a.

Try taking the cube root of a^3. The result would be a. To do this we have to use rational exponent of 1/3. The radical version does not simplify.

The $|a|$ would be true for any even root and a value of a would be true for any odd root. This result and other rules lead us to the *Properties for Radicals*.

In the *Properties of Radicals*, m and n are positive integers and a and b are real numbers provided the indicated roots exists.

Properties of Radicals

1. $\left(\sqrt[n]{a}\right)^n = a$

2. $\sqrt[n]{a^n} = a$ if n is odd

3. $\sqrt[n]{a^n} = |a|$ if n is even

4. $\sqrt[n]{a \cdot b} = \sqrt[n]{a} \cdot \sqrt[n]{b}$

5. $\sqrt[n]{\dfrac{a}{b}} = \dfrac{\sqrt[n]{a}}{\sqrt[n]{b}}$

6. $\sqrt[m]{\sqrt[n]{a}} = \sqrt[mn]{a}$

Let us look at illustrations of how the HP Prime handles properties 1-3.

HP Prime Family Properties of Radicals

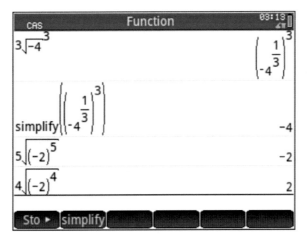

Begin by selecting the **CAS** key on the HP Prime. If the **CAS** view of the screenshot has computations, clear the **history** first. To clear the **history**, press the **Clear** key.

Key in as shown.

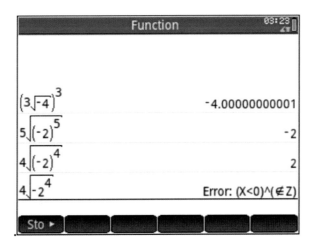

Begin by selecting the **HOME** key on the HP Prime. If the **HOME** view of the screenshot has computations, clear the **history** first. To clear the **history**, press the **Clear** key.

Use the **Menu** key "Get from CAS" to transfer the problems over. Key in entry four as shown. Using a negative value for entry four with an even index gives an error message.

Entry one: the cube root of -4 exist, so raising to the third power gives us back the *radicand*, -4. The precision of the real solution in the **HOME** screen view comes into play.

With Property 1 of Radicals we have to be careful that the given root exists. For example if we did the fourth root of -2 raised to the fourth power we would get an error message. Entry four of **HOME** screen view shows this. On the earlier **CAS** view screen, the fourth root of -2 raised to the fourth power would result in a complex number (not shown). The **CAS** view result would be same as <u>our earlier problem</u>, where we needed to use **cSolve** to show all of the solutions.

Entry three **CAS**, two **HOME**: n is odd so we get back the number that was raised to the power, that is, -2.

Entry four **CAS**, three **HOME**: n is even so we get back the absolute value of number that was raised to the power, that is, absolute value of -2 which is 2.

HP Prime Properties of Radicals

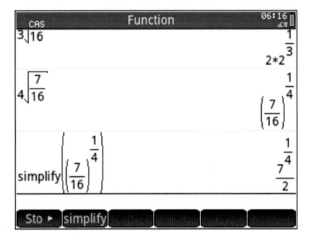

Begin by selecting the **CAS** key on the HP Prime. If the **CAS** view of the screenshot has computations, clear the **history** first. To clear the **history**, press the **Clear** key.

Key in as shown.

HP Prime Family Properties of Radicals – Part 2

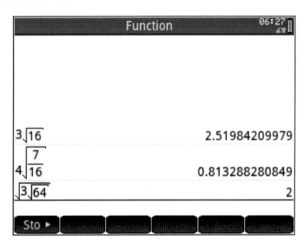

Begin by selecting the **HOME** key on the HP Prime. If the **HOME** view of the screenshot has computations, clear the **history** first. To clear the **history**, press the **Clear** key.

Use the **Menu** key "Get from CAS" to transfer the problems over. Key in as shown.

The cube root of a square root of 64 for the HP Prime **CAS** view would also be 2. It is not shown in the **CAS** screen.

Note: From our work so far we can conclude that both the HP Prime **CAS** view and HP Prime HOME view perform simplification of exact radicals flawlessly. From the two previous screenshots we can see that the HP Prime **CAS** can be used with numerical values for algebraic solutions for radicals that are not exact. However, the radicals are switched to rational exponents. The HP Prime **HOME** view as expected converts them to numerical values.

The first screenshot solutions also lead us into the next topic for this section, defining rational exponents using radicals.

Remark: The HP Prime **CAS** writes the solution for properties 4-6 in rational exponent form rather than radical form. However, this behavior various with the property and complexity of the problem and the solution may or may not help us see how the *Properties of Radicals* is manually performed or appear to be in a very useful form.

To work these problems manually use the *Properties of Radicals* or alternately use a combination of the *Properties of Radicals* and the following rule. The rule is a mechanical technique that can assist us with the simplification of perfect nth powers.

In general, simplification of radicals involves three steps. First, removal of all perfect nth powers; second, making the index of the radical is as small as possible; and third, having no fractions in the radicand, i.e. removal of the radical from the denominator. We will cover the second and third steps at the conclusion of this section.

To use the rule to remove all perfect nth powers, we combine radicals if necessary. We then factor any constant if necessary. For each factor, constant or variable, we divide the power by the index. Where the quotient is greater than zero we rewrite the factor's power with the power now being written as the quotient on the outside and the remainder on the inside of the radical. If there is no remainder, then nothing is written in the inside.

If the quotient is not greater than zero, we leave the factor in the radicand alone. For an even index add absolute value to the removed factors. Lastly, use absolute value rules to remove absolute value notation from factors where notation is not necessary.

Simplification of Radicals - nth Power Removal

1. If necessary combine radicals
2. If possible factor the constant
3. Do the division for each factor

$$\sqrt[index]{a^{power}} \qquad index\overline{)\,power}^{\;quotient\;remainder}$$

4. Rewrite the radical

    i. For odd index

    $$a^{quotient} \cdot \sqrt[index]{a^{remainder}}$$

    ii. For even index

    $$\left| a^{quotient} \right| \cdot \sqrt[index]{a^{remainder}}$$

    Simplify the absolute value

    $$|a \cdot b| = |a| \cdot |b|$$
    $$|k \cdot a| = |k| \cdot |a| = c \cdot |a| \qquad |k| = c > 0$$
    $$\left| a^{even\ power} \right| = a^{even\ power}$$

Enter the problem into HP Prime **CAS**. We will be able with many of the solutions to see that the manual and HP Prime **CAS** solutions are equivalent. However, if the manual and HP Prime **CAS** solutions final forms are not obviously equivalent, do not spend a lot of time seeing that they are equivalent.

It should also be noted that HP Prime **CAS** solutions that use improper rational exponent can be beneficial in calculus when performing differentiation and integration of variables raised to a power.

Example 1 Removing Factors from Radicals

(a) Simplify: $\sqrt[3]{375}$

Factor largest cube	$\sqrt[3]{375}$
$\sqrt[n]{a \cdot b} = \sqrt[n]{a} \cdot \sqrt[n]{b}$	$= \sqrt[3]{3 \cdot 125} = \sqrt[3]{3 \cdot 5^3}$
$\sqrt[n]{a^n} = a \quad n \text{ is odd}$	$= \sqrt[3]{3} \cdot \sqrt[3]{5^3}$
	$= 5\sqrt[3]{3}$

(b) Simplify: $\sqrt{x^{10}}$

Properties of Exponents	$\sqrt{x^{10}}$
$\sqrt[n]{a^n} = |a| \quad n \text{ is even}$	$= \sqrt{(x^5)^2}$
	$= \left| x^5 \right|$

(c) Simplify: $\sqrt[3]{54x^8y^3z^5}$

Arrange as a cube	$\sqrt[3]{54x^8y^3z^5}$
Properties of Exponents	$= \sqrt[3]{(2x^2z^2) \cdot (27x^6y^3z^3)}$
$\sqrt[n]{a \cdot b} = \sqrt[n]{a} \cdot \sqrt[n]{b}$	$= \sqrt[3]{(2x^2z^2) \cdot (3x^2y \cdot z)^3}$
$\sqrt[n]{a^n} = a \quad n \text{ is odd}$	$= \sqrt[3]{2x^2z^2} \cdot \sqrt[3]{(3x^2y \cdot z)^3}$
	$= 3x^2y \cdot z\sqrt[3]{2x^2z^2}$

Alternate Approach

(a) Simplify: $\sqrt[3]{375}$

Factor	$\sqrt[3]{375}$
nth Power Removal – odd	$= \sqrt[3]{3 \cdot 5^3}$
	$= 5\sqrt[3]{3}$

(b) Simplify: $\sqrt{x^{10}}$

nth Power Removal – even	$\sqrt{x^{10}}$
	$= \left| x^5 \right|$

(c) Simplify: $\sqrt[3]{54x^8y^3z^5}$

Factor	$\sqrt[3]{54x^8y^3z^5}$
nth Power Removal – odd	$= \sqrt[3]{2 \cdot 3^3 x^8 y^3 z^5}$
	$= 3x^2y \cdot z\sqrt[3]{2x^2z^2}$

HP Prime **Removing Factors from Radicals**

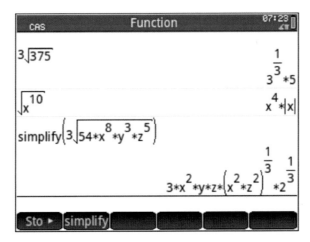

Begin by selecting the **CAS** key on the HP Prime. If the **CAS** view of the screenshot has computations, clear the **history** first. To clear the **history**, press the **Clear** key.

Key in entry one and two as shown. For entry three we deleted the original radical entry and left the simplified entry so it would fit on one screen.

HP Prime **CAS's** part (a) is written in exponent form, but we can see that the manual solution is equivalent. Part (b) solution is again equivalent for both HP Prime **CAS** and manual solution. Part (c) answer is equivalent but we would have to use the *nth Power Removal* rule extended to rational exponents.

Exercise 1 **Removing Factors from Radicals**

Simplify:

(a) $\sqrt[4]{x^8 y^8}$

(b) $3\sqrt[4]{x^3 y} \cdot \sqrt[4]{x^2 y^2}$

(b) $\sqrt[3]{\sqrt{128}}$

<u>Solution</u> >>

Simplification by the Properties of Radicals is often used to combine like radicals in an expression. The Distributive Property is used to factor out the radicals and simplify where possible. The next two-part illustration allows us to see these principles at work.

(a) Simplify: $\sqrt{50} - \sqrt{18}$

$\sqrt[n]{a \cdot b} = \sqrt[n]{a} \cdot \sqrt[n]{b}$

$\sqrt[n]{a^n} = |a|$ n is even & Simplify absolute value

Distributive property

$$\sqrt{50} - \sqrt{18}$$
$$= \sqrt{2 \cdot 25} - \sqrt{2 \cdot 9}$$
$$= 5\sqrt{2} - 3\sqrt{2}$$
$$= 2\sqrt{2}$$

(b) Simplify: $\sqrt[3]{27x^3 y^2} + \sqrt[3]{-x^3 y^2}$

Arrange as cubes

$\sqrt[n]{a \cdot b} = \sqrt[n]{a} \cdot \sqrt[n]{b}$

$\sqrt[n]{a^n} = a$ n is odd

Distributive property

$$\sqrt[3]{27x^3 y^2} + \sqrt[3]{-x^3 y^2}$$
$$= \sqrt[3]{(3x)^3 y^2} + \sqrt[3]{(-x)^3 y^2}$$
$$= \sqrt[3]{(3x)^3} \sqrt[3]{y^2}$$
$$+ \sqrt[3]{(-x)^3} \sqrt[3]{y^2}$$
$$= 3x\sqrt[3]{y^2} - x\sqrt[3]{y^2}$$
$$= 2x\sqrt[3]{y^2}$$

HP Prime Family Combining Like Radicals

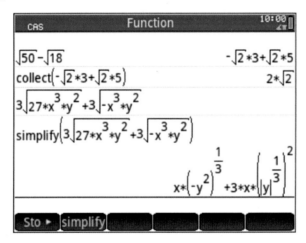

Begin by selecting the **CAS** key on the HP Prime. If the **CAS** view of the screenshot has computations, clear the **history** first. To clear the **history**, press the **Clear** key.

Key in entry one as shown. Press the **Toolbox** key and select **Toolbox > CAS > Algebra > Collect**. Copy the result from the history area. Press **Enter** to see the result. For entry three we **simplify** the entry. No commands appear to work. We are better off working this problem manually.

Rational Exponents

We now give meaning to **rational exponents** by defining them so that the properties of exponents hold. As we have noted, the TI-Nspire makes frequent use of the relationship between radicals and rational exponents and their properties.

HP Prime Family **Rational Exponents and Corresponding Radicals Results**

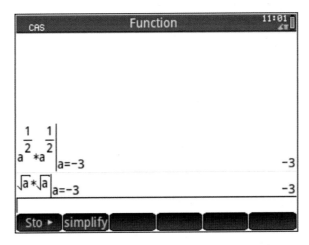

Begin by selecting the **CAS** key on the HP Prime. If the **CAS** view of the screenshot has computations, clear the **history** first. To clear the **history**, press the **Clear** key.

Key in as shown.

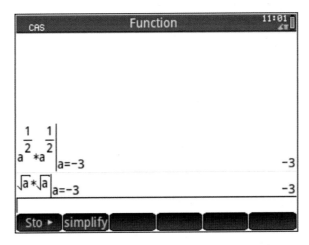

Begin by selecting the **CAS** key on the HP Prime. If the **CAS** view of the screenshot has computations, clear the **history** first. To clear the **history**, press the **Clear** key.

Key in as shown. We have to be careful for one half power and square root whose input's domain is restricted to greater than or equal to zero where result's domain can be all *real numbers*. A restricted input situation ends up with incorrect result being displayed. In this case when we use a negative value of -3 instead of *a*, we end with a -3 as the result. This is not correct for reals since no negative numbers are allowed in the original domain. The odd powers and roots do not have this problem.

Remark: Technically on the HP Prime the answers to the last two entries on the last screen are correct. The HP Prime handles the domain of input as complex. The "$\sqrt{}$-3" is "$\sqrt{}$3i". The "$\sqrt{}$3i"$*$ "$\sqrt{}$ 3i" is $3i^2$ or -3. The same thing would be true for the one half power.

Since entry one has the same result as entry two, it suggest that *a* to the one-half power is the same square root of *a*. Similarly with entry three and four, it suggest *a* to the one-third power is the same cube root of *a*. Generalizing we have part (1) of the following definition.

If the property for multiplying exponents is to hold, this would suggest part (2) of the definition. Applying (1) to part (2) we have part (3) of the definition.

Definition of Rational Exponents

Let m/n be a rational number where n is a counting number greater than 1, and a is a real number such that $\sqrt[n]{a}$ exist, then

(1) $a^{1/n} = \sqrt[n]{a}$

(2) $a^{m/n} = (\sqrt[n]{a})^m = \sqrt[n]{a^m}$

(3) $a^{m/n} = (a^{1/n})^m = (a^m)^{1/n}$

As we noted earlier the HP Prime **CAS** provides algebraic manipulation of radical numerical expressions with the results shown as rational exponents except in case of square roots.

HP Prime Family Using the Definition of Rational Exponents

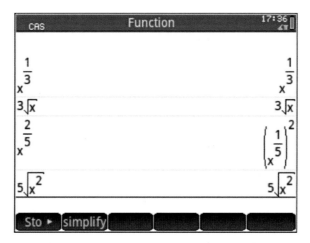

Begin by selecting the **CAS** key on the HP Prime. If the **CAS** view of the screenshot has computations, clear the **history** first. To clear the **history**, press the **Clear** key.

Key in as shown.

We see from the screen that when dealing with variables and not numerical values the input as rational exponent or radicals does not convert to a different form.

The next two-part illustration shows using the Definition of Rational Exponents with numerical values.

(a) Simplify: $\left(\dfrac{16}{81}\right)^{3/4}$

$a^{m/n} = (\sqrt[n]{a})^m$

$\left(\dfrac{16}{81}\right)^{3/4}$

$\sqrt[n]{a^n} = |a|$ n is even & Simplify $= \left(\sqrt[4]{\dfrac{16}{81}}\right)^3$

absolute value

$\left(\dfrac{a}{b}\right)^n = \dfrac{a^n}{b^n}$ $= \left(\dfrac{2}{3}\right)^3$

$= \dfrac{8}{27}$

(b) Simplify: $(32)^{-1/5}$

Definition Negative Exponents $(32)^{-1/5}$

$a^{1/n} = \sqrt[n]{a}$ $= \dfrac{1}{32^{1/5}}$

$\sqrt[n]{a^n} = a$ n is odd $= \dfrac{1}{\sqrt[5]{32}}$

$= \dfrac{1}{2}$

HP Prime Family Using the Definition of Rational Exponents with Numerical Values

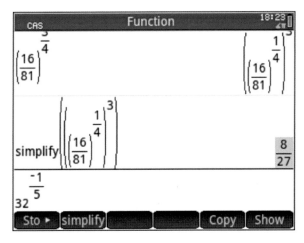

Begin by selecting the **CAS** key on the HP Prime. If the **CAS** view of the screenshot has computations, clear the **history** first. To clear the **history**, press the **Clear** key.

Key in as shown. The command line result is ½.

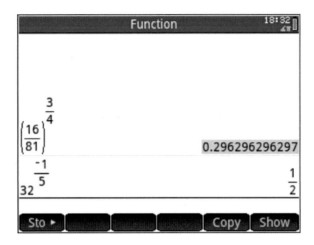

Begin by selecting the **HOME** key on the HP Prime. If the **HOME** view of the screenshot has computations, clear the **history** first. To clear the **history**, press the **Clear** key.

Use the **Menu** key "Get from CAS" to transfer the problems over. Highlight entry one. Pressing the **mixed numeral** key will toggle the decimal to 8/27.

Note: It seems strange that the **HOME** view gave an exact answer for an implied repeating decimal not the actual decimal highlighted.

HP Prime Family Making a Table of Powers

Press the **Apps** key. Highlight the **Spreadsheet** icon on the Application Library screen. Press the soft **Start** key. The above screen will appear. Tap on the cell with the HP logo in it. Alternatively, you can use the cursor keys to move to that cell. Enter the command as shown. Press the **Vars** key to find spreadsheet variable **Row** and **Col** by using **Vars** > **App** > **Spreadsheet** > **Numeric** > **Row** or **Col**.

	Square	Cube	Fourth	Fifth	Sixth
1	1	1	1	1	1
2	4	8	16	32	64
3	9	27	81	243	729
4	16	64	256	1,024	4,096
5	25	125	625	3,125	15,625
6	36	216	1,296	7,776	46,656
7	49	343	2,401	16,807	117,64
8	64	512	4,096	32,768	262,14
9	81	729	6,561	59,049	531,44
10	100	1,000	10,000	100,000	1,000.0

Spreadsheet — Square: — Format | Go To | Select | Go ↓ — 22:04

Press the soft **OK** key. See the above spreadsheet with its values for Square, Cube, Fourth, Fifth, and Sixth. Add these labels by pressing the soft **Format** key and then the **Name** option.

Note: Each column gives the nth power of the row number starting with the squares in column 2. Thus 4^4 is 256 and 8^5 is 32,768. Column 2 is square, 3 is cube, 4 is fourth. 5 is fifth, 6 is sixth and so forth.

Knowing squares through row 12, cubes through row 7, powers of 4 through row 6, powers of 5 through row 4, and powers of 6 through row 2 can help if you need to manually work with exponents and radicals. We either use these values directly or a multiple of them.

This is how we came up with the equivalent expression or value that was used in the simplification of various parts of the last and previous two-part illustrations. Other or higher values then the ones mentioned in the last paragraph would need to be calculated.

Example 2 Using the Properties of Exponents with Rational Numbers

(a) Simplify: $(-8)^{2/3} \cdot 9^{3/2}$

$a^{m/n} = (\sqrt[n]{a})^m$

$\sqrt[n]{a^n} = |a|$ n is even

$\sqrt[n]{a^n} = a$ n is odd

$(-8)^{2/3} \cdot 9^{3/2}$

$= \left(\sqrt[3]{-8}\right)^2 \cdot \left(\sqrt{9}\right)^3$

$= \left(\sqrt[3]{-8}\right)^2 \cdot |3|^3$

$= (-2)^2 \cdot 27 = 108$

(b) Simplify: $(x^4 y^{10})^{-1/5}$

Definition Negative Exponents

$a^{1/n} = \sqrt[n]{a}$

$\sqrt[n]{a \cdot b} = \sqrt[n]{a} \cdot \sqrt[n]{b}$

$\sqrt[n]{a^n} = a$ n is odd

or direct using $(ab)^n = a^n b^n$

$(x^4 y^{10})^{-1/5}$

$= \dfrac{1}{(x^4 y^{10})^{1/5}}$

$= \dfrac{1}{\sqrt[5]{x^4 (y^2)^5}}$

$= \dfrac{1}{\sqrt[5]{x^4} \cdot \sqrt[5]{(y^2)^5}}$

$= \dfrac{1}{y^2 \cdot \sqrt[5]{x^4}} = \dfrac{1}{x^{4/5} \cdot y^2}$

HP Prime Family Using the Properties of Exponents with Rational Numbers

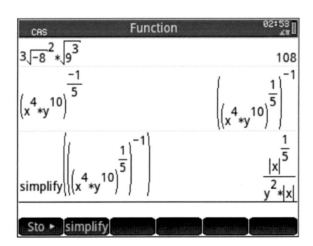

Begin by selecting the **CAS** key on the HP Prime. If the **CAS** view of the screenshot has computations, clear the **history** first. To clear the **history**, press the **Clear** key.

Key in as shown. Entry one showed the result as a complex number. One complex solution of who knows how many complex solutions.

For entry two we switched to radicals to get the real number solution we were looking for. Thought we tried this approach directly with part (b) of our problem. Here it echoed back our input. Tried using the soft **simplify** key and got a compound fraction with absolute values in the results (not shown).

Started over with part (b). See next screen.

Continuing. After deleting our last attempts from the history area using the **backspace** key, we tried the original form. Then used the soft **simplify** key.

If in the last calculator result, we combined numerator and denominator together in the denominator we would get our $x^{4/5}$ manual result. That is when in our combining, we ignore the absolute value of the x's that are in both the numerator and denominator.

Note: We can see why textbook and tutorials throw in "Assume all variables represent nonnegative real number" statement in their explanations and exercise directions when working with property of exponents using rational numbers. A luxury that CAS systems do not have. Thus the need for CAS systems to add absolute value.

Let us finish by looking at the **HOME** view part (a) results.

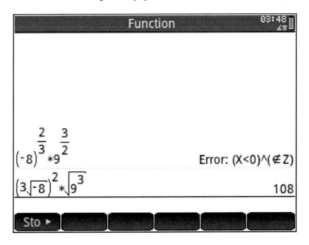

Begin by selecting the **HOME** key on the HP Prime. If the **HOME** view of the screenshot has computations, clear the **history** first. To clear the **history**, press the **Clear** key.

Use the **Menu** key "Get from CAS" to transfer the problems over. Entry one gives us an error message.

In both the **CAS** view and **HOME** view it looks like combining was happening where the calculator was attempting to take powers (roots) of a negative even exponent (index). The **CAS** view switched to complex numbers and the **HOME** view gave us an error message.

Exercise 2 **Using the Properties of Exponents with Rational Numbers**

Simplify:

(a) $\left(\dfrac{x^{1/3}}{y^{1/3}}\right)^{3/2}$

(b) $\left(\dfrac{3x^{1/3}}{y^{2/3}}\right)^{2}\cdot\left(\dfrac{2x^{-3/4}}{y^{1/2}}\right)$

<u>Solution</u> >>

The second step of simplification, making the index of the radical as small as possible, will be covered next.

Reducing the Index

A radical is in simplest form if the index is as small as possible. Our HP Prime CAS uses this in its simplification of radicals and rational exponents.

Let us begin by looking at two illustrations. One is with even radicand powers and the other is with an odd radicand power. We will use the HP Prime CAS for the illustrations. We see in the following screenshot that entry two, three, and four that the index has been reduced in value. Entry one shows the entry being transformed from radical to rational exponent form. Entry three and four are equivalent and both show the result with a reduced index.

HP Prime Family Reducing the index

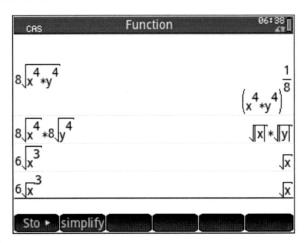

Begin by selecting the **CAS** key on the HP Prime. If the **CAS** view of the screenshot has computations, clear the **history** first. To clear the **history**, press the **Clear** key.

Key in as shown. To get the solution for entry one that we were looking for we had to change the input to an equivalent form by using part (4) of the *Definition of Rational Exponents*. We then entered the equivalent form as entry two and it produced close to the solution we were looking for. To get what we were looking for we need to put the product back together as one with absolute value around both x an y in inside the combined square root. Using part (4) again but in the reverse direction.

Note: We may need to use a mathematically equivalent form in our HP Prime CAS to produce the result we are looking for. Many times the best technique is to work the problem manually rather than look for a technique that works with the HP Prime CAS.

We need to use absolute value in the radicand when even power factors in the radicand are reduced to odd powers (x^4 to x^1 in the above screen - x being x^1).

Recall that the radicand cannot represent negative values. For an odd power factor in the radicand no absolute value is necessary, however the original domain restrictions applies to the simplified form. As in entry two's input and entry three's equivalent result, *x* cubed in the input and *x* in the result cannot be negative.

Note: Just as we mentioned earlier, many texts and tutorials to get around the problem of absolute value in the radicand and absolute value in removing perfect *n*th powers, make a statement in directions such as "Assume all variables represent nonnegative real numbers." With this added comment, no absolute values are necessary in the result. Our HP Prime CAS has no such restrictions, thus the need for absolute value in its solutions.

To reduce the index of the radical to as small as possible use the following procedure. This procedure can also be used for simplification of many radical expressions.

Simplifying Radical Expressions

1. Convert radicals to exponents
2. Use arithmetic and properties of exponents
3. As necessary, convert back to radical notation

The next illustration is using *Simplifying Radical Expressions* to simplify two different radical by reduce the index of each of the two radicals.

(a) Simplify: $\sqrt[6]{27x^3}$

$(a \cdot b)^n = a^n \cdot b^n$	$\sqrt[6]{27x^3} = \sqrt[6]{3^3 x^3}$
$a^{1/n} = \sqrt[n]{a}$ and $(a^m)^n = a^{m \cdot n}$	$= \sqrt[6]{(3x)^3}$
reduce fraction	$= (3x)^{3/6}$
$a^{1/n} = \sqrt[n]{a}$	$= (3x)^{1/2}$
	$= \sqrt{3x}$

(b) Simplify: $\sqrt[8]{25x^2y^8}$

$(a \cdot b)^n = a^n \cdot b^n$	$\sqrt[8]{25x^2y^8} = \sqrt[8]{5^2 x^2 y^8}$
$a^{1/n} = \sqrt[n]{a}$ and $(a^m)^n = a^{m \cdot n}$	$= \sqrt[8]{(5x \cdot y^4)^2}$
reduce fraction	$= (5x \cdot y^4)^{2/8}$
and add absolute value	
$a^{1/n} = \sqrt[n]{a}$	$= (5|x| \cdot y^4)^{1/4}$
$\sqrt[n]{a \cdot b} = \sqrt[n]{a} \cdot \sqrt[n]{b}$	$= \sqrt[4]{5|x| \cdot y^4}$
$\sqrt[n]{a^n} = |a|$ n is even	$= \sqrt[4]{5|x|} \cdot \sqrt[4]{y^4}$
	$= |y|\sqrt[4]{5|x|}$

HP Prime Family Simplifying Radical Expressions

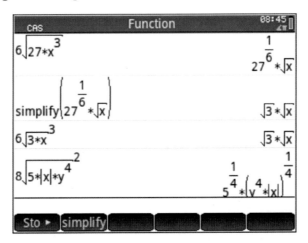

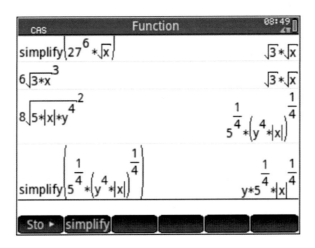

Begin by selecting the **CAS** key on the HP Prime. If the **CAS** view of the screenshot has computations, clear the **history** first. To clear the **history**, press the **Clear** key.

Key in as shown. Screen two is given to show the soft **simplify** key entry for the last entry of screen one.

Another way to get the solution for entry one first screen was to change the input to an equivalent form by using part (4) of the *Definition of Rational Exponents*. We then entered the equivalent form as entry three first screen and it produced close to the solution we were looking for. To get what we were looking for in entry two and three first screen we need to put the product back together as one with absolute value around both 3 an x in inside the combined square root. Using part (4) again but in the reverse direction.

For the illustration (b) solution, we switched to the equivalent form as the original form did not work. In the equivalent form it was necessary for us to add the absolute value to the radicand.

As mentioned above *Simplifying Radical Expressions* can be used for other simplification as well. For example, one use is to determine equivalent radical expressions when operations of multiplication and division do not have the same index.

What we do is follow the rule. First converting the radicals to exponents; adding the exponents for multiplication, subtracting the exponents for division; and then converting the exponent result back to a radical. See the following illustration.

(a) Simplify: $\sqrt{a} \cdot \sqrt[5]{a}$

$a^{1/n} = \sqrt[n]{a}$

$a^m \cdot a^n = a^{m+n}$

Add fractions

$a^{1/n} = \sqrt[n]{a}$

$\sqrt{a} \cdot \sqrt[5]{a}$
$= a^{1/2} a^{1/5}$
$= a^{1/2+1/5}$
$= a^{7/10}$
$= \sqrt[10]{a^7}$

(b) Simplify: $\dfrac{\sqrt[4]{a^3}}{\sqrt[3]{a}}$

$a^{1/n} = \sqrt[n]{a}$

$\dfrac{a^m}{a^n} = a^{m-n}$

Subtract fractions

$a^{1/n} = \sqrt[n]{a}$

$\dfrac{\sqrt[4]{a^3}}{\sqrt[3]{a}}$
$= \dfrac{a^{3/4}}{a^{1/3}}$
$= a^{3/4-1/3}$
$= a^{5/12}$
$= \sqrt[12]{a^5}$

TI-Nspire CAS Simplifying Radical Expressions – Different Indices

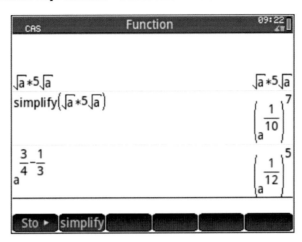

Begin by selecting the **CAS** key on the HP Prime. If the **CAS** view of the screenshot has computations, clear the **history** first. To clear the **history**, press the **Clear** key.

Key in as shown. As has been case, rational exponent form is used in both results. For the second part of the illustration it was necessary to change the input to rational exponent subtraction as well. The manual solutions has part (a) and part (b) final rational exponent as the product of the exponents showing in the calculator screen.

Rationalizing Denominators

The final step in simplify radicals is to have to no fractions in the denominator of the radical. This translates into have no radicals in the denominator of the quotient of two roots. Each of these situations may allow us to simplify some radicals, but to completely accomplish this final step; it is often necessary to *rationalize the denominator.*

With the *Properties of Radicals*, the root of a quotient can be expressed as the quotient of two roots. We can simplify the root of a quotient if the denominator is a perfect nth powers by expressing as the quotient of two roots and simplifying the denominator root and if possible the numerator root.

The reverse is also true; the quotient of two roots can be expressed as the root of a quotient. If simplification is possible, express the quotient of two roots as the root of a quotient and simplify.

If expressing as the quotient of two roots and reverse do not totally simplify the radical, we can eliminate the fraction in the radical or the radical in the denominator by a process known as *rationalizing the denominator.* If there is a fraction left in the radical or no simplification was possible thus far, we need if necessary, to convert our expression to the quotient of two radicals. Then to eliminate the radical in the denominator, multiplying both the numerator and denominator by the same appropriate expression. What we are doing is changing the quotient to an equivalent quotient.

See the following numerical illustrations.

(a) Simplify: $\sqrt[3]{\dfrac{8}{27}}$

$\sqrt[n]{\dfrac{a}{b}} = \dfrac{\sqrt[n]{a}}{\sqrt[n]{b}}$

$\sqrt[n]{a^n} = a \quad n \text{ is odd}$

$\sqrt[3]{\dfrac{8}{27}}$

$= \dfrac{\sqrt[3]{8}}{\sqrt[3]{27}}$

$= \dfrac{2}{3}$

(b) Simplify: $\dfrac{4\sqrt[3]{108}}{\sqrt[3]{2}}$

$\sqrt[n]{\dfrac{a}{b}} = \dfrac{\sqrt[n]{a}}{\sqrt[n]{b}}$

$\sqrt[n]{a \cdot b} = \sqrt[n]{a} \cdot \sqrt[n]{b}$

$\sqrt[n]{a^n} = a \quad n \text{ is odd}$

$\dfrac{4\sqrt[3]{108}}{\sqrt[3]{2}}$

$= 4\sqrt[3]{\dfrac{108}{2}} = 4\sqrt[3]{54}$

$= 4\sqrt[3]{27}\sqrt[3]{2}$

$= 12\sqrt[3]{2}$

(c) Simplify: $\sqrt[3]{\dfrac{5}{4}}$

$\sqrt[n]{\dfrac{a}{b}} = \dfrac{\sqrt[n]{a}}{\sqrt[n]{b}}$

Multiply by 1, $\sqrt[n]{a \cdot b} = \sqrt[n]{a} \cdot \sqrt[n]{b}$

$\sqrt[n]{a^n} = a \quad n \text{ is odd}$

$\sqrt[3]{\dfrac{5}{4}}$

$= \dfrac{\sqrt[3]{5}}{\sqrt[3]{4}} \cdot \dfrac{\sqrt[3]{2}}{\sqrt[3]{2}}$

$= \dfrac{\sqrt[3]{10}}{\sqrt[3]{8}}$

$= \dfrac{\sqrt[3]{10}}{2}$

HP Prime Family Rationalizing Denominator – Numerical Values

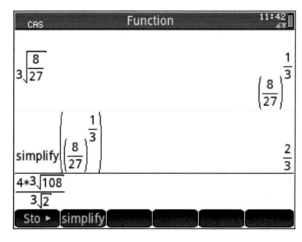

Begin by selecting the **CAS** key on the HP Prime. If the **CAS** view of the screenshot has computations, clear the **history** first. To clear the **history**, press the Clear key.

Key in as shown. Press **enter** to see the command line result.

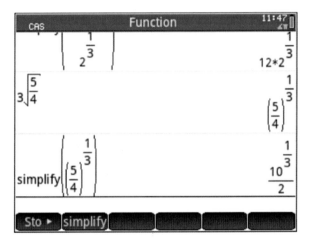

Continuing. We used the soft **simplify** key.

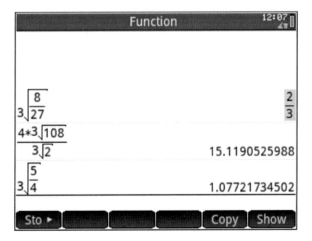

Continuing. We used the soft **simplify** key.

Begin by selecting the **HOME** key on the HP Prime. If the **HOME** view of the screenshot has computations, clear the **history** first. To clear the **history**, press the **Clear** key.

Use the **Menu** key "Get from CAS" to transfer the problems over. Highlight entry one. Pressing the **mixed numeral** key will toggle the 2/3 to a repeating decimal.

Our numerical illustrations showed all three techniques being used that is simplification of a quotient by changing to the quotients of roots, simplification of the quotients of roots by changing to quotient of a root, and simplification by rationalizing the denominator.

We could use the same techniques with radicals using numerical and variable factors and quotients. We could formalize the rule for *Rationalizing the Denominator*. It is shown next. It requires that we perform all simplification first.

Rationalizing the Denominator

If factors in the denominator are of the form $\sqrt[n]{a^m}$ with $m < n$ then multiplying both the numerator and denominator by each denominator factor

$$\sqrt[n]{a^{n-m}}$$

will rationalize the denominator.

However, another option is to simplify at the end. We still multiply by 1 but make the factors that we multiple by, be a perfect root, or a multiple of the index. We will show that next.

In part (a) of example 3 that follows, we pick $3x$ for the radicand that we use to multiply both the numerator and denominator by. This makes the combined denominator radicand 3 squared times x to the fourth. The 3 squared, or 9, is the perfect square root and the x to the fourth is a multiple of the square root, which allows the combined denominator to easily be simplified.

In part (b) of example 3 we could use the above *Rationalizing the Denominator* Rule since all factor powers are less then the index's power, that is m<n.

Example 3 Rationalizing Denominators

(a) Simplify: $\sqrt{\dfrac{4y}{3x^3}}$

$\sqrt[n]{\dfrac{a}{b}}=\dfrac{\sqrt[n]{a}}{\sqrt[n]{b}}$ $\qquad\qquad \sqrt{\dfrac{4y}{3x^3}}$

Multiply by 1, $\sqrt[n]{a\cdot b}=\sqrt[n]{a}\cdot\sqrt[n]{b}$ $\quad =\dfrac{\sqrt{4y}}{\sqrt{3x^3}}\cdot\dfrac{\sqrt{3x}}{\sqrt{3x}}$

$\sqrt[n]{a^n}=|a|\ n$ is even $\qquad =\dfrac{\sqrt{4}\sqrt{3x\cdot y}}{\sqrt{9x^4}}$

Simplify absolute value $\qquad =\dfrac{2\sqrt{3x\cdot y}}{3\left|x^2\right|}$

$\qquad\qquad\qquad\qquad\qquad =\dfrac{2\sqrt{3x\cdot y}}{3x^2}$

(b) Simplify: $\sqrt[5]{\dfrac{2x^4y^{11}}{4y^2}}$

$\sqrt[n]{\dfrac{a}{b}}=\dfrac{\sqrt[n]{a}}{\sqrt[n]{b}}$ $\qquad\qquad \sqrt[5]{\dfrac{2x^4y^{11}}{4y^2}}$

Multiply by 1, $\sqrt[n]{a\cdot b}=\sqrt[n]{a}\cdot\sqrt[n]{b}$ $\quad =\dfrac{\sqrt[5]{2x^4y^{11}}}{\sqrt[5]{4y^2}}\cdot\dfrac{\sqrt[5]{8y^3}}{\sqrt[5]{8y^3}}$

$\sqrt[n]{a^n}=a\ n$ is odd $\qquad =\dfrac{\sqrt[5]{16x^4(y^2)^5y^4}}{\sqrt[5]{32y^5}}$

$\dfrac{a^m}{a^n}=a^{m-n}$ $\qquad\qquad =\dfrac{y^2\sqrt[5]{16x^4y^4}}{2y}$

$\qquad\qquad\qquad\qquad\qquad =\dfrac{y\sqrt[5]{16x^4y^4}}{2}$

HP Prime Family Rationalizing Denominators

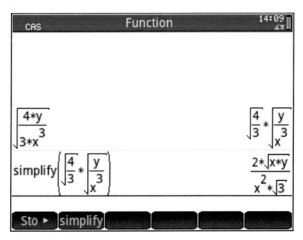

Begin by selecting the **CAS** key on the HP Prime. If the **CAS** view of the screenshot has computations, clear the **history** first. To clear the **history**, press the **Clear** key.

Key in as shown. To finish we need to manually rationalize the square root of 3.

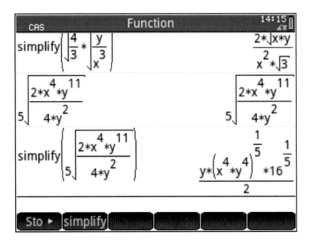

Continuing. To finish put all the 1/5 power back into one radical with index of 5.

Exercise 3 **Rationalizing Denominators**

Simplify:

(a) $\sqrt{\dfrac{1}{2x \cdot y^3}}$

(b) $\sqrt[4]{\dfrac{3x^9 y^2}{8x^2}}$

Solution >>

Explanation 1.5 - Algebraic Expressions

In this section we discuss **algebraic expressions**, the most used form being a **polynomial**. We will go over the definition of a polynomial, operations with polynomials, and special product formulas.

A letter that represents any number from a set of numbers is called a **variable**. A symbol that represents a specific number is called a **constant**. Starting with variables x and y, some real numbers, and combining using addition, subtraction, multiplication, divisions, powers, and roots, we form **algebraic expressions** such as

$$\frac{3y}{x^2+4}, \ 2x+\sqrt{x}-11, \ 4x^2, \ x^2+5x+6, \ -8, \ x^2-16.$$

A **monomial** in x would be of the form ax^k, where k is a nonnegative integer and a is a real number. A **binomial** in x would be the sum of two monomials in x and a trinomial in x would be the sum of three monomials in x. A monomial or the sum of monomials in x would be a **polynomial** in x. The last four expressions would be examples of polynomials in x, or one variable. For now, we are only discussing polynomials of one variable.

> **Definition of Polynomial**
>
> A **polynomial** in x is a monomial or a sum of monomials in x
>
> $$a_n x^n + a_{n-1} x^{n-1} + \cdots + a_1 x + a_0$$
>
> where n is a nonnegative integer, and a_i is a real number. If $a_n \neq 0$ then the polynomial has **degree** n.

The monomial $4x^2$, the trinomial $x^2 + 5x + 6$, and binomial $x^2 - 16$ have degree 2. The monomial -8 can be thought of as $-8x^0$ therefore the degree is 0. We need to note that the term 0 itself has no degree since 0 times any power of x would produce zero.

Polynomials represent real numbers, therefore we can use the properties discussed in Section 1.2, to perform the operations on polynomials.

Adding and Subtracting Polynomials

To add and subtract polynomials we use the procedures in Section 1.2, for Collecting Like Terms – Part 1 and Part 2. The next example shows the procedures applied to the addition and subtraction of polynomials.

Example 1 Adding and Subtracting Polynomials

(a) Find the sum $(-2x^2 + 4x) + (5x^2 - 7x)$

Replacing with 1	$(-2x^2 + 4x) + (5x^2 - 7x)$
Distributive − expand	$= 1(-2x^2 + 4x) + 1(5x^2 - 7x)$
Combine like terms	$= -2x^2 + 4x + 5x^2 - 7x$
	$= 3x^2 - 3x$

(b) Find the difference $(3x^2 - 2x + 4) - (2x^2 + 6x)$

Replacing with 1, −1	$(3x^2 - 2x + 4) - (2x^2 + 6x)$
Distributive − expand	$= 1(3x^2 - 2x + 4) - 1(2x^2 + 6x)$
Combine like terms	$= 3x^2 - 2x + 4 - 2x^2 - 6x$
	$= x^2 - 8x + 4$

First we insert 1's or -1 in front of the parentheses, use the expand mnemonic to remove the parentheses, and then combine like terms mentally.

To combine like terms mentally, we can either use the traditional approach of visualizing subtraction as "addition of the opposite" or the Alternate Rule - Addition and Subtraction.

HP Prime Family Adding and Subtracting Polynomials

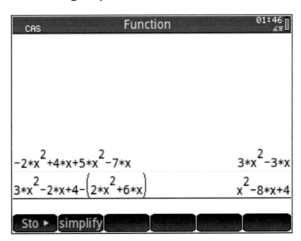

Begin by selecting the **CAS** key on the HP Prime. If the **CAS** view of the screenshot has computations, clear the **history** first. To clear the **history**, press the **Clear** key.

Key in as shown. Both entries were entered with parentheses. The HP Prime CAS dropped all but the subtraction parenthesis.

Exercise 1 Adding and Subtracting Polynomials

(a) Find the sum $(3x^3 - 4x^2 - 5) + (-2x^3 + 3)$

(b) Find the difference $(5x^2 - 4x - 1) - (x - 2)$

<u>Solution</u> >>

Multiplying Polynomials

To multiply polynomials we will make use of the right and left distributive property. First, we look at multiplying binomials.

HP Prime Family Multiplying **Binomials - FOIL**

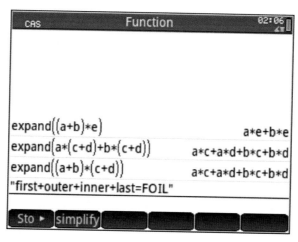

Begin by selecting the **CAS** key on the HP Prime. If the **CAS** view of the screenshot has computations, clear the **history** first. To clear the **history**, press the **Clear** key.

Key in as shown. Press the **Toolbox** key use **Toolbox > CAS > Algebra > Expand** to show the entries as terms. Press **Enter** for all entries. Delete the last result. The HP Prime CAS leaves products as factors, thus the need for us to use the **expand** command.

When we multiply binomials we take the two terms in the first factor times the second factor. We then expand the results and if possible collect like terms.

Thus in binomial multiplication of $(a+b)(c+d)$, we take $a(c+d)$ and $b(c+d)$ resulting in $ac+ad+bc+bd$. In the above screenshot we show how the right distributive property, $(a+b)e$ results in $ae+be$ with e representing $(c+d)$. The second entry has $(c+d)$ substituted in for e thus we now evaluate $a(c+d)$ and $b(c+d)$. Entry two's, $a(c+d)$ and $b(c+d)$, then uses the left distributive property twice resulting in $ac+ad+bc+bd$.

Entry three show us the HP Prime working the problem directly with the result being known as the FOIL technique. FOIL is a mnemonic that means that we take the first, outer, inner, and last terms of each factor times themselves. We would use the full distributive property expand or our <u>distributive expand mnemonic</u> to write the FOIL's result. The final step in multiplying binomials would if possible combine like terms.

When multiplying binomials of the form $(ax+b)(cx+d)$ it is possible to proceed to the results by combining mentally the outer and inner of the FOIL technique.

In general to multiply polynomials we use the following procedure.

Multiplying Polynomials

1. Multiply all the terms in the first factor times the second factor.

2. Use the distributive expand mnemonic to remove the parentheses.

3. If possible, combine like terms.

Example 2 Multiplying Polynomials

(a) Find the product $(2x+1)\cdot(3x^3-5)$

Right distributive	$(2x+1)\cdot(3x^3-5)$
Left distributive	$=2x\cdot(3x^3-5)+1\cdot(3x^3-5)$
Standard form	$=6x^4-10x+3x^3-5$
	$=6x^4+3x^3-10x-5$

(b) Find the product $(3x-4)\cdot(2x+1)$

FOIL	$(3x-4)\cdot(2x+1)$
Combine like terms	$=6x^2+3x-8x-4$
	$=6x^2-5x-4$

For part (b) the "outer" and "inner" products plus the result of combining are shown in red. We could by using the FOIL technique and combining the "outer" and "inner" products mentally go directly to $6x^2 - 5x - 4$ by doing the red parts in our head.

HP Prime Family Multiplying Polynomials

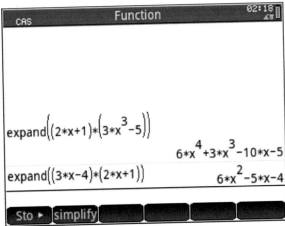

Begin by selecting the **CAS** key on the HP Prime. If the **CAS** view of the screenshot has computations, clear the **history** first. To clear the **history**, press the **Clear** key.

Key in as shown. Press the **Toolbox** key use **Toolbox > CAS > Algebra > Expand** to show the entries as terms. Press **Enter** for all entries. Both entries were entered using multiplication between the factors. The HP Prime CAS will issue a warning that it will be evaluated as a function not as a product if we leave the multiplication symbol out. This will not produce the results we are looking for.

Note: The HP Prime requires a multiplication symbol between parentheses used to indicate multiplication of two factors. This is shown in the two entries of the previous screen.

For polynomial multiplication where one of the factors has three or more terms, we can alternately write out step 1 in the form of a table. See exercise 2's solution for illustration of the table form.

Exercise 2 Multiplying Polynomials

Find the product $(3x^2 - 1) \cdot (2x^3 - x + 4)$

<u>Solution</u> **>>**

Special Product Formulas

We now look at some product formulas that are worth knowing. These formulas could be found by performing the multiplications.

Special Products Formulas

Let u and v be real numbers or algebraic expressions.

Squares of a Binomial

$(u + v)^2 = u^2 + 2uv + v^2$

$(u - v)^2 = u^2 - 2uv + v^2$

Sum and Difference of a Binomial

$(u + v)(u - v) = u^2 - v^2$

Cubes of a Binomial

$(u + v)^3 = u^3 + 3u^2v + 3uv^2 + v^3$

$(u - v)^3 = u^3 - 3u^2v + 3uv^2 - v^3$

We can use the HP Prime CAS to display them as well.

HP Prime Family Special Product Formulas

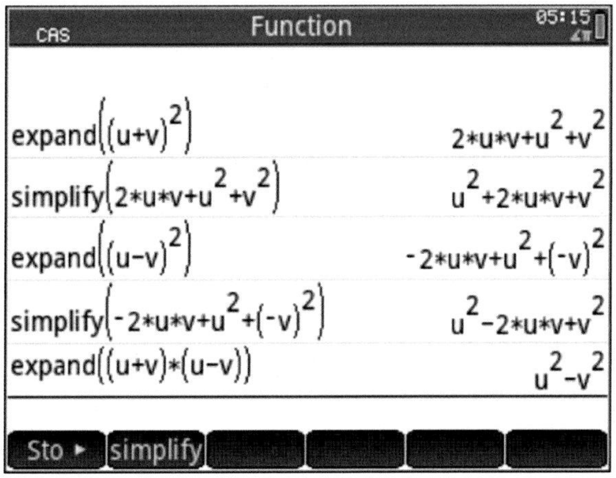

Begin by selecting the **CAS** key on the HP Prime. If the **CAS** view of the screenshot has computations, clear the **history** first. To clear the **history**, press the **Clear** key.

Key in as shown. Press the **Toolbox** key use **Toolbox > CAS > Algebra > Expand** to show the entries as terms. Press **Enter** for all entries. Press the soft **simplify** key for all entries except the last. The HP Prime CAS leaves products as factors, thus the need for us to use the **expand** command. We used the Paste key to select a listing of previous entries. Choose the closest one and then edited it.

We used the **simplify** command to write the formula in standard form.

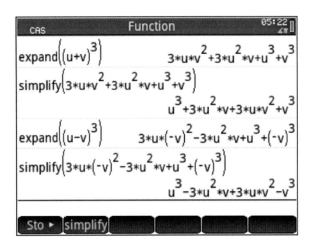

Begin by selecting the **CAS** key on the HP Prime. To clear the **history**, press the Clear key.

Key in as shown. Press the **Toolbox** key use **Toolbox > CAS > Algebra > Expand** to show the entries as terms. Press **Enter** for both entries. Press the soft **simplify** key for both entries. The HP Prime CAS leaves products as factors, thus the need for us to use the **expand** command. We used the Paste key to select a listing of previous entries. Choose the sum version and then edited it.

Example 3 Special Product Formulas

(a) Find the product $(3x+4)^2$

The product takes the form $(u+v)^2 = u^2 + 2uv + v^2$

Replace u and v $(3x+4)^2$

Simplify
$$= (3x)^2 + 2(3x)(4) + 4^2$$
$$= 9x^2 + 24x + 16$$

(b) Find the product $(2x-3)^3$

Product form $(u-v)^3 = u^3 - 3u^2v + 3uv^2 - v^3$

Replace u and v $(2x-3)^3$

Exponents
$$= (2x)^3 - 3(2x)^2(3) + 3(2x)(3)^2 + 3^3$$

Simplify
$$= 8x^3 - 3(4x^2)(3) + 3(2x)(9) + 27$$
$$= 8x^3 - 36x^2 + 54x + 27$$

HP Prime Family Special Product Formulas

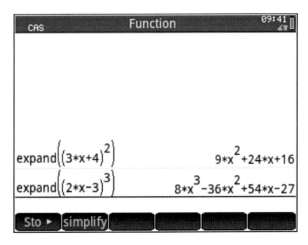

Begin by selecting the **CAS** key on the HP Prime. To clear the **history**, press the Clear key.

Key in as shown. Press the **Toolbox** key use **Toolbox > CAS > Algebra > Expand** to show the entries as terms. Press **Enter** for both entries. The HP Prime CAS leaves products as factors, thus the need for us to use the **expand** command. We used the Paste key to select a listing of previous entries. Choose the closest version and then edited it for both entries.

Exercise 3 Special Product Formulas

(a) Find the product $(\sqrt{x} - 3y)(\sqrt{x} + 3y)$

(b) Find the product $(2x + y - 3)(2x + y + 3)$

Solution >>

Explanation 1.6 - Factoring

In this section we discuss **factoring**. We will go over common factors, factoring a trinomial, factor by grouping, and special factoring formulas.

Factoring is where we express the sum of terms as a product. Remember expand and factor are the opposite directions of the distributive property. Factoring is the reverse of expand.

Factoring is used to reduce complicated expressions to several simpler expressions or a single expression, which can aid us in simplifying expressions and finding solutions to algebraic equations.

HP Prime Family Simplifying Expressions – Solving Algebraic Equations

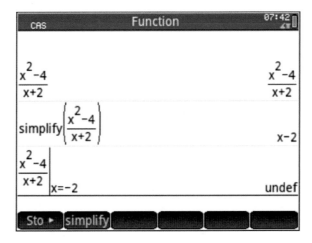

Begin by selecting the **CAS** key on the HP Prime. If the **CAS** view of the screenshot has computations, clear the **history** first. To clear the **history**, press the **Clear** key.

Key in as shown. Notice that in entry one -2 is not allowed in the original expression. In the past we had some complex rational expression where it erroneously was allowed in the result. Entry three shows that not to be the case here. It must be checking for division by zero before simplification.

This use of factoring in expression simplification will be covered in section 1.7.

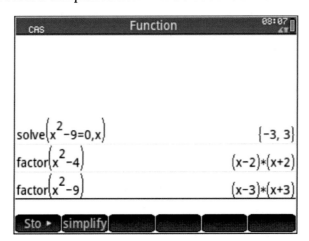

Begin by selecting the **CAS** key on the HP Prime. If the **CAS** view of the screenshot has computations, clear the **history** first. To clear the **history**, press the **Clear** key.

Key in as shown. Press the **Toolbox** key to use **Toolbox > CAS > Solve > Solve** to show the solution of an algebraic equation containing a polynomial. We will be covering the use of factoring to solve algebraic equations in the next tutorial. For now, we will say if the product $ab = 0$ then either $a = 0$ or $b = 0$ or both a and b equal 0, thus the need to use factoring to change the algebraic expression to products of simpler expressions.

In entries three and four press the **Toolbox** key to use **Toolbox > CAS > Algebra > Factor** to show the difference of terms as products.

Note: For the HP Prime CAS simplifications and algebraic solutions there is no need to use factor. We displayed entries three and four to help us see the processes that we use in manually simplify and solving algebraic equations.

Each term of a polynomial can be thought of as $a_n x^n$ with n a non-negative integer. The a_n is considered the **coefficient** of that term. Factoring requires us to specify the number system that the coefficients will be using. Unless otherwise stated, we will restrict our manual factoring to factoring with integer coefficients. Polynomials that cannot be factored using integer coefficients are **prime**, or **irreducible** over the integers. When we talk about prime or irreducible, we need to talk about a set of numbers. Factoring is the process where we express a polynomial as the product of irreducible polynomials.

In our next screenshot we show a polynomial that is irreducible over the real numbers but not over the complex. The HP Prime CAS when using the **factor** command only allows factoring with real results. Thus $x^2 + 3$ is irreducible over the real for the HP Prime CAS. Entry two shows $x^2 - 3$ is irreducible over the integers but not reals. Entry three shows us that the HP Prime CAS is able to factor rational coefficients. Entry four and five shows that $x^2 + 3$ can be obtained by multiplying two complex factors even though the $x^2 + 3$ is irreducible over real numbers.

HP Prime CAS Factor Command

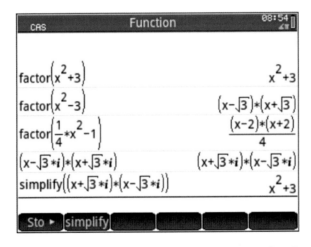

Begin by selecting the **CAS** key on the HP Prime. If the **CAS** view of the screenshot has computations, clear the **history** first. To clear the **history**, press the **Clear** key.

Key in as shown. Press the **Toolbox** key to use **Toolbox > CAS > Algebra > Factor** to show the difference of terms as products. Use the soft **simplify** key for the last entry.

Notice in entry one that the HP Prime CAS gives back our original expression because the original expression is irreducible over real numbers. The HP Prime CAS uses the real coefficients for the **factor** command.

We see that entry two factors out one-fourth but writes it in the denominator. As we previously mentioned we will not manually factor rational values unless factoring rational coefficients is stated in the directions or there is a need to do so. Earlier we talked about graphing a parabola. This would be a case where there is a need to factor out rational numbers if possible and then factor the remaining equivalent expression into rational coefficients.

Before we present our factoring rules let us take a look at how we could manually factor entry one and two in the previous screenshot. We will use <u>Difference of Squares</u> and <u>Common Factor</u>.

(a) Factor the polynomial $x^2 - 3$ over reals

Radical rules $\qquad x^2 - 3$

Difference of squares $\qquad = x^2 - \sqrt{3}^2$

$\qquad\qquad\qquad\qquad = (x - \sqrt{3})(x + \sqrt{3})$

(b) Factor the polynomial $\frac{1}{4}x^2 - 1$ over rationals

Multiply by 1 $\qquad \frac{1}{4}x^2 - 1$

Distributive – factor $\frac{1}{4}$ $\quad = \frac{1}{4}x^2 - 1 \cdot \frac{4}{4}$

Difference of squares $\quad = \frac{1}{4}(x^2 - 4)$

$\qquad\qquad\qquad\qquad = \frac{1}{4}(x - 2)(x + 2)$

Part (a) looks at manually factoring using real numbers. We make the second term a perfect square by using the rules of radicals. The second term would be the square root of 3 raised to the second power. After making if a perfect square we use the special factor formula for difference of two squares to change the expression to factored form. The special factor formulas are discussed at the end of this section.

Part (b) looks at manually factoring using rational numbers. If the manual directions for the expression stated that we were to factor with rational numbers we would need to factor out one-fourth from both terms. To manually do this we would need to multiply the -1 term by 4/4 so we could factor out one-fourth from the both the first and second terms. Multiplying by 4/4 is an example of using the identity for multiplication, $a \times 1 = a$, with the 1 being 4/4. The identity properties of multiplying by 1 and adding 0 are often used to change expressions to an equivalent expression in a form that allows us to complete the solution. After factoring out the one-fourth we again use the special factor formula for difference of two squares to change the expression to factored form

Entry three used the expand component of the distributive property. Since each factor has radicals it is not necessary to use the TI-Nspire CAS **expand** command. Reading this entry in reverse shows us that under the real numbers x² – 3 is factorable by using radicals.

Common Factors

When factoring polynomials it is advisable to factor common factors first. We look at each term of the polynomial to see if there are factors common to all the terms. We factored out the smallest non-zero exponent found in any term. The product of these is the **greatest common factor (gcf)**.

Greatest Common Factor

The **greatest common factor** is the product of the factors that appear in all terms. The smallest non–zero exponent found in any term is factored out.

When factoring polynomials with two or more terms, it is advantageous for leading coefficient to be positive. To accomplish this factor a -1 out of every term.

Example 1 Common Factors

(a) Factor the polynomial $3x^2 - 6$

3 is the gcf $\qquad\qquad 3x^2 - 6$

Distributive $-$ factor $\qquad = 3x^2 - 3\cdot 2$

$\qquad\qquad\qquad\qquad = 3(x^2 - 2)$

(b) Factor the polynomial $-3x^3 + 9x^2 - 18x$

Factor -1 $\qquad\qquad -3x^3 + 9x^2 - 18x$

3x is the gcf $\qquad\quad = -1(3x^3 - 9x^2 + 18x)$

Distributive $-$ factor $\quad = -1(3x\cdot x^2 - 3x\cdot 3x + 3x\cdot 6)$

$\qquad\qquad\qquad\qquad = -3x(x^2 - 3x + 6)$

When factoring we need to factor completely. In part (a) we ended up with a constant times a prime polynomial. It is prime since unless stated otherwise, we are factoring over integers coefficients and there is no integer that squared gives us 2.

In part (b) we have a monomial times an irreducible trinomial. Trinomials of the form $x^2 + bx + c$ are prime, that is irreducible, when no factors using the FOIL technique produce it. Demonstrating that a trinomial is irreducible over integer coefficients will be discussed next.

Common Factors

1. Factor out the gcf.

2. Write as the product of gcf and a blank:
   gcf $\cdot$ ( )

3. Supply value for missing factor. Use the distributive expand mnemonic.

For common factors we work the problem mentally by placing the gcf in front of an empty set of parenthesis and think what we need to multiply the gcf by to get our original polynomial. We then use the full distributive property expand or our distributive expand mnemonic to aid us in supplying the terms of the missing factor. See exercise 1 for an example of this procedure.

HP Prime Family Common Factors

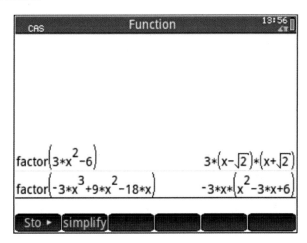

Begin by selecting the **CAS** key on the HP Prime. If the **CAS** view of the screenshot has computations, clear the **history** first. To clear the **history**, press the **Clear** key.

Key in as shown. Press the **Toolbox** key to use **Toolbox > CAS > Algebra > Factor**. Entry one factors the x^2 -2 since the HP Prime factors the difference of real squared terms to irrationals. The second entry has an irreducible trinomial.

Exercise 1 Common Factors

(a) Factor the polynomial $-4x-12$

(b) Factor the polynomial $8x^3y-16x^2y^2$

<u>Solution</u> **>>**

Factoring Trinomials

When dealing with two or more terms we commented earlier that it is advantageous for the leading coefficient to be positive. We find it advantageous to have trinomials in descending order. Some tutorials or textbooks will keep trinomials in ascending order if the x^2 coefficient is negative. We prefer to always keep ours in descending order.

Before using the **Factoring Trinomials** procedure shown next, remember to factor out common factors first. We like to break our trinomials $ax^2 + bx + c$, into the case where $a = 1$ and case where $a >$ 1. If a is negative we will factor out a -1 so that we end up with a trinomial that has an a being 1 or an a greater than 1.

Factoring Trinomials

ac Test

$ax^2 + bx + c,\ a > 0$

find $|a|\cdot|c|$

list positive pairs of factors of $|a|\cdot|c|$

i) If c positive, add the pair of factors

    If b positive, each factor of the pair is positive

    If b negative, each factor of the pair is negative

ii) If c negative, subtract the pair of factors

    If b positive, largest positive, smallest negative

    If b negative, largest negative, smallest positive

If no pairs work for i) or ii) then trinomial is prime.
If $a=1$ then we have the factors. If $a>1$ then we
regroup bx using these values.

We will next look at the above type of trinomials with the leading coefficient being 1. There are four cases that factor as described by the ac test above. Everything else not having a b of the four cases will be prime.

Trinomials of this type with $a > 1$ can also be factored using this technique or they can be factored by trial and error. To use this technique with $a > 1$ we will split bx into the pair that allows us to factor by grouping.

We will cover the $a > 1$ type of trinomials plus other polynomials that factor using grouping in the next section For the $a > 1$ type of trinomials, there are four cases that factor as described by the ac test above. Everything else not having a b of the four cases will be prime.

If you wish to use trial and error for the $a > 1$ type of trinomials see online tutorials or a textbook that demonstrates how trial and error works.

Example 2 Factoring Trinomials

(a) Factor the polynomial x^2+6x+8

$|a|\cdot|c|=1\cdot8=8$ pairs: 1,8; 2,4

$c>0, b>0$ add $1+8=9$; $2+4=6$

pair is positive x^2+6x+8

$$=(x+2)(x+4)$$

(b) Factor the polynomial $36-12x-3x^2$

Factor -3 $36-12x-3x^2$

Decending order $=-3(-12+4x+x^2)$

$$=-3(x^2+4x-12)$$

$|a|\cdot|c|=1\cdot12=12$ pairs: 1,12; 2,6; 3,4

$c<0, b>0$ subtract $12-1=11$; $6-2=4$; $4-3=1$

largest, positive $-3(x^2+4x-12)$

$$=-3(x+6)(x-2)$$

In part (b) by factoring out a -3, we perform both common factor of the terms and negative removal of the x^2 term in a single step. We complete the common factor mentally by filling in the blank parenthesis with $x^2 + 4x$ -12. We then use our Factoring Trinomial procedure on $x^2 + 4x$ -12.

HP Prime Family Factoring Trinomials

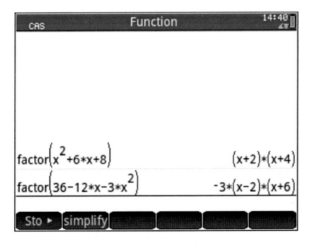

Begin by selecting the **CAS** key on the HP Prime. If the **CAS** view of the screenshot has computations, clear the **history** first. To clear the **history**, press the **Clear** key.

Key in as shown. Press the **Toolbox** key to use **Toolbox > CAS > Algebra > Factor**.

Exercise 2 Factoring Trinomials

(a) Factor the polynomial $x^2-7x+12$

(b) Factor the polynomial $2x^2-6x-8$

<u>Solution >></u>

Before considering factor by grouping, lets us look at algebraic expressions with fractional exponents. We will need to factor algebraic expressions with fractional exponents in later tutorials.

Factor the expression $x^{5/3} - 16x^{2/3} + 48x^{-1/3}$

Factor $x^{-1/3}$ $\qquad$ $x^{5/3} - 16x^{2/3} + 48x^{-1/3}$

$$= x^{-1/3}(x^2 - 16x + 48)$$

$|a| \cdot |c| = 1 \cdot 48 = 48$ pairs: 1,48; 2,24; 3,16; 4,12; 6,8

$c > 0, b < 0$ add $\qquad$ 1+48 = 49; 2+24 = 26;

$\qquad\qquad\qquad$ 3+16=19; 4+12=16; 6+8=14

pair is negative $\qquad x^{-1/3}(x^2 - 16x + 48)$

$$= x^{-1/3}(x-4)(x-12)$$

We factored out the smallest power of x, $x^{-1/3}$. Factor using our standard procedure, use the original exponent subtracting the factored out exponent to find the exponent to use inside the parenthesis.

The first term's exponent of the second factor would be 5/3 – (-1/3) = 6/3 = 2, the second term exponent would be 2/3 – (-1/3) = 3/3 = 1 and the last term would have the whole $x^{-1/3}$ factored out. Use the Factor Trinomial procedure to finish the problem.

HP Prime Family Expression with Fractional Exponents

Begin by selecting the **CAS** key on the HP Prime. If the **CAS** view of the screenshot has computations, clear the **history** first. To clear the **history**, press the **Clear** key.

Key in as shown. Press the **Toolbox** key to use **Toolbox > CAS > Algebra > Factor**. Notice the HP Prime CAS switches the negative exponent to the denominator. The soft **simplify** key does not help. Copy the result to command line. Delete the denominator. Press **Enter**. Press the **Toolbox** key to use **factor**. Copy the x²-16x+48 to the command line. Press **Enter**. Manually put these two parts together we see the result is equivalent to our manual solution.

The next type of problem is the result that occurs in calculus from using the Product Rule to take the derivative of the cube root of 4 + x times x, $(4 + x)^{1/3}x$. We then use factoring to simplify this result.

Factor the expression $(4+x)^{1/3}+\frac{1}{3}\cdot(4+x)^{-2/3}\cdot x$

Multiply by 1 $\qquad (4+x)^{1/3}+\frac{1}{3}\cdot(4+x)^{-2/3}\cdot x$

Factor $\frac{1}{3}(4+x)^{-2/3}$ $\quad =\frac{3}{3}(4+x)^{1/3}+\frac{1}{3}\cdot(4+x)^{-2/3}\cdot x$

Simplify $\qquad\qquad =\frac{1}{3}(4+x)^{-2/3}[3(4+x)^{1}+x]$

Factor 4 $\qquad\qquad =\frac{1}{3}(4+x)^{-2/3}(12+4x)$

$\qquad\qquad\qquad =\frac{4}{3}(4+x)^{-2/3}(3+x)$

We factored out the smallest power of $4 + x$, $(4 + x)^{-2/3}$. Use the original exponent subtracting the factored out exponent to find the exponent to use inside the parenthesis.

The first term's exponent of the second factor would be $1/3 – (-2/3) = 3/3 = 1$ and the last term would have the whole $1/3(4 + x)^{-2/3}$ factored out leaving x. Simplify and factor out 4 to finish the problem.

HP Prime Family Algebraic Expressions with Fractional Exponents

Begin by selecting the **CAS** key on the HP Prime. If the **CAS** view of the screenshot has computations, clear the **history** first. To clear the **history**, press the **Clear** key.

Key in as shown. Press the **Toolbox** key to use **Toolbox > CAS > Algebra > Factor**. Notice the HP Prime CAS switches the negative exponent to the denominator. The soft **simplify** key does not help. Copy the result to command line. Delete the denominator. Press **Enter**. Press the **Toolbox** key to use **expand**. Copy the 3*(x+4)+x to the command line. Press **Enter**. Use **factor** again. Manually put these two parts together we see the result is equivalent to our manual solution.

In the next section we will cover Compound Rational Expressions. Compound Rational Expressions are also known as compound fractions or complex fractions. Various forms exist, usually fractions inside of fractions or multiple complex terms.

The problem in our screenshot is a multiple complex term problem.

There are three manual ways to deal with Compound Rational Expressions. Method one is to factor out negative, which is the manual technique that we used.

Method two and three normally deal with fractions inside of fractions. Method two and three use the least common denominator (lcd) and/or inverting and multiplying. Method two can be used with multiple complex terms problems as well.

We will cover manually working with <u>method 2 and 3</u> in section 1.7.

Factor by Grouping

We first take a general look at how to factor common binomial terms by grouping and then apply it to our Factoring Trinomial procedure for a > 1.

When a polynomial contains four or more terms we may be able to factor common binomial terms by grouping.

We will need to find a common binomial term by grouping the polynomial into two groups of two terms. Sometimes to factor we will have to rearrange the four terms. Remember that the polynomial can turn out to be prime as well.

Example 3 Factor by Grouping

(a) Factor the polynomial $2x^3 - 2x^2 + 3x - 3$

Group	$2x^3 - 2x^2 + 3x - 3$
Factor $2x^2$, 3	$= (2x^3 - 2x^2) + (3x - 3)$
Factor $x - 1$	$= 2x^2(x-1) + 3(x-1)$
	$= (2x^2 + 3)(x-1)$

(b) Factor the polynomial $9x^2 - 15x + 4$

$|a| \cdot |c| = 9 \cdot 4 = 36$ pairs: 1,36; 2,18; 3,12; 4,9; 6,6

$c > 0, b < 0$ add $36 + 1 = 37$; $2 + 18 = 20$; $3 + 12 = 15$;

$\qquad\qquad\qquad 4 + 9 = 13$; $6 + 6 = 12$

pair is negative	$9x^2 - 15x + 4$
Factor 3x, -4	$= 9x^2 - 3x - 12x + 4$
Factor $3x - 1$	$= 3x(3x - 1) - 4(3x - 1)$
	$= (3x - 4)(3x - 1)$

In part (a) we use the associative property to group the first two and last two terms. Then we use the left distributive property to factor each group. We then use the right distributive property to factor out the x – 1.

In part (b) we show how to factor trinomials with a > 1 by splitting the middle into two terms. In the next section we cover Special Factor Formulas. If the middle term of part (b) trinomial were -12x this would be an example of a perfect square. Because the middle is 15, it is not a perfect square. Thus to factor, we need to use grouping or trial and error. If the middle were not any of the sum values, then the trinomial would be prime under integer coefficients.

Unlike part (a) we did not show the associative property's grouping, but extended our mental common factor approach to factor each of the parts. Since the first part common factor produced 3x – 1 it was necessary to factor out a -4 from the second part to produce 3x – 1. Factor by grouping needs the same expression for both parts. We then use the right distributive property to factor out the $3x - 1$.

HP Prime Family Factor by Grouping

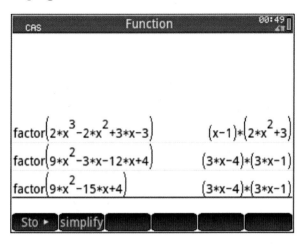

Begin by selecting the **CAS** key on the HP Prime. If the **CAS** view of the screenshot has computations, clear the **history** first. To clear the **history**, press the **Clear** key.

Key in as shown. Press the **Toolbox** key to use **Toolbox > CAS > Algebra > Factor**.

Notice in entry 3 that the HP Prime CAS can work the problem directly.

Exercise 3 Factor by Grouping

(a) Factor the polynomial $2bx - 2cx + cy - by$

(b) Factor the polynomial $8x^2 + 10x - 3$

Solution >>

Special Factoring Formulas

In this section we make use of the first two groups, Square of a Binomial and Sum and Difference of a Binomial, of the Special Products Formulas. We will use these in reverse. The third group, Cubes of Binomial, is generally not reversed and designated as a Special Factoring Formulas. However another third group involving the Difference of Cubes and Sum of Cubes is added. We need to be careful when considering cubes because the product and factoring special formulas are not reverses of each other where all of the other special product and factoring formulas are.

To summarize, in this section we will look at factoring the two Perfect Square Trinomials, the Difference of Squares, the Difference of Cubes, and Sum of Cubes Binomials.

Special Factoring Formulas

Let u and v be real numbers or algebraic expressions.

Perfect Square Trinomials

$$u^2 + 2uv + v^2 = (u+v)^2$$
$$u^2 - 2uv + v^2 = (u-v)^2$$

Difference of Squares Binomial

$$u^2 - v^2 = (u+v)(u-v)$$

Difference of Cubes Binomial

$$u^3 - v^3 = (u-v)(u^2 + uv + v^2)$$

Sum of Cubes Binomial

$$u^3 + v^3 = (u+v)(u^2 - uv + v^2)$$

We can use the HP Prime CAS to display them as well.

HP Prime Family Special Factoring Formulas

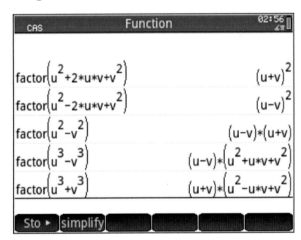

Begin by selecting the **CAS** key on the HP Prime. If the **CAS** view of the screenshot has computations, clear the **history** first. To clear the **history**, press the Clear key.

Key in as shown. Press the **Toolbox** key to use **Toolbox > CAS > Algebra > Factor**.

We used the **up arrow Enter** combination to transfer a previous entry to the edit line in the creation of each of the above entries

Example 4 Special Factoring Formulas

(a) Factor the polynomial $x^2 - 12x + 36$
The trinomial takes the form $u^2 - 2uv + v^2 = (u-v)^2$

Replace u and v $x^2 - 12x + 36$

Change form $= x^2 - 2(x)(6) + 6^2$
                $= (x-6)^2$

(b) Factor the polynomial $x^6 - y^6$
The binomial takes the form $u^2 - v^2 = (u-v)(u+v)$

Replace u and v $x^6 - y^6$

Change form $= (x^3)^2 - (y^3)^2$
                $= (x^3 - y^3)(x^3 + y^3)$

The binomial takes the form
    $u^3 \pm v^3 = (u \pm v)(u^2 \mp uv + v^2)$

Change form $= (x-y)(x^2 + xy + y^2)(x+y)$
                $(x^2 - xy + y^2)$

In part (b) we used the Difference of Squares Binomial followed by Difference of Cubes Binomial and Sum of Cubes Binomial. To manually factor we need to work the problem in this order.

HP Prime Family Special Factoring Formulas

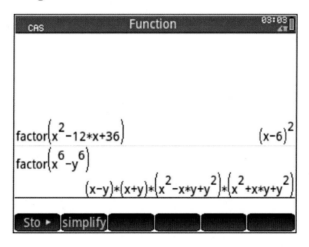

Begin by selecting the **CAS** key on the HP Prime. If the **CAS** view of the screenshot has computations, clear the **history** first. To clear the **history**, press the **Clear** key.

Key in as shown. Press the **Toolbox** key to use **Toolbox > CAS > Algebra > Factor**.

Exercise 4 Special Factoring Formulas

(a) Factor the polynomial $4x^2 + 20x + 25$

(b) Factor the polynomial $x^6 + 125$

Solution >>

Explanation 1.7 – Rational Expressions

Expressions formed by an algebraic expressions over non-zero algebraic expressions are called **fractional expressions**. If the numerator and denominator are polynomials then they are called **rational expressions**. We will look at how to simplify, multiply and dividing, add and subtract rational expressions. We conclude with simplifying compound rational expressions.

Graphing rational expressions will be cover in later tutorials. It is helpful for a discussion of **domain** for us to look at the HP Prime App generated graph and related HP Prime CAS calculator screens at this time.

HP Prime Family Domain of Rational Expressions

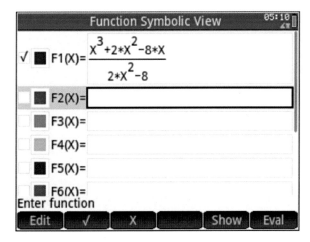

Press the **Apps** key. Highlight the **Function** icon on the Application Library screen. Press the soft **Start** key. Press the soft **Edit** key. The above screen will appear. Enter function as shown. Press the soft **OK** key.

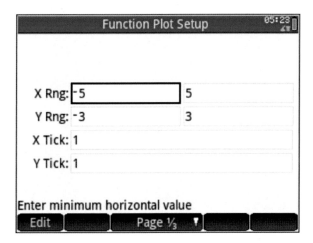

Press the Plot **Setup** key. Page 1/3, change these values X Rng: -5, 5; Y Rng: -3, 3. Page 2/3, check the Labels box.

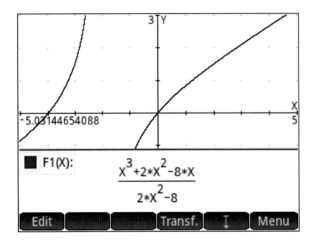

Press the **Plot** key to see a graph of the function. Press the soft **Menu** key. Use the **Fcn Extremum**. Press the soft **OK** key and then soft **Menu** key. Use the **Fcn Defintion** to display the function.

Simplify the expression $\dfrac{x^3+2x^2-8x}{2x^2-8}$

Factor out x, 2 $\quad\dfrac{x^3+2x^2-8x}{2x^2-8}$

Factor x^2-4 $\quad =\dfrac{x(x^2+2x-8)}{2(x^2-4)}$

$\quad =\dfrac{x(x^2+2x-8)}{2(x-2)(x+2)}$

Factor x^2+2x-8

$\quad |a|\cdot|c|=1\cdot8=8\quad$ pairs: 1,8; 2,4

$\quad c<0, b>0\quad$ subtract $\quad 8-1=7;\ 4-2=2;$

largest, positive $\quad =\dfrac{x(x+4)(x-2)}{2(x-2)(x+2)}$

Cancel $\quad =\dfrac{x(x+4)(x-2)}{2(x-2)(x+2)}$

$\quad =\dfrac{x(x+4)}{2(x+2)}\ x\neq2$

The **domain** for a rational expression is all values that are allowed. Unless otherwise specified we will be using the real numbers.

In our manual solution we show the restriction for the canceled out factor. In most tutorials and textbooks after a brief introduction with restrictions given for reduced rational expressions, the tutorials and textbooks leave them out. For the rest of this tutorial, in our manual solutions we will leave them out as well. We need to note that when the HP Prime CAS will show reduced form, it is up to us to realize that the domain of reduced form is larger than the domain of the original. For the first few instances we will show this. After the first few instances we will just note it.

We should also note that in calculus tutorials and calculus textbooks the cancelation restrictions are very important and are usually stated.

For the rational expressions that are reduced or are not reducible it is up to us to see what values are not allowed in their domain. Taking this and the restriction for the reduced rational expression into account, the domain for the original rational expression is all reals except 2 and -2.

Turning to the function F1 that is associated with the Function app we look at the how the HP Prime **CAS** and **HOME** view handles these restrictions. We see that the function defined in the Function app is available to both the **CAS** and **HOME** views.

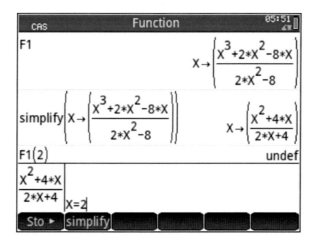

Begin by selecting the **CAS** key on the HP Prime. If the **CAS** view of the screenshot has computations, clear the **history** first. To clear the **history**, press the Clear key.

Key in as shown. We will need to press **Enter** to see the edit line result. The **with** (|) operator is located by pressing the **symbol template** key. Notice the use of capital X with the **with** (|) since the function and reduced function are in capitals.

Continuing. Key in as F1(-2). Copy the **with** rational expression and change the 2 to -2.

Next we look at the **HOME** view.

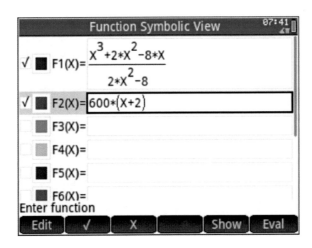

Begin by selecting the **HOME** key on the HP Prime. If the **HOME** view of the screenshot has computations, clear the **history** first. To clear the **history**, press the **Clear** key.

Use the **Menu** key "Get from CAS" to transfer F1 over. Key in F1(2) andF1(-2) as shown. Notice the difference in the two error message. F1(2) is the error 0/0 and F1(-2) is the error X/0. Use the **Menu** key "Get from CAS" to transfer the simplified rational expression over. Notice that 2 is allowed in the simplified form. The domain of the simplified form is larger than the domain of the original rational expression.

We should note that in both original and simplified x would not be defined at -2. The domain of the original function does not include -2 and 2 where the reduced simplified version only excludes -2. Using F1(2) produces the correct result of undef in **CAS** view and error message in **HOME** view. Substituting in the simplified using the width operator produces the value for the whole. Thus, the domain of the result is larger than the input's domain.

With the HP Prime CAS we need to explicitly prohibit their value in the simplified version since the simplified version's domain allows the prohibited value.

We next add a vertical asymptote and look at the trace function to help our understanding of the rational expression graph at the discontinuities, X=-2 and X=2.

Press the **Apps** key. Highlight the **Function** icon on the Application Library screen. Press the soft **Start** key. Press the soft **Edit** key. The above screen will appear. Enter functions as shown. Press the soft **OK** key. No vertical lines in the Function App. A line close to the vertical line at X=h is drawn using F(X)=big number(X-h). Large big numbers will not show that is why we picked 600, a large number that shows. Since h=-2 for our vertical asymptote, we have F2(X)=600*(X+2).

The Function Plot Setup is the same as before.

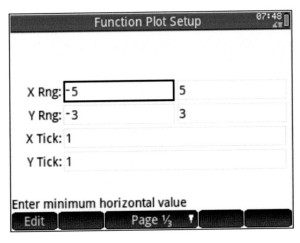

Press the Plot **Setup** key. Change if necessary. Page 1/3, values X Rng: -5, 5; Y Rng: -3, 3. Page 2/3, the Labels box is checked.

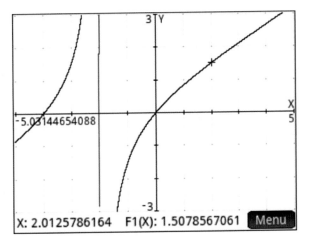

Press the **Plot** key to see a graph of the function. Press the soft **Menu** key. Use the **Trace** to see close to the hole's X and Y values. Close to X=-2 vertical line is shown as F2.

We can see from our graph why our HP Prime represent X/0 as ±∞ and 0/0 as undefined. The vertical asymptote is as X=-2 and the hole at (2,1.5).

Let take a quick look at the Advanced Graphing App.

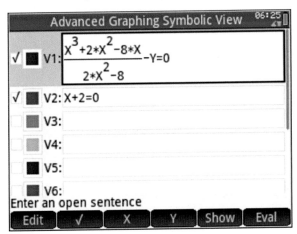

Press the **Apps** key. Highlight the **Advanced Graphing** icon on the Application Library screen. Press the soft **Start** key. Press the soft **Edit** key. The above screen will appear. Enter functions as shown. Press the soft **OK** key.

For V1 and V2 we set our original rational function and vertical asymptote equal to zero.

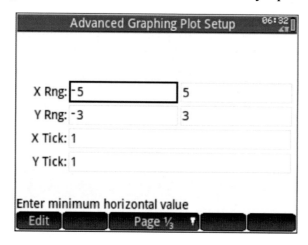

Press the Plot **Setup** key. Change if necessary. Page 1/3, values X Rng: -5, 5; Y Rng: -3, 3. Page 2/3, the Labels box is checked.

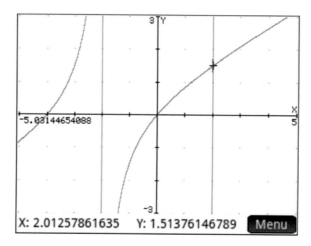

Press the **Plot** key to see a graph of the function. Press the soft **Menu** key. Use the **Trace** to see close to the hole's X and Y values.

Both the function and X=-2 vertical asymptote are shown as relations equal to zero. Notice a second line at what appears to be X=2 in the same color as the function. Originally the trace area was messier. As time went on the program was removing extraneous points. Technically the entire vertical line at X=2 is extraneous. This is the reason it appears as the same color as our relation because our HP Prime thinks all these points are part of the relation.

The variables in the rational expressions represent real numbers. We can use our <u>Properties of Fractions</u> thinking of the letters as polynomials.

Simplifying Rational Expressions

To **simplify rational expressions** factor the numerator and denominator and using the following property.

Simplifying Rational Expressions

$$\frac{a \cdot d}{b \cdot d} = \frac{a}{b}$$

This property allows us to cancel the common factors occurring in both the numerator and denominator.

Example 1 Simplifying Rational Expressions

Simplify the expression $\dfrac{3x^2 - 7x + 2}{9x^2 - 1}$

Factor $9x^2 - 1$ $\qquad \dfrac{3x^2 - 7x + 2}{9x^2 - 1}$

pair is negative $\qquad = \dfrac{3x^2 - 7x + 2}{(3x - 1)(3x + 1)}$

Factor $3x^2 - 7x + 2$

$\quad |a| \cdot |c| = 3 \cdot 2 = 6 \quad$ pairs: 1,6; 2,3

$\quad c > 0, b < 0 \quad$ add $\qquad 1 + 6 = 7; \ 2 + 3 = 5$

Factor x, -2 $\qquad = \dfrac{3x^2 - 1x - 6x + 2}{(3x - 1)(3x + 1)}$

Factor $3x - 1$ $\qquad = \dfrac{x(3x - 1) - 2(3x - 1)}{(3x - 1)(3x + 1)}$

Cancel $\qquad = \dfrac{(x - 2)(3x - 1)}{(3x - 1)(3x + 1)}$

$\qquad = \dfrac{x - 2}{3x + 1}$

HP Prime Family Simplifying Rational Expressions

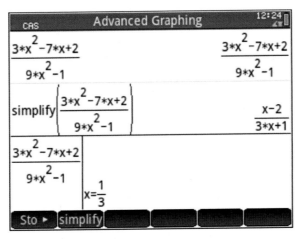

Begin by selecting the **CAS** key on the HP Prime. If the **CAS** view of the screenshot has computations, clear the **history** first. To clear the **history**, press the **Clear** key.

Key in as shown. Use the soft **simplify** key. We will need to press **Enter** to see the edit line result. The **with** (|) operator is located by pressing the **symbol template** key. The x=1/3 result will be **undef** for the original expression but have a value if used **with** the simplified result. We need to exclude x=-1/3 from the domain of the original and simplified result.

Exercise 1 Simplifying Rational Expressions

Simplify the expression $\dfrac{x^2+x-6}{x^2-4}$

<u>Solution</u> >>

Multiplying and Dividing Rational Expressions

To **multiply rational expressions** use the following property.

Multiplying Rational Expressions

$$\frac{a}{b} \cdot \frac{c}{d} = \frac{a \cdot c}{b \cdot d}$$

This property is where we multiplying the numerator and denominator of each of the factors.

To **divide rational expressions** use the following property.

Dividing Rational Expressions

$$\frac{a}{b} \div \frac{c}{d} = \frac{a}{b} \cdot \frac{d}{c} = \frac{a \cdot d}{b \cdot c}$$

To divide rational expression we invert the second factor and multiply the numerator and denominator of each of the factors.

Example 2 Multiplying and Dividing Rational Expressions

(a) Multiply $\dfrac{2x-4}{x+1} \cdot \dfrac{x^2+2x+1}{x^2-4}$

Factor rationals $\qquad \dfrac{2x-4}{x+1} \cdot \dfrac{x^2+2x+1}{x^2-4}$

Multiply $\qquad\qquad = \dfrac{2(x-2)}{x+1} \cdot \dfrac{(x+1)^2}{(x-2)(x+2)}$

Cancel, Exponents $\qquad = \dfrac{2(x-2)(x+1)^2}{(x+1)(x-2)(x+2)}$

$\qquad\qquad\qquad = \dfrac{2(x+1)}{x+2}$

(b) Divide $\dfrac{x^2-8x+16}{3x-9} \div \dfrac{2x^2-8x}{x^2-9}$

Invert and multiply $\dfrac{x^2-8x+16}{3x-9} \div \dfrac{2x^2-8x}{x^2-9}$

Factor rationals $\qquad = \dfrac{x^2-8x+16}{3x-9} \cdot \dfrac{x^2-9}{2x^2-8x}$

Multiply $\qquad\qquad = \dfrac{(x-4)^2}{3(x-3)} \cdot \dfrac{(x-3)(x+3)}{2x(x-4)}$

Cancel, Exponents $\qquad = \dfrac{(x-4)^2(x-3)(x+3)}{6x(x-3)(x-4)}$

$\qquad\qquad\qquad = \dfrac{(x-4)(x+3)}{6x}$

All factoring in part (a) and part (b) involved common factors or special factoring formulas. At this point you should be able to recognize common factors and special factoring formulas and be able to change them to their factored form.

You also might want at this point also to recognize factorable trinomials with an a coefficient of 1 can be done mentally. Because the ac Test comes down to the $|c|$ and its possible factors that make a correct b, it is possible to visualize this process mentally, and directly write these type of trinomials in factored form.

Those with an a coefficient other than 1 will need a positive a coefficient and the ac Test result to assist with regrouping bx and the remaining factoring process. In the next exercise we will see how we can automate the regrouping procedure.

The trial and error method is another method used for trinomials where a is not equal to 1. When $|a||c|$ is small trial and error can get the answer quickly, but when $|a||c|$ is large trial and error can be very involved where regrouping is straight forward and when automated as shown in the next exercise, is easy to use.

HP Prime Family Multiplying and Dividing Rational Expressions

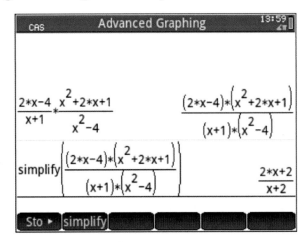

Begin by selecting the **CAS** key on the HP Prime. If the **CAS** view of the screenshot has computations, clear the **history** first. To clear the **history**, press the **Clear** key.

Key in as shown.

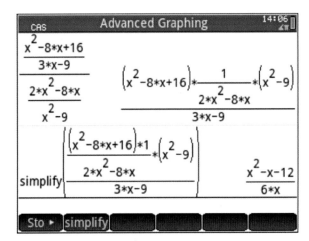

Continuing. Entry one was entered using the divide symbol with the HP Prime CAS changing the input form to a compound fraction. Use the soft **simplify** key.

Exercise 2 Multiplying and Dividing Rational Expressions

(a) Multiply $\dfrac{9x^2+6x+4}{3x^2-4x-4} \cdot \dfrac{9x^3-4x}{27x^5-8x^2}$

(b) Divide $\dfrac{x^4-81}{5x^2-9x+4} \div \dfrac{x^2-3x}{5x-4}$

<u>Solution</u> >>

Adding and Subtracting Rational Expressions

To **add or subtract rational expression** we need to find the least common denominator and use one of the Addition of Rational Expressions properties.

To find the **least common denominator (lcd)** of fractions, we factor each of the denominators into primes. We then find the **least common multiple (lcm)** by taking the highest power of each of the prime factors and multiply them together. The least common denominator is the least common multiple.

Least Common Multiple

The **least common multiple (lcm)** for two or more expressions is the product of the prime factors to the highest power that occurs in the prime factorization of any one expression.

The **least common denominator (lcd)** or **lowest common denominator** is the **least common multiple**.

If the least common denominator is the product of the two denominators we can use the second property of the Addition of Rational Expressions properties.

We note that this second property is sometimes used for any denominators if the problem involves rational numbers but we would only want to use it with rational expressions when there is no common factor between the two denominators.

Addition of Rational Expressions

$$\frac{a}{b} + \frac{c}{b} = \frac{a+c}{b}$$

$$\frac{a}{b} + \frac{c}{d} = \frac{a \cdot d + b \cdot c}{b \cdot d}$$

To add rational expression we write the sum of both the numerator and denominator over the least common denominator. For subtraction this would be the difference.

Addition and or subtraction of rational expressions is extended for three or more terms.

We start by looking at how we add rational numbers. This is helpful because the procedure for adding rational expressions is the same as adding rational numbers. The only difference is that prime factorization of polynomials is used instead of prime factorization of integers.

First we take a look at how the HP Prime does fraction. The HP Prime gives us the answer directly. We could use HP Prime commands **LCM** and **Factors** displayed as **lcm** and **ifactor** to help us manually solve the problem.

Next, we look at the manual technique. The manual technique for rational numbers provides a model that we can use for manually simplifying rational expressions.

HP Prime Family **Adding Rational Numbers**

Begin by selecting the **CAS** key on the HP Prime. If the **CAS** view of the screenshot has computations, clear the **history** first. To clear the **history**, press the **Clear** key.

Key in as shown. Press the **Toolbox** key to use **Toolbox > CAS > integer > LCM** and **Toolbox > CAS > Integer > Factors**.

(a) Add $\dfrac{3}{20}+\dfrac{2}{15}$

Prime Factorization $\quad\dfrac{3}{20}+\dfrac{2}{15}$

Multiply by 1, lcd $\quad=\dfrac{3}{2^2\cdot5}+\dfrac{2}{3\cdot5}$

Exponents $\quad=\dfrac{3}{2^2\cdot5}\cdot\dfrac{3}{3}+\dfrac{2}{3\cdot5}\cdot\dfrac{2^2}{2^2}$

Add $\quad=\dfrac{3^2}{2^2\cdot3\cdot5}+\dfrac{2^3}{2^2\cdot3\cdot5}$

Simplify $\quad=\dfrac{3^2+2^3}{2^2\cdot3\cdot5}$

$\quad=\dfrac{17}{60}$

(b) Add $\dfrac{3}{8}+\dfrac{4}{9}$

No common factors $\quad\dfrac{3}{8}+\dfrac{4}{9}$

Simplify $\quad=\dfrac{3\cdot9+8\cdot4}{8\cdot9}$

$\quad=\dfrac{59}{72}$

In part (a) we need to find the **least common denominator (lcd)** of the two fractions. We factor each of the denominators into primes. To find the **least common multiple (lcm)** we take the highest power of each of the prime factors and multiply them together. The least common denominator is the least common multiple. We then multiply each term by 1 using the missing factor(s) of the lcm. Now we are able to add the two fractions numerators together. Simplifying we get 17/60.

In part (b), since there are no common factors between the denominators the least common denominator is the product of the two denominators. We are thus able to use the second property. Simplifying we get 59/72.

Example 3 Adding and Subtracting Rational Expressions

(a) Add $\dfrac{1}{x^2-4}+\dfrac{1}{x^2-4x+4}$

Factor $\qquad \dfrac{1}{x^2-4}+\dfrac{1}{x^2-4x+4}$

Multiply by 1, lcd $\quad =\dfrac{1}{(x-2)(x+2)}+\dfrac{1}{(x-2)^2}$

Add, Expand $\quad =\dfrac{1}{(x-2)(x+2)}\cdot\dfrac{(x-2)}{(x-2)}$

$\qquad\qquad +\dfrac{1}{(x-2)^2}\cdot\dfrac{(x+2)}{(x+2)}$

Simplify $\qquad =\dfrac{x-2+x+2}{(x-2)^2\cdot(x+2)}$

$\qquad\qquad =\dfrac{2x}{(x-2)^2\cdot(x+2)}$

In part (a) we need to find the **least common denominator (lcd)** of the two rational expression. We factor each of the denominators into polynomials. To find the **least common multiple (lcm)** we take the highest power of each of the polynomial factors and multiply them together. The least common multiple is the least common denominator. We then multiply each term by 1 using the missing factor(s) of the lcm. Now we are able to add the two numerators together.

(b) Subtract $\dfrac{x}{x-3}-\dfrac{2}{x+1}$

No common factors $\quad \dfrac{x}{x-3}-\dfrac{2}{x+1}$

Expand $\qquad\qquad =\dfrac{x(x+1)-2(x-3)}{(x-3)(x+1)}$

Simplify $\qquad\qquad =\dfrac{x^2+x-2x+6}{(x-3)(x+1)}$

$\qquad\qquad =\dfrac{x^2-x+6}{(x-3)(x+1)}$

In part (b), since there are no common factors between the denominators the least common denominator is the product of the two denominators. We are thus able to use the second property. Notice that the numerator is a prime, irreducible, trinomial

HP Prime Family Adding and Subtracting Rational Expressions

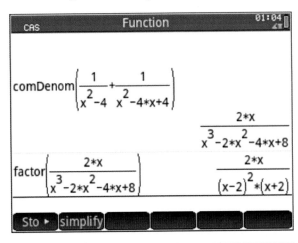

Begin by selecting the **CAS** key on the HP Prime. If the **CAS** view of the screenshot has computations, clear the **history** first. To clear the **history**, press the **Clear** key.

Key in as shown. Press the **Toolbox** key to use **Toolbox > Catlg > comDenom**. Press the **Toolbox** key to use **Toolbox > CAS > Algebra > Factor** to display the result in factored form. This is our first instance in our tutorial using rational expressions, where the domain of the result is same as the domain of the input. The domain of result does not have any values in the result that are not in the domain of the input.

Exercise 3 Adding and Subtracting Rational Expressions

Simplify $\dfrac{4x}{x^2-1}+\dfrac{4}{x-1}-\dfrac{2}{x+1}$

<u>Solution</u> >>

Compound Fractions

Compound fractions are where the numerator, denominator, or both are composed of algebraic fractions. They are also referred to as <u>complex fractions</u>.

There are three ways to simplify compound fractions. Method 1 is to get the numerator and denominator to be a rational expression, and then we invert and multiply. Method 2 is to multiply the numerator and denominator by a common denominator for the problem clearing out any fractional terms in the numerator or denominator. Method 3 is where a problem has a negative power. We factor out the <u>greatest common factor</u> (gcf) that includes the negative power common factor. See our previous discussion on factoring out negative fractional exponents. The second gcf illustration came from the use of the product rule in calculus.

Let's look at some calculus definitions and formulas that lead to compound fractions.

Calculus is the study of change. There are two main branches, differential and integral calculus. Compound fractions have many uses in the study of differential calculus. The investigations and concurrent development of calculus are credited to Gottfried Wilhelm Leibnitz (1646-1716) and Isaac Newton (1642-1727). Use a search engine to investigate more about calculus and its discovery.

Finding the slope of secant and tangent lines and using the calculus definition for the derivative with functions, which are quotients, results in the creation of compound fractions. Using the quotient rule to differentiate a function with radicals or rational exponents in the numerator or denominator results in compound fractions.

We use the definition of slope, $m = (y_2 - y_1)/(x_2 - x_1)$, to come up with a formula for the slope of the secant line. We pick a point, $P_1(a, f(a))$, on the curve and consider a point h units away, $P_2(a+h, f(a+h))$.

Slope of Secant Line

Slope secant line based on $P_1(a, f(a))$ and $P_2((a+h, f(a+h))$.

$$m_{sec} = \frac{y_2 - y_1}{x_2 - x_1} = \frac{f(a+h) - f(a)}{a+h-a} = \frac{f(a+h) - f(a)}{h}$$

We can see that from this definition for slope of a secant line that for functions which are quotients the initial substitution of $f(a)$ and $f(a+h)$ results in a compound fraction. We have a numerator composed of algebraic fractions over h.

We let the value for h in the formula take on smaller and smaller values. This is known as taking the limit as h approaches 0. If we take the formula for the slope of the secant line and take the limit as h approaches 0 we get the slope of the tangent line at $P_1(a, f(a))$.

Remark: We encountered problems setting up the Slope of Tangent Line for the HP Prime/ Pro/ Virtual using the limit as h approaches 0. We decided to switch to the alternate definition that uses $P_1(a,f(a))$ and $P_2(x,f(x))$. The alternated definition uses the slope of the secant line being $(f(x)-f(a))/(x-a)$. Then using the limit as x approaches a to get the slope of the tangent line at $P_1(a, f(a))$. The tangent line is then defined as the lim x->a (f(x)-f(a))/(x-a).

Once we got the alternate Slope of Tangent Line working we applied the same technique to get the limit as h approaches 0 version working. In our program listing we left the alternate version in and labeled it mtan2.

Slope of Tangent Line

The **slope** of a tangent line at point $P(a, f(a))$ for the function $f(x)$ is given by

$$m_{tan} = \lim_{h \to 0} \frac{f(a+h) - f(a)}{h}$$

provided the limit exists.

To manually find the slope of a tangent line we use the first form to evaluate the limit as h approaches 0 for the secant line. The first step to find the slope of a tangent line for a function, such as f(x) = 1/(x – 2) would be to find the slope of the secant line for $P_1(a, f(a))$ and $P_2(a+h, f(a+h))$.

Find the slope of secant for $f(x) = \dfrac{1}{x-2}$ for $P_1(a, f(a))$ and $P_2(a+h, f(a+h))$.

Substitute $f(a+h)$ and $f(a)$ $\quad \dfrac{f(a+h) - f(a)}{h}$

Combine quotients, invert $\quad = \dfrac{\dfrac{1}{a+h-2} - \dfrac{1}{a-2}}{h}$

Expand, Multiply $\quad = \dfrac{1(a-2) - 1(a+h-2)}{(a+h-2)(a-2)} \cdot \dfrac{1}{h}$

Simplify $\quad = \dfrac{a-2-a-h+2}{h(a+h-2)(a-2)}$

$$= \dfrac{-1}{(a+h-2)(a-2)}$$

$$m_{tan} = \lim_{h \to 0} \dfrac{-1}{(a+h-2)(a-2)} = \dfrac{-1}{(a+0-2)(a-2)} = \dfrac{-1}{(a-2)^2}$$

Since there are no common factors in the denominator, we used the second property of Addition of Rational to combine the quotients in the numerator. We then use method 1 to invert and multiply the rational expression in the numerator by 1/h. This result is simplified to arrive at a formula for finding the slope of secant line at points, $P_1(a, f(a))$ and $P_2(a+h, f(a+h))$.

To get the formula for slope of the tangent line at the point, $P_1(a, f(a))$, we need to take the limit as h approaches 0 of secant slope's formula. This is done by substituting in 0 for h in the secant formula, resulting in the tangent slope formula of -1/(a – 2)^2 for the point at $P_1(a, f(a))$.

Remark: For the rest of Section 1.7 HP Prime Free calculator users need only pay attention to the manual technique shown and built-in HP Prime features. HP Prime handheld, Pro, Virtual users will use the programmed functions and commands created in the CalcSecTan and CalcSketch program libraries or use our created FncSecTanLines, FncIncDecConvUpDn, or GraphPlus Application Library.

Go to computerlearningservice.com/html/products.html to download the files.

HP Prime Family Graph of Tangent and Secant Line – Function Library App

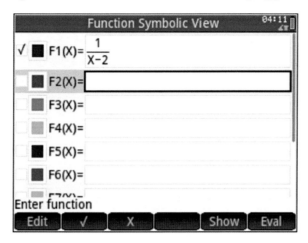

Note: For the HP Prime/ Pro/ Virtual illustration of tangent line and secant line we have added a library, CalcSecTan, to our HP Prime/ Pro/ Virtual device. Subsequent instructions for this illustration assume that you have added the CalcSecTan library to your HP Prime/ Pro/ Virtual device. Instructions for adding the CalcSecTan library are given following this illustration. Add the CalcSecTan library to your HP Prime/ Pro/ Virtual device before proceeding.

Go to computerlearningservice.com/html/products.html to download the file.

HP Prime Free will do the tangent and secant line entries by manually entering entries F2(X)= and F3(X)= of the Function Symbolic View screen. HP Prime Free will use the values shown by the HP Prime/ Pro/ Virtual CalcSecTan library's *secline* and *tanline* functions. For function other than F1(X)=1/(X-2) HP Prime Free will have to manually calculate the secant and tangent lines functions.

Both HP Prime/ Pro/ Virtual and HP Prime Free will do the above and next screens. HP Prime Free will then skip two screens. The individual directions for the screens will let you know what HP Prime/ Pro/ Virtual and HP Prime Free need to do.

Press the **Apps** key. Highlight the **Function** icon on the Application Library screen. Press the soft **Start** key. Press the soft **Edit** key. The above screen will appear. Enter function as shown. Press the soft **OK**. To erase all functions press the **Clear** key. Both HP Prime/ Pro/ Virtual and HP Prime Free need to do this screen.

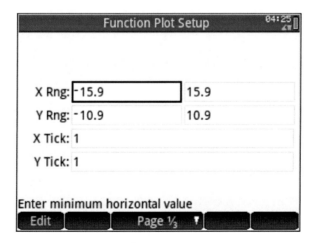

Press the Plot **Setup** key. Page 1/3, change to the default values X Rng: -15.9, 15.9; Y Rng: -10.9, 10.9. Page 2/3, check the Labels box. To set page 1/3 back to defaults press the **Clear** key. Both HP Prime/ Pro/ Virtual and HP Prime Free need to do this screen.

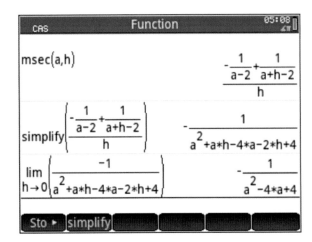

Begin by selecting the **CAS** key on the HP Prime. If the **CAS** view of the screenshot has computations, clear the **history** first. To clear the **history**, press the **Clear** key. HP Prime Free does not have the function **msec**. HP Prime Free will not do this screen.

However, the HP Prime Free could use the definition of secant line and built-in simplify function if they wished. This would actually be entry two above with numerator of entry two terms reversed.

Key in as shown. Press the **Toolbox** key to use **Toolbox > User > CalcSecTan > msec**. The program function **msec** uses the function **F1** from the **Function Symbolic View**. Press the soft **simplify** key to simplify the compound fraction. The **lim** command is located by pressing the **symbol template** key.

The above screens shows how to use the relationship between defining a function using the **Function App** and the defined function subsequent use of **F1** in the **CAS** view. Here our function **msec** is using the function **F1** from the Function App's **Function Symbolic View**.

In the next screen, **HOME** view's entry one, **F1**, shows what is stored in the **Function Symbolic View** for **F1**. The next two entries store their results into the **Function Symbolic View's F2** and **F3** functions. Here our functions, **secline** and **tanline**, are being used to add **F2** and **F3** to the Function App's **Function Symbolic View**.

CAS view could have been used as well, but the form of functions in the history area is cleaner in **HOME**'s view. Beside the function in the history area being cleaner, the default entry in **CAS** view is lower case and we would need to use the **Shift** with **ALPHA** for **F1**, **F2**, and **F3**.

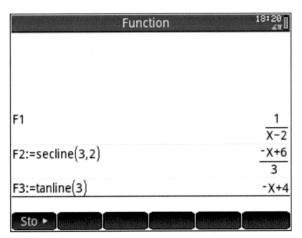

Note: The instructions for this screenshot assume that you have added the CalSecTan library to your HP Prime/ Pro/ Virtual device. Instructions for adding the CalSecTan library are given following this illustration. If you have not added the CalSecTan library, do so now.

Go to computerlearningservice.com/html/products.html to download the file.

Begin by selecting the **HOME** key on the HP Prime. If the **HOME** view of the screenshot has computations, clear the **history** first. To clear the **history**, press the **Clear** key. HP Prime Free does not have the **secline** and **tanline** commands. HP Prime Free will not do this screen.

Alternately, HP Prime Free users would need to manually calculate slope of secant line and slope of tangent line. HP Prime Free users would then manually apply to y=m(x-x$_1$)+y$_1$. The slope of the tangent line could be done by taking the derivative at the point on the HP Prime Free **CAS** view, diff(F1(x),x=3). The slope of secant line could be done on HP Prime Free **CAS** view by following the steps we did two screens earlier and substituting in the values for a and h.

Key in as shown. Press the **Toolbox** key to use **Toolbox > User > CalcSecTan > secline** and **Toolbox > User > CalcSecTan > tanline**.

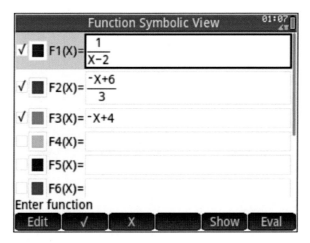

HP Prime/ Pro/ Virtual users press the **Symb** key to see the three functions in the **Function Symbolic View** window. If necessary use the **Apps** key to select the **Function** app.

HP Prime Free users press the **Symb** key. HP Prime Free users need to manually enter the expressions shown in **F2** and **F3** since their **F2** and **F3** are blank. As stated earlier, for any other **F1** HP Prime Free users will need to manually calculate **F2** and **F3**.

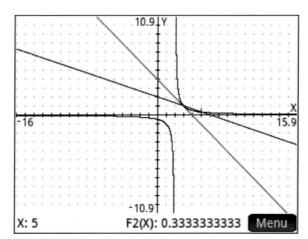

Press the **Plot** key to see a graph of the function. Both HP Prime/ Pro/ Virtual and HP Prime Free need to do this screen.

Pressing the 5 key gives us the message 'Enter the value to witch to jump' with 5 set as the value. Press **Enter**. Press the soft **Menu** key. Use the soft **Fcn** key **Definition** to enable the soft **F1(X)** key. Change the function to **F2(X)**, Experiment with soft **Menu** and **Trace** key and clicking on graph of **F2**. Notice in our plot the trace's cross hair at **X: 5, F2(X): 0.3333333333**.

The blue line is our function **F1**. The red line is the secant line **F2** generated by its library function using an *x* value of 3 for *a* with an *h* value of 2. The green line is the tangent line **F3** generated by its library function using an *x* value of 3 for *a*.

We see from the graphs that the function, secant line, and tangent line intercepting at the point $P_1(3,1)$ and the secant line intercepts the function again at the point $P_2(5,1/3)$, 2 x-units from our first point.

We next look at our Library App FcnSecTanLines that draws the same results.

HP Prime Family Graph of Tangent and Secant Line – FncSecTanLines Library App

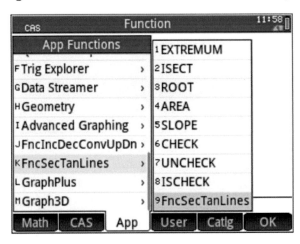

Note: The instructions for this screenshot assume that you have added the CalSecTan library and FncSecTanLines Application Library to your HP Prime/ Pro/ Virtual device. Go to for instructions on adding the required library. Go to FncSecTanLines for instructions on adding this Application Library.

Go to computerlearningservice.com/html/products.html to download the files.

Begin by selecting the **CAS** key or **HOME** key on the HP Prime. If the **CAS** view or **HOME** view of the screenshot has computations, clear the **history** first. To clear the **history**, press the Clear key. HP Prime Free does not have the Application Library **FncSecTanLines**. HP Prime Free will not do this screen.

Press the **Toolbox** key to use **Toolbox > App > FncSecTanLines**. Press **Enter** to transfer the result to the command line. Press **Enter** to execute the app from the command line (now shown).

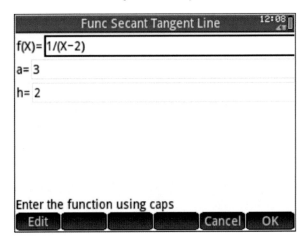

Key in the fields as shown. Be sure to use capital X. Press the soft **Edit** key. Use **Esc** to clear each field's default entry. Press **Enter** or soft **OK** key to update the field. Press **Enter** or soft **OK** key to see the plot. HP Prime Free will not do this screen.

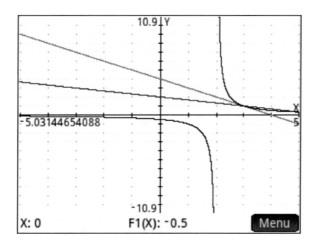

The graphs of the function, secant line, and tangent line are drawn with **FncSecTanLines** last Plot **Settings**. HP Prime Free will not do this screen.

Remark: The earlier manual solution's final form for slope of secant and tangent differ from our CAS derived version form. Many times it is possible to use HP Prime commands to turn the CAS result into the form that the manual solution produced. This may also be necessary in verifying HP Prime results with tutorial and textbook results since tutorial and textbook results were likely produced manually. If through visual inspection we can see the HP Prime and manual solutions are equivalent there is no need to perform the extra HP Prime manipulations.

By adding the additional **secline** and **tanline** functions to our CalcSecTan library we can see the applications of the slope of the secant and tangent at a physical point and with a physical h value. Since the FncSecTanLines App use the CalcSecTan library we executed the **secline** and **tanline** functions as code in the App. In the case of HP Prime Free we are manually adding secline and tanline equations. The added visual picture increases our understanding of the algebraic concepts.

For HP Prime/ Pro/ Virtual we create the CalSecTan library. The library gives us functions for finding formulas for the slope of the secant and tangent lines; actual slope of the secant and tangent line values at a specific x value and an h value in the case of secant; plus equations for the secant and tangent lines given an x and an h value in the case of secant.

The CalcSecTan Library shown in the following two listing is © Larry Schroeder 2018. All rights reserved. We create a template with our HP Prime and replace the template's shell with the Notepad++ contents.

For the FncSecTanLines Library App we use a very similar procedure to create it. The difference is how the FncSecTanLines template is created.

The amount of code makes it better to create the program CalcSecTan and FncSecTanLines Library App using a text editor. See the previous notes on this.

Next we will look at creating the CalcSecTan application library. We will go over the details to creating the FncSecTanLines Library App right before our summary list of the steps using for creating a program library or Library App.

Start by creating the CalcSecTan application library template. HP Prime Free will not be able to create the CalcSecTan application library since the HP Prime Free lacks the programming feature.

HP Prime/ Pro/ Virtual Creating the CalcSecTan Library

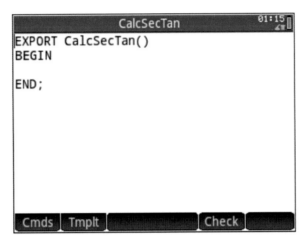

On our HP Prime/ Pro/ Virtual press the **Program** key. Remember the HP Prime Free does not have the programming function. Next, press the **New** soft key. Type in **CalcSecTan** to the **Name**: field. Leave the **CAS**: field unchecked. Press the **OK** soft key twice. Leave the template **CalcSecTan** program blank. HP Prime Free will not do this screen.

Go to computerlearningservice.com/html/products.html to download the file.

Shown next is the Notepad++ with the HP PPl plug-in listing of the first 22 lines of the library CalcSecTan, The remaining 15 lines of the CalcSecTan Library is shown following the explanation of the first 22 lines.

```
1    CalcSecTan;|
2
3    msec();
4    mtan();
5    secline();
6    tanline();
7
8    EXPORT msec(a,h)
9    BEGIN
10    return CAS.exact((F1(a+h)-F1(a))/h);
11   END;
12
13   EXPORT mtan(a)
14   BEGIN
15    return CAS.limit(CAS.simplify((F1(a+'H')-F1(a))/'H'),H,0);
16   END;
17
18   EXPORT mtan2(a)
19   BEGIN
20    return CAS.limit(CAS.simplify((F1('X')-F1(a))/('X'-a)),X,a);
21   END;
22
```

From the Notepad++ select all and copy. This will copy the complete listing. That is both the above and next listing into the windows clipboard.

```
                   CalcSecTan              01:25
CalcSecTan;

msec();
mtan();
secline();
tanline();
                                              ►
EXPORT msec(a,h)
BEGIN
 return CAS.exact((F1(a+h)-F1(a))/h);
END;

EXPORT mtan(a)                ▼
  Cmds   Tmplt    Page    ▼  Check
```

Remember the HP Prime Free does not have the programming function. With the CalcSecTan template showing, press the Copy key on the HP Prime. Press the soft key **All**, followed by pressing the soft key **Cut**. Use the paste function of the HP Prime Pro or HP Prime Virtual Calculator to paste from the system clipboard the listing from Notepad++. Scroll to the top. At this point, we will see the above screen. Press the **Check** soft key. Press **OK** soft key to message "No errors in the program". HP Prime Free will not do this screen.

As we mentioned with Key_user scientific notation application library, the process of creating CalcSecTan is more involved than our earlier programs in first section of the book. But once we get our update/ debugged code into the template, the execution is no different than the one-line functions and our program library one-line functions. Returning to the **HOME** view or **CAS** view command line means that the program library syntax is correct. That the functions are ready to be executed/ tested.

Now let's look at the explanation of the code in the first listing.

The function **msec** returns the exact slope of the secant line. The **CAS.exact** is used to change any decimal representation to an exact form.

The function **mtan** returns the slope of the tangent line. The function **mtan2** is the alternative definition of the slope of the tangent line. It is not needed because **mtan** produces the same result. However, it can be executed if so desired.

It is included to help with understanding of **mtan**'s code. Notice in **mtan** and **mtan2** the use of system global Real variables H and X respectively. In the **CAS.simplify** we use literal 'H' and 'X' in quote marks to manipulate the algebraic slope formulas. By not including the quote marks in the **CAS.limit** we use the values stored in H and X which the limit function sets to 0 and a respectively. It is hoped that seeing both **mtan** and **mtan2** declared with literal notation, quotes, for the nested command and value notation, no quotes, for the outside command helps you see the logic behind using a literal for the **simplify** command and a value representation for the **limit** command.

```
23    EXPORT secline(x1,h)
24    BEGIN
25     local a,m;
26     m:=msec(x1,h);
27     a:=CAS.simplify(m*('X'-x1)+F1(x1));
28     return a;
29    END;
30
31    EXPORT tanline(x1)
32    BEGIN
33     local a,m;
34     m:=mtan(x1);
35     a:=CAS.simplify(m*('X'-x1)+F1(x1));
36     return a;
37    END;
```

Shown is the final 15 lines of the CalcSecTan library. Let's take a look at this listing explanations.

The function **secline** called on the **msec** function declared in the first 22 lines of code. Then it used m(x-x1)+y1 expression of the point slope formula combined with **CAS.Simplify** to produce the **secline** expression for point slope formula.

The function **tanline** called on the **mtan** function declared in the first 22 lines of code. Then it used m(x-x1)+y1 expression of the point slope formula combined with **CAS.Simplify** to produce the **tanline** expression for point slope formula.

Notice in both **secline** and **tanline** the use of 'X' literal.

The above two listings illustrates how adding our own functions in libraries can greatly enhance the HP Prime's power and capabilities.

Remark: In the Plot submenu at the bottom of the screen there is command **Fcn** to graph the **Tangent** Line. There is merit in creating our own plus using the built-in command. As we see later with our command minmax, the rigor of the built-in commands is missing but the understanding from generalizing a process and creating our own plus their usefulness as long as we understand their limitations is well worth the effort.

At this point you can return to the HP Prime CAS Slope of Tangent and Secant screenshot and use the CalcSecTan library to find the slope of the tangent and secant.

Another option for *secline* and *tanline* would be to use a library from our future second volume that contain *lineptm*. The CLSlines Library has a function that find the slope of a line – *slopeln* given two points; find the equation of line given a point and slope - *lineptm*; given two points - *linep1p2*; or given the *x* and *y* intercepts - *linexy*. The screenshots of this library and modification to the CalcSecTan Library are shown next. All Libraries shown next are © Larry Schroeder 2018. All rights reserved.

We use the prefix CLS to make our lines library name unique. It stands for our publisher, Computer Learning Service. This naming scheme allows us to differentiate our library functions from other library that happen to have a function that use the same function name as ours. It probably would have been better to use this prefix with all our libraries but we choose for our other libraries to use shorter somewhat meaningful library names. For example CalcSecTan library name was for Calculus, Secant, and Tangent.

Library CLSlines

```
 1    CLSlines;
 2
 3    slopeln();
 4    lineptm();
 5    linept1pt2();
 6    linexy();
 7
 8    EXPORT slopeln(x1,y1,x2,y2)
 9    BEGIN
10     return (y2-y1)/(x2-x1);
11    END;
12
13    EXPORT lineptm(x1,y1,m)
14    BEGIN
15     local a;
16     a:=m*('X'-x1)+y1;
17     return CAS.expand(a);
18    END;
19
```

Library CLSlines continued

```
20    EXPORT linept1pt2(x1,y1,x2,y2)
21    BEGIN
22     local a,sl;
23     sl:=slopeln(x1,y1,x2,y2);
24     a:=lineptm(x1,y1,sl);
25     return a;
26    END;
27
28    EXPORT linexy(x1,y1)
29    BEGIN
30     local a;
31     a:= linept1pt2(x1,0,0,y1);
32     return a;
33    END;
34
```

Go to computerlearningservice.com/html/products.html to download the file.

HP Prime Free will not do this.

Library CalcSecTan modifications using CLSlines Library function *lineptm*

```
23    EXPORT secline(x1,h)
24    BEGIN
25     local a,m;
26     m:=msec(x1,h);
27     a:=CAS.simplify(lineptm(x1,F1(x1),m));
28     return a;
29    END;
30
31    EXPORT tanline(x1)
32    BEGIN
33     local a,m;
34     m:=mtan(x1);
35     a:=CAS.simplify(lineptm(x1,F1(x1),m));
36     return a;
37    END;
```

Go to computerlearningservice.com/html/products.html to download the file.

HP Prime Free will not do this .

Building Global Libraries is a very powerful feature. Being able to call one of our added functions from another library is a very useful feature. We should also add a comment statement to our modified CalcSecTan library saying it is dependent on the CLSlines library existing on our HP Prime.

Remark: Even though it is more complex to use Global libraries, writing the *lineptm* function once and using it outside its Library is the best procedure. Updating, extending, and correcting a function's definition should be done from one spot, that way we are sure that all occurrences of the function will use the most recent up-to-date version.

For now, we will concentrate on creating and using simpler self-contained Libraries. Later as we gain more experience with creating and using Libraries we will follow the more complex but also more reliable approach that was just illustrated.

Remark: The ability to add one-line global functions enhances our math abilities in general and amplifies our understanding of the underlying math concept behind the one line global function or group of related one-line global functions. As shown by our earlier plot screenshot, the HP Prime's generation of the equation for the secant and tangent lines made it easy for us to investigate the relationship between a function and its secant and tangent lines at a point. Even though there are built-in functions to do many things the ability to add new global one-line functions gives us unlimited potential besides the learning from generalizing a process to produce a new global function or group of global functions that greatly enhances the process.

As shown in the modified CalcSecTan library, the nesting of functions adds an additional dimension and power to our already powerful and useful CalcSecTan library.

Next we show how to create Application Libraries that run from the **HOME** view or **CAS** view command line.

HP Prime/ Pro/ Virtual Creating the FncSecTanLines Library Application

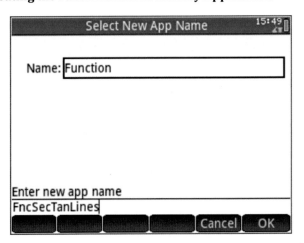

On our HP Prime/ Pro/ Virtual highlight the Function App in the Application Library. Press the soft **Save** key. The above screen appears. Remember the HP Prime Free does not have the programming function. Even though the HP Prime Free can Save a new App. It cannot add code to the new app. The HP Prime Free will not do this procedure.

Type in **FncSecTanLines** to the **Name**: field. Press the **OK** soft key twice. The **FncSecTanLines** icon appears on the Application Library.

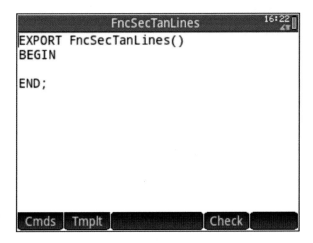

On our HP Prime/ Pro/ Virtual press the **Program** key. Select the **FncSecTanLines (App)**. Leave the template **FncSecTanLines** program blank. HP Prime Free will not do this screen.

Go to computerlearningservice.com/html/products.html to download the files.

Shown next is the Notepad++ with the HP PPl plug-in listing of the FncSecTanLines Library Application.

```
#pragma mode( separator(.,;) integer(h32) )

EXPORT FncSecTanLines()
BEGIN
// Initialization
LOCAL a,h,f;
a:=2; h:=3; f:='X^2';

STARTAPP("FncSecTanLines");

  if input(
    {{f,[8]},a,h},
    "Func Secant Tangent Line",
    {"f(X)=", "a=", "h="},
    {
      "Enter the function using caps",
      "Enter the x-value for a",
      "Enter the x-value, h units away"
    },
    {f,a,h}
  ) then
    F1:=f;
    F2:=secline(a,h);
    F3:=tanline(a);
  end;

CHECK(1);
CHECK(2);
CHECK(3);
STARTVIEW(1,1);
END;
```

```
                    FncSecTanLines            16:35
#pragma mode( separator(.,;) integer(h

EXPORT FncSecTanLines()
BEGIN
// Initialization
LOCAL a,h,f;
a:=2; h:=3; f:='X^2';                          ▶

STARTAPP("FncSecTanLines");

  if input(
    {{f,[8]},a,h},
Cmds   Tmplt      Page  ▼  Check
```

Remember the HP Prime Free does not have the programming function. With the **FncSecTanLines** template showing, press the **Copy** key on the HP Prime. Press the soft key **All**, followed by pressing the soft key **Cut**. Use the paste function of the HP Prime Pro or HP Prime Virtual Calculator to paste from the system clipboard the listing from Notepad++. Scroll to the top. At this point, we will see the above screen. Press the **Check** soft key. Press **OK** soft key to message "No errors in the program".

HP Prime Free will not do this screen.

Now let's look at the explanation of the code.

The app EXPORT FncSecTanLines line allows the code to run from the **HOME** view or **CAS** view command line.

The input command prevents the FncSecTanLines Library Application from being directly executed.

The Library Application FncSecTanLines has no override functions. All Library Application functions are inherited from the Application Library Functions. None of the Application Library functions are disabled since there are no blank functions listed.

The two line F2:=secline(a,h) and F3:=tanline(a) require that the program CalcSecTan application library be loaded.

HP Prime/ Pro/ Virtual Creating the FncIncDecConvUpDn Library Application

Go to computerlearningservice.com/html/products.html to download the files.

HP Prime Free will not do this procedure.

Shown next is the Notepad++ with the HP PPl plug-in listing of the FncIncDecConvUpDn Library Application. Use the exact same procedure as we used to create the FncSecTanLines Library Application.

```
#pragma mode( separator(.,;) |integer(h32) )

EXPORT FncIncDecConvUpDn()
BEGIN
// Initialization
LOCAL f;
f:='X^2';
STARTAPP("FncIncDecConvUpDn");

  if input(
    {{f,[8]}},
    "Func Increase Decrease Concavity",
    {"f(X)="},
    {
      "Enter the function using caps"
    },
    {f}
  ) then
    F1:=f;
    F2:="incdec("+'X'+")";
    F3:="2*concaveupdown("+'X'+")";

  end;

CHECK(1);
CHECK(2);
CHECK(3);
STARTVIEW(1,1);
END;
```

Now let's look at the explanation of the code.

The app EXPORT FncIncDecConvUpDn line allows the code to run from the **HOME** view or **CAS** view command line.

The input command prevents the FncIncDecConvUpDn Library Application from being directly executed.

The Library Application FncIncDecConvUpDn has no override functions. All Library Application functions are inherited from the Application Library Functions. None of the Library Application functions are disabled since there are no blank functions listed.

The two line F2:="incdec("+'X'+")" and F3:="2*concaveupdowm("+'X'+")" require that the program CalcSketch application library be loaded.

Next we show how to create an Library Applications that run from the Application Library icon.

HP Prime/ Pro/ Virtual Creating the GraphPlus Library Application

Go to computerlearningservice.com/html/products.html to download the file.

HP Prime Free will not do this procedure.

Shown next is the Notepad++ with the HP PPl plug-in listing of the GraphPlus Library Application. Use the exact same procedure as we used to create the FncSecTanLines Library Application.

```
#pragma mode( separator(.,;) integer(h32) )

gGP_setdefault();
incdec();
concaveupdown();

initGP=0;

view "Edit Function",START()
begin
  if initGP==0 then
    gGP_setdefault();
  end;
  startview(0,1);
end;

View "Reset Plot Settings",RESET()
begin
  gGP_setdefault();
end;

Symb()
begin
  startview(0,1);
end;
```

Part 1 of GraphPlus listing.

```
view "Plot the Function",Plot()
begin
  if initGP==0 then
    gGP_setdefault();
  end;
  F2:="incdec("+'X'+")";
  F3:="2*concaveupdown("+'X'+")";
  CHECK(1);
  CHECK(2);
  CHECK(3);
  startview(1,1);
end;

gGP_setdefault()
begin
  F1:=""; F2:=""; F3:=""; F4:=""; F5:="";
  F6:=""; F7:=""; F8:=""; F9:=""; F0:="";
  initGP:=1;
end;

incdec(x)
BEGIN
 LOCAL c;
 F0:=CAS.diff(F1(X));
 c:=SIGN(F0(x));
END;

concaveupdown(x)
BEGIN
 LOCAL c;
 F9:=CAS.diff(F1(X));
 F0:=CAS.diff(F9);
 c:=SIGN(F0(x));
END;
```

Part 2 of GraphPlus listing.

Now let's look at the explanation of the code.

The absence of EXPORT GraphPlus line prevents the code from running from the **HOME** view or **CAS** view command line. This app needs F1 to be input from the Symb view.

The use of Start, Reset, Symb, and Plot function in the GraphPlus code allow the GraphPlus Library Application to override these functions from the inherited Application Library Functions. All other Application Library App functions are inherited. None of the Application Library App functions are disabled since there are no blank functions listed.

The view content menu is populated with Start, Reset, and Plot directives.

The presence of local function incdec and concaveupdown allow F2:="incdec("+'X'+")" and F3:="2*concaveupdowm("+'X'+")"to be executed without the external program library CalcSketch. Thus, the app is a standalone app. However, how they were coded prevents us from using modified **Symb** values to display a wider Y-range.

Go to computerlearningservice.com/html/products.html to download all the program library and Library Application files.

Let's summarize the steps needed to create and use a program library of functions or create executable Library Application:

· Create a HP Prime enhanced Notepad++ version of the program library of functions or Library App.

· For a program library add a HP Prime function template using the name of the library as the function name or for a Library App Save a copy of the Library App that we will be using for our new Library App with a new name.

· Edit the HP Prime function template or copy of the Library App by using the **Copy** key of the HP Prime. Press the soft key **All**, followed by the soft key **Cut**.

· In the HP Prime enhanced Notepad++ select All, followed by Copy.

· On the HP Prime Pro or HP Prime Virtual Calculator Paste from the system clipboard.

· Press the HP Prime soft **Check** key. Press the soft OK key to message "No errors in the program".

· Run a program library function or execute a Library Application. For the program library of functions use the **Toolbox** > **User** > **Program Function** > **function name** from the **CAS** view or **HOME** view. For the Library Application App, if it has an Export function of the application in the code, use the **Toolbox** > **App** > **App Functions** > **app name** from the **CAS** view or **HOME** view. No Export function of the application in the code, execute it from Application Library screen soft **Start** key.

Definition of Derivative

The **derivative** of $f(x)$ is given by

$$f'(x) = \lim_{h \to 0} \frac{f(x+h) - f(x)}{h}$$

provided the limit exists.

The derivative may also be symbolized using

$$\frac{dy}{dx}, y', D_x y, \frac{d[f(x)]}{dx}, \frac{d}{dx}[f(x)].$$

In part (a) of example 4 we will take a look at using the limit definition to find the derivative of a function. Part (b) of example 4 will look at using the quotient rule with a radical in the denominator. We will switch the radical to a rational exponent.

The product and quotient rules do not use the limit definition of the derivative but are two of the basic differentiation rules. The product and quotient rules use the other basic differentiation rules plus a technique to handle composite functions called the chain-rule.

We will work the quotient rule problem in part (b) from the simplification point.

Example 4 Compound Factions

(a) Find the derivative for $f(x) = \dfrac{1}{x^2}$

Substitute $f(x+h)$ and $f(x)$ $\qquad \dfrac{f(x+h) - f(x)}{h}$

Combine quotients, invert $\qquad = \dfrac{\dfrac{1}{(x+h)^2} - \dfrac{1}{x^2}}{h}$

Expand, Multiply $\qquad = \dfrac{1 \cdot x^2 - 1(x+h)^2}{x^2(x+h)^2} \cdot \dfrac{1}{h}$

Simplify $\qquad = \dfrac{x^2 - x^2 - 2xh - h^2}{x^2 h(x+h)^2}$

$\qquad = \dfrac{h(-2x-h)}{x^2 h(x+h)^2} = \dfrac{-2x-h}{x^2(x+h)^2}$

$$f'(x) = \lim_{h \to 0} \frac{-2x-h}{x^2(x+h)^2} = \frac{-2x-0}{x^2(x+0)^2} = \frac{-2x}{x^2 x^2} = \frac{-2}{x^3}$$

For simplifying the compound fraction we used method 1 to invert and multiply the rational expressions. To get the derivative, take the limit as h approaches 0 by substituting in 0 for h. With the exception of using x instead of a, this is the same procedure we used to find the tangent slope formula. Taking the derivative at a point is finding the slope of the tangent line at that point.

HP Prime Family Compound Factions – Part (a)

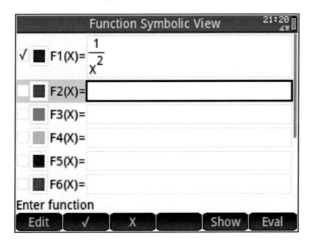

Press the **Symb** key to see the functions in the **Function Symbolic View** window. If necessary use the **Apps** key to select the **Function** app. Press the **Clear** key. To the message "Clear all Expressions?" press the soft **OK** key. Key in F1(X) as $1/X^2$. HP Prime Free users need to do this step as we will be using the function F1(X).

Begin by selecting the **CAS** key on the HP Prime. If the **CAS** view of the screenshot has computations, clear the **history** first. To clear the **history**, press the Clear key. HP Prime Free does not have the function **msec**. HP Prime Free will not do this screen. HP Prime Free could use the definition of secant line and built-in simplify function if they wished. This would actually be entry two above with numerator of entry two terms reversed.

Key in as shown. Press the **Toolbox** key to use **Toolbox > User > CalcSecTan > msec**. The program function **msec** uses the function **F1** from the **Function Symbolic View**. Press the soft **simplify** key to simplify the compound fraction. The **lim** command is located by pressing the **symbol template** key.

Begin by selecting the **CAS** key on the HP Prime. If the **CAS** view of the screenshot has computations, clear the **history** first. To clear the **history**, press the Clear key. HP Prime Free does not have the function **mtan**. HP Prime Free will do everything else that is shown on this screen.

HP Prime/ Pro/ Virtual Key in entry one as shown. Press the **Toolbox** key to use **Toolbox > User > CalcSecTan > mtan**. The program function **mtan** uses the function **F1** from the **Function Symbolic View**.

For shown entry two and three select the **derivative** template by pressing the **Symbolic Template** key. We need to use the lower case x. By looking at entry two result, uppercase X has 3 stored in it and we do not get the result we are looking for. For shown entry four **diff()** press the **Toolbox** key to use **Toolbox > CAS > Calculus > Differentiate**. Key in the F1(x). Press **Enter**.

In the command line key in F1'(x). We use a single quote to get the derivative. The single quote can follow the F1 as shown or be after the final parenthesis. To get the single quote press the ' ' key and delete the extra quote mark. Press **Enter** to see that it gives the same result. We cannot use the **apostrophe** that comes from **shift 9**.

In our work so far, we have used limits to manually find the derivative or the slope of the tangent line. Finding the derivative or the slope of the tangent line was done by using algebraic rules to obtain simpler functions from more complicated functions and then substituting in the value given by the limit formula.

The next manual step in Calculus is to use a set of rules to find the derivative for additional functions. We will do additional function's derivatives by the use of the product, quotient, and chain rules. This story will be left to a Calculus class with our algebra skills being vital to our success in Calculus.

The HP Prime CAS has a built-in derivative function that is uses to find derivatives for all functions. Notice in the above screen, that there are three built-in ways to find the derivative. The customized formula **mtan** would not be needed since we could use any of the three built-in forms for derivative.

Beside the single-variable Calculus we just talked about, the derivative template is the more general multiple-variable Calculus **partial derivative**. The Calculus menu **diff()** also can also be the more general multiple-variable by use of a second optional parameter.

However, knowing what values the derivative or the slope of the tangent line exist for and what values it does not exist requires that we begin our study of the derivative and the slope of the tangent line from the perspective of limits rather than use a set of rules or the HP Prime CAS's built-in derivative. Using CalSecTan library for the derivative's definition allowed us to use the limit definition.

In part (b) when we start with the result of the quotient rule. Using a rule such as the quotient rule puts us at a point in the study of calculus where basic differentiation rules are being established and the built-in HP Prime CAS derivative and a costumed second derivative functions can be used in the solution of problems. We will examine in part (b) how the HP Pfrime CAS built-in derivative and costumed second derivative functions can be used to add costumed functions to a new library, CalcSketch, that can help us work real world math problems.

The HP Prime Free will be able to work the problem by using the built-in functions and applying individual strategy to an individual solution. The HP Prime Free won't have the generalized solutions of the new CalcSketch library that allows us to work multiple problems efficiently.

(b) Simplify
$$\frac{(x^2-1)^{1/2}3x^2 - x^3\frac{1}{2}(x^2-1)^{-1/2}2x}{\left[(x^2-1)^{1/2}\right]^2}$$

Multiply by 1
$$\frac{(x^2-1)^{1/2}3x^2 - x^3\frac{1}{2}(x^2-1)^{-1/2}2x}{\left[(x^2-1)^{1/2}\right]^2}$$

Expand
$$= \frac{(x^2-1)^{1/2}3x^2 - \dfrac{x^4}{(x^2-1)^{1/2}}}{(x^2-1)} \cdot \frac{(x^2-1)^{1/2}}{(x^2-1)^{1/2}}$$

Simplify
$$= \frac{(x^2-1)\cdot 3x^2 - x^4}{(x^2-1)^{3/2}}$$

Factor
$$= \frac{3x^4 - 3x^2 - x^4}{(x^2-1)^{3/2}} = \frac{2x^4 - 3x^2}{(x^2-1)^{3/2}}$$

$$= \frac{x^2(2x^2-3)}{(x^2-1)^{3/2}}$$

The simplification of the compound fraction used method 2 of multiplying the fractional expression numerator and denominator by the least common multiple (lcm) of the fractional expression numerator and denominator. The remaining steps are simplification. As we will see next this is the solution to the derivative of $f(x)= x^3/\sqrt{(x^2 -1)}$.

HP Prime Family Compound Factions – Part (b)

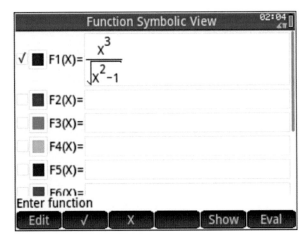

Note: For the HP Prime/ Pro/ Virtual illustration of part (b) we have added the CalcSketch library. Instructions for creating the CalcSketch library are given following the discussion of part (b). Add the CalcSketch library before proceeding..

Go to computerlearningservice.com/html/products.html to download the file

HP Prime Free will use individual commands instead of the CalcSketch library.

Press the **Apps** key. Highlight the **Function** icon on the Application Library screen. Press the soft **Start** key. Press the soft **Edit** key. The above screen will appear. Enter function as shown. Press the soft **OK**. To erase all functions press the **Clear** key. Both HP Prime/ Pro/ Virtual and HP Prime Free need to do this screen.

Let's look at the derivative of this function from **mtan** and the various forms of built-in HP Prime commands. Even though their initial results vary we can see that after the **factor** command that the various results it produced are all equivalent to the manual solution shown above.

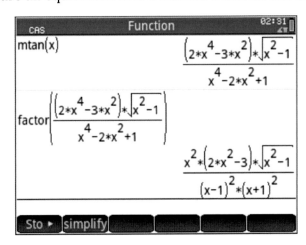

Note: The instructions for this screenshot assume that you have added the CalSecTan library to your HP Prime/ Pro/ Virtual device. Instructions for adding the CalSecTan library are given following this illustration. If you have not added the CalSecTan library, do so now.

Go to computerlearningservice.com/html/products.html to download the files.

Begin by selecting the **CAS** key on the HP Prime. If the **CAS** view of the screenshot has computations, clear the **history** first. To clear the **history**, press the **Clear** key. HP Prime Free does not have the function **mtan**. HP Prime Free will not do this screen.

HP Prime/ Pro/ Virtual Key in as shown. Press the **Toolbox** key to use **Toolbox > User > CalcSecTan > mtan**. The program function **mtan** uses the function **F1** from the **Function Symbolic View**.

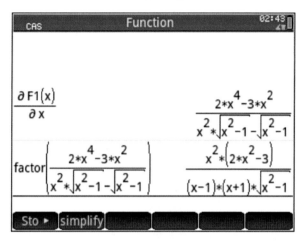

Begin by selecting the **CAS** key on the HP Prime. If the **CAS** view of the screenshot has computations, clear the **history** first. To clear the **history**, press the **Clear** key. Both HP Prime/ Pro/ Virtual and HP Prime Free need to do this screen.

Key in as shown. Use the **derivative** template by pressing the **Symbolic Template** key. Remember to use the lower case *x*. For **factor** press the **Toolbox** key to use **Toolbox > CAS > Algebra > Factor**.

We know from our earlier limit definition know that the derivative is only available where the limit exists. A misuse of the derivative would be to use it at places where the limit does not exist. This would apply to **mtan(x)** as well. The function and derivative do not exist between 0 and 1. Zero, one, and any value in-between cause complex results in the function and the derivative.

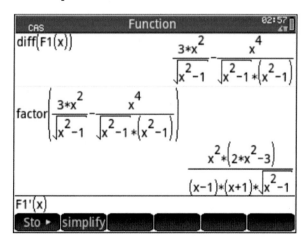

Begin by selecting the **CAS** key on the HP Prime. If the **CAS** view of the screenshot has computations, clear the **history** first. To clear the **history**, press the **Clear** key. Both HP Prime/ Pro/ Virtual and HP Prime Free need to do this screen.

For **diff()** press the **Toolbox** key to use **Toolbox > CAS > Calculus > Differentiate**. Key in the F1(x). Press **Enter**.

In the command line key in F1'(x). We use a single quote to get the derivative. The single quote can follow the F1 as shown or be after the final parenthesis. To get the single quote press the ' ' key and delete the extra quote mark. Press **Enter** to see that it gives the same result. We cannot use the **apostrophe** that comes from **shift 9**. The result is identical to **diff.**.

We next add the graph of CalcSketch library functions *incdec* and *concaveupddown* to our plot page. The updated Plot page screen is shown below. The functions *incdec* and *concaveupddown* are based on the first derivative and in *concaveupddown* case the second derivative as well. Remember that a misuse of the first derivative and second derivative would be to use it at places where the limit does not exist. Such a misuse of the first derivative's and second derivative's result or the results of a function that use the first derivative could result in unpredictable results.

A prime example of unpredictable results is the math field of catastrophe theory (Barunik). Stock market crashes may depend on internal forces, October 19, 1987 or external forces, September 11, 2001. Applying the catastrophe model to where the stock market had a sudden drop may better explain internal forces causing the 1987 crash where alternate models better explain the crash of 2001. Use a search engine to investigate more about catastrophe theory, its discovery, and its uses.

Applying the wrong model to a crash can lead us to erroneous results. In the same vein under the real number system we cannot use the HP Prime CAS original function, derivative operation, basic differentiation rules, or derived functions where the graph of the original function is discontinuous or the limit of the function does not exist.

We may in these situations be able to find a manual result or get a solution from our HP Prime CAS but in these cases the solution are erroneous or using complex number system results. Thus, there is the need for us to study discontinuities, limits and definitions, so that we do not attempt to use Algebra, Calculus, and HP Prime where it is not applicable.

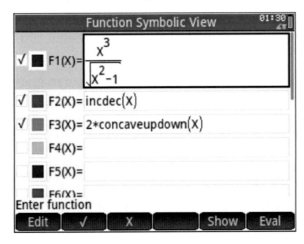

Note: The instructions for this screenshot assume that you have added the CalcSketch library on your HP Prime/ Pro/ Virtual device. Instructions for adding the Calc Sketch library are given following the discussion of part (b). If you have not added the CalcSketch library, do so now.

Go to computerlearningservice.com/html/products.html to download the file.

Press the **Symb** key to see the functions in the **Function Symbolic View** window. The above screen will appear. HP Prime Free does not have the function **incdec** or **concaveupdown**. HP Prime Free will not do this screen.

Prime/ Pro/ Virtual Key in as shown. Press the **Toolbox** key to use **Toolbox > User > CalcSketch** > **incdec** and **Toolbox > User > CalcSketch > concaveupdown**. Notice the capital X as the parameter in both functions. The program function **incdec** and **concaveupdown** uses the function **F1**. The function **incdec** assigns **F0** a value and the function **concaveupdown** assigns **F9** and **F0** a value that they use In their calculations. The values assigned to **F0** and **F9** are not graphed.

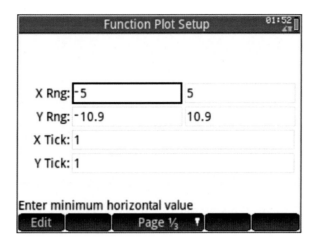

Press the Plot **Setup** key. Page 1/3, change to the default values X Rng: -15.9, 15.9; Y Rng: -10.9, 10.9. Page 2/3, check the Labels box. To set page 1/3 back to defaults press the **Clear** key. HP Prime Free will do this screen.

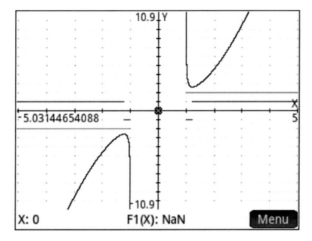

Press the **Plot** key to see a graph of the function. HP Prime Free does not have the red graph F2, **incdec**, or green graph F3, **2*concaveupdown**. HP Prime Free will do this screen. The HP Prime Free plot will only show the original blue graph, F1.

X	F1	F2	F3
-1.6	-3.27942459	1	-2
-1.5	-3.01869177	1	-2
-1.4	-2.80058327	1	-2
-1.3	-2.64487719	1	-2
-1.2	-2.60505802	-1	-2
-1.1	-2.90448012	-1	-2
-1	NaN	NaN	NaN
-0.9	NaN	NaN	NaN
-0.8	NaN	NaN	NaN
-0.7	NaN	NaN	NaN
-1.6			

Zoom   More   Go To   Defn

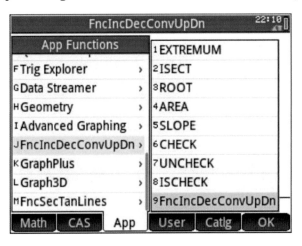

X	F1	F2	F3
0.7	NaN	NaN	NaN
0.8	NaN	NaN	NaN
0.9	NaN	NaN	NaN
1	NaN	NaN	NaN
1.1	2.90448012	-1	2
1.2	2.60505802	-1	2
1.3	2.64487719	1	2
1.4	2.80058327	1	2
1.5	3.01869177	1	2
1.6	3.27942459	1	2

Press the **Symb** key to see the functions in the <u>Function</u> **Symbolic View** window. Use **the directional pad**. The above screens will appear. **incdec**, or F3, **2*concaveupdown**. HP Prime Free does not have the functions F2 or F3. HP Prime Free will not do these screens.

The two above screens are data representations of the graphs.

We next look at our Library App <u>FcnIncDecConvUpDn</u> and GraphPlus draws the same results. We begin with the FcnIncDecConvUpDn app.

HP Prime/ Pro/ Virtual Graph of Tangent and Secant Line – FcnIncDecConvUpDn Library App

Note: The instructions for this screenshot assume that you have added the CalSketch library and FncIncDecConvUpDn Application Library to your HP Prime/ Pro/ Virtual device. Go to <u>CalSketch</u> for instructions on adding the required library. Go to <u>FncIncDecConvUpDn</u> for instructions on adding this Application Library.

Go to computerlearningservice.com/html/products.html to download the files.

Begin by selecting the **CAS** key or **HOME** key on the HP Prime. If the **CAS** view or **HOME** view of the screenshot has computations, clear the **history** first. To clear the **history**, press the **Clear** key. HP Prime Free does not have the Application Library **FncIncDecConvUpDn**. HP Prime Free will not do this screen.

Press the **Toolbox** key to use **Toolbox > App > FncIncDecConvUpDn**. Press **Enter** to transfer the result to the command line. Press **Enter** to execute the app from the command line (now shown).

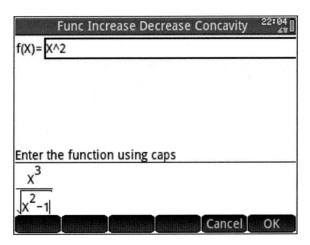

Key in the function as shown. Be sure to use capital X. Press the soft **Edit** key. Use **Esc** to clear the default function, x^2. Key in the new function, $x^3/\sqrt{(x^2-1)}$. Press **Enter** or soft **OK** key to update the field. Press **Enter** or soft **OK** key to see the plot.

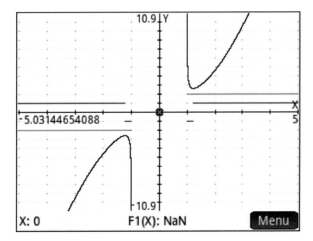

The graphs of the function, secant line, and tangent line are drawn with **FncIncDecConvUpDn** last Plot Settings.

We now look at the GraphPlus app.

HP Prime/ Pro/ Virtual Graph of Tangent and Secant Line – GraphPlus Library App

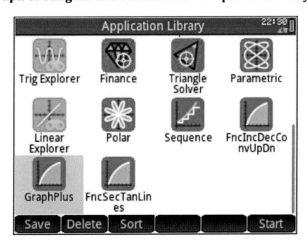

Note: The instructions for this screenshot assume that you have added the GraphPlus Application Library to your HP Prime/ Pro/ Virtual device. Go to GraphPlus for instructions on adding this Application Library.

Press the **Apps** key. Select the **GraphPlus** icon. Press the soft **Start** key.

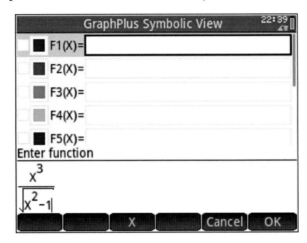

Key in the function as shown. Be sure to use capital X. Press the soft **Edit** key. Key in the function, $x^3/\sqrt{(x^2 -1)}$. Press **Enter** or soft **OK** key to update the field.

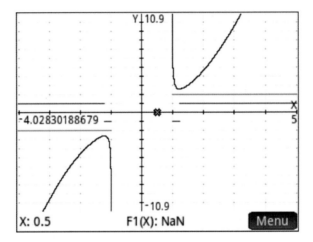

The graphs of the function, secant line, and tangent line are drawn with **GraphPlus** last Plot **Settings**.

We now look at how the CalcSketch library functions *incdec*(X) and *concaveupdwn*(X) help with interpreting a graph behavior but because of our earlier concerns about the first derivative and these functions being based on first derivative and second derivative respectively the possibility of errors or complex number system results exists. Therefore, their results need to be viewed with reservations. The same concerns would hold for GraphPlus Library Application internal local versions of *incdec*(x) and *concaveupdwn*(x).

Here we see a picture of the graph and two functions dealing with where the graph changes its behavior. Function F2 uses the sign of the first derivative to tell where the function is increasing or decreasing. Function F3 use double the sign of the second derivative to tell where the graph is concave up or concave down. We doubled the sign so that F3 would not overlay F2's graph.

Our function F1 is not defined over the closed interval from -1 to 1. Our CalcSketch library function *incdec*, F2, show a value of -1 over the closed interval $-\sqrt{6}/2$ to $\sqrt{6}/2$, approximately -1.22474 to 1.22474. These values are where the <u>local maximums and local minimums</u> occur. Our *incdec* function takes the sign of the first derivative. A result of -1 for a value of x indicates decreasing and a result of 1 indicates increasing. Nothing is shown over the closed interval from -1 to 1 since F1 is not defined over that interval and thus not continuous. The rest of the graph of F1 is correct. Later in our **CAS** view we find F1(0) to be 0. The **HOME** view gives the result 'Error: Invalid input" for F1(0). The **CAS** View result is the reservation we are talking about.

Remark: The check box for Complex is off in the HOME settings. Looks like from all our work so far that **CAS** view always allows Complex where **HOME** view only does with box checked.

The graph of our library function *concaveupdown*, F3, is correct over the entire interval.

For HP Prime/ Pro/ Virtual we now create the CalcSketch library. The library gives us functions for finding x-intercept of a function; possible maximums and minimums for a function; possible inflection points; an increasing and decreasing sign function for a function; and a concave down and concave up sign function for a function.

Note: HP Prime Free will want to read the listing explanation to see the code found in the functions and execute this code directly from the CAS command line.

The CalcSketch Library shown in the following two listing is © Larry Schroeder 2018. All rights reserved. We create a template with our HP Prime and replace the template's shell with the Notepad++ contents.

The amount of code makes it better to create the program using a text editor. See the previous notes on this.

HP Prime/ Pro/ Virtual Creating the CalcSketch Library

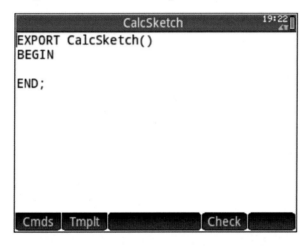

The HP Prime Free does not have the programming function. The HP Prime will not do this screen.

On our HP Prime/ Pro/ Virtual press the **Program** key. Next, press the **New** soft key. Type in **CalcSketch** to the **Name**: field. Leave the **CAS**: field unchecked. Press the **OK** soft key twice. Leave the template **CalcSketch** program blank.

Go to computerlearningservice.com/html/products.html to download the file.

Shown next is the Notepad++ with the HP PPl plug-in listing of the first 25 lines of the library CalcSketch, The remaining 23 lines of the CalcSketch Library are shown following the explanation of the first 25 lines

```
1    CalcSketch;
2
3    xintcpt();
4    minmax();
5    inflpt();
6    incdec();
7    concaveupdown();
8
9    EXPORT xintcpt()
10   BEGIN
11    LOCAL a,b,c,d;
12    d:=F1;
13    a:=d+"="+"0";
14    b:="X";
15    c:=CAS.solve(EVAL(a),EVAL(b));
16   END;
17
18   EXPORT minmax()
19   BEGIN
20    LOCAL a,b,c,d;
21    d:=CAS.diff(F1(X));
22    a:=d+"="+"0";
23    b:="X";
24    c:=CAS.solve(EVAL(a),EVAL(b));
25   END;
```

From the Notepad++ select all and copy. This will copy the complete listing. That is both the above and next listing into the windows clipboard.

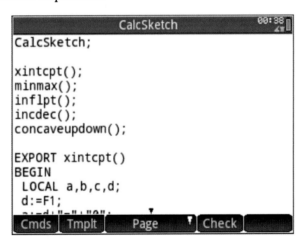

The HP Prime Free does not have the programming function. The HP Prime will not do this screen.

With the **CalcSketch** template showing, press the **Copy** key on the HP Prime. Press the soft key **All**, followed by pressing the soft key **Cut**. Use the paste function of the HP Prime Pro or HP Prime Virtual Calculator to paste from the system clipboard the listing from Notepad++. Scroll to the top. At this point, we will see the above screen. Press the **Check** soft key. Press **OK** soft key to message "No errors in the program".

As we mentioned with Key_user scientific notation and CalcSecTan application libraries, the process of creating CalcSketch is more involved than our earlier programs in first section of the book. But once we get our update/ debugged code into the template, the execution is no different than the one-line functions and our program library one-line functions. Returning to the **HOME** view or **CAS** view command line means that the program library syntax is correct. That the functions are compiled and ready to be executed/ tested.

Now let's look at the explanation of the code in the first listing.

With the function **xintcpt** we are using <u>CAS solve</u>(F1(X)=0,X) from either the **HOME** view or **CAS** view. This requires us to use local variables, string parameters for the solve, capital letter X, and the Eval function with each parameter. See lines 13-15 in the above listing. HP Prime Free could find possible x-intercepts from the command line of the **CAS** view by keying in solve(F1(x)=0,x). Note the lower case x.

With the function **minmax** we are using <u>CAS solve</u>(diff(F1(X))=0,X) from either the **HOME** view or **CAS** view. This requires us to use local variables, string parameters for the solve, capital letter X, and the Eval function with each parameter. See lines 21-24 in the above listing. HP Prime Free could find possible maximums and minimums from the command line of the **CAS** view by keying in solve(diff(F1(x))=0,x). Note the lower case x.

```
27    EXPORT inflpt()
28    BEGIN
29     LOCAL a,b,c,d;
30     d:=CAS.diff(CAS.diff(F1(X)));
31     a:=d+"="+"0";
32     b:="X";
33     c:=CAS.solve(EVAL(a),EVAL(b));
34    END;
35
36    EXPORT incdec(x)
37    BEGIN
38     LOCAL c;
39     F0:=CAS.diff(F1(X));
40     c:=SIGN(F0(x));
41    END;
42
43    EXPORT concaveupdown(x)
44    BEGIN
45     LOCAL c;
46     F9:=CAS.diff(F1(X));
47     F0:=CAS.diff(F9);
48     c:=SIGN(F0(x));
49    END;
```

Shown is the final 23 lines of the CalcSketch library. Let's take a look at this listing explanations.

With the function **inflpt** we are using <u>CAS solve</u>(diff(diff(F1(X)))=0,X) from either the **HOME** view or **CAS** view. This requires us to use local variables, string parameters for the solve, capital letter X, and the Eval function with each parameter. See lines 31-33 in the above listing. HP Prime Free could find possible inflection points from the command line of the **CAS** view by keying in solve(diff(diff(F1(x)))=0,x). Note the lower case x.

The function **incdec** returns a 1 when the function is increasing and -1 when the function is decreasing. HP Prime Free will need to use maximums and minimums plus the graph of the function F1 to decide whether increasing or decreasing.

The function **concaveupdown** returns a 1 when the function is concaved up and -1 when the function is concaved down. HP Prime Free will need to use maximums, minimums, and inflection points plus the graph of the function F1 to decide whether concave up or concave down.

The last two functions, *incdec*(*x*) and *concaveupdwn*(*x*), need *x* as a parameter. The first three functions, *xincpt*(), *minmax*(), and *inflpt*() have no parameters.

The functions *xincpt*(), the *x*-I ntercept of F1(*x*); *minmax*(), the *x*-value for type I candidates for local minimums and maximums of F1(*x*); *inflpt*(), the *x*-value for type I candidates for inflection points of F1(*x*); *incdec*(*x*), places where the function F1(*x*) is increasing or decreasing, with 1 designating increasing and -1 decreasing; and *concaveupdwn*(*x*), places where the function F1(*x*) is concave up or concave down, with 1 designating concave down and -1 concave up.

Note: We need to note two facts. The maximums, minimums, and inflection points are candidates to be maximums, minimums, and inflection points. It does not mean that they will actually turn out to be maximums, minimums, and inflection points. The functions we created are for Type 1 maximums, minimums, and inflection points. We did not cover Type 2 maximums, minimums, and inflection points.

At this point we can return to the HP Prime Family Compound Fractions – Part (b) screenshot.

We next continue on by using some of our additional functions with our function $f1(x) = x^3/\sqrt{(x^2 - 1)}$ that was defined in the Graph page editor.

HP Prime/ Pro/ Virtual CalcSketch Library Functions except F1

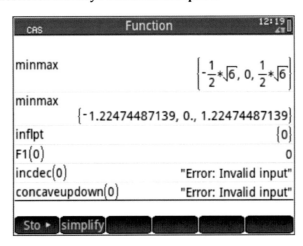

Begin by selecting the **CAS** key on the HP Prime. If the **CAS** view of the screenshot has computations, clear the **history** first. To clear the **history**, press the **Clear** key. HP Prime Free only entry four.

The HP Prime free will only do **F1(0)**. The HP Prime Free will does not have any of the other functions on this screen.

HP Prime/ Pro/ Virtual key in the above functions as shown. For **minmax** press the **Toolbox** key to use **Toolbox > User > CalcSketch > minmax**. For **inflpt** press the **Toolbox** key to use **Toolbox > User > CalcSketch > inflpt**. . For **incder()** press the **Toolbox** key to use **Toolbox > User > CalcSketch > indec**. For **concaveupdown()** press the **Toolbox** key to use **Toolbox > User > CalcSketch > concaveupdown**.

Notice the **CAS** view extraneous **minmax**, **inflpt**, and **F1(0)** solutions of 0. However, **incdec(0)** and **concaveupdown(0)** correctly display an error message.

Next we look at using the built-in CAS's **solve** and **diff** to do **xintcpt**, **minmax**, and **inflpt**. This is the technique that we use for the HP Prime Free to calculate the x-intercept, possible maximums and minimums, and possible inflection points.

Begin by selecting the **CAS** key on the HP Prime. If the **CAS** view of the screenshot has computations, clear the **history** first. To clear the **history**, press the Clear key.

The HP Prime free will only do entry one, two, and three. The HP Prime Free will does not have the last three functions on this screen. For **solve** press the **Toolbox** key to use **Toolbox > CAS > Solve > Solve**. For **diff** press the **Toolbox** key to use **Toolbox > CAS > Calculus > Differentiate**.

HP Prime/ Pro/ Virtual key in the above as shown. For the first three entries follow the HP Prime Free instructins. For **xintcpt** press the **Toolbox** key to use **Toolbox > User > CalcSketch** > **xintcpt**. For **minmax** press the **Toolbox** key to use **Toolbox > User > CalcSketch** > **minmax**. For **inflpt** press the **Toolbox** key to use **Toolbox > User > CalcSketch** > **inflpt**.

Notice the **CAS** view extraneous entry one, two, and three solutions of 0. The use of the built-in functions can produce extraneous solutions as well.

The last three entries are the generalized versions of the first three entries. For example, entry one in the above screen is replaced by lines 11-15 of **xintcpt** in CalcSketch's listing. This allow the code to work from **Run** soft key of **Program Catalog**, **HOME** view, and **CAS** view. The HP Prime Free will need to use the non-generalized entry one, two, and three for each F1 that we use.

Begin by selecting the **HOME** key on the HP Prime. Select the **Menu** key. Select the **Get from CAS** entry. Select the each entry using the soft **OK** key. Press **Enter**. Use the approx key for the second entry. With non-CAS, **HOME** view, it correctly displayed **F1(0)** answer as "Error: Invalid input".

Notice the **HOME** view extraneous **minmax** and **inflpt** solutions of 0. However, **F1(0)**, **incdec(0)**, and **concaveupdown(0)** correctly display an error message.

We see that **minmax** and **inflpt** can be run from the **HOME** view as well. This would also be true for **xintcpt**.

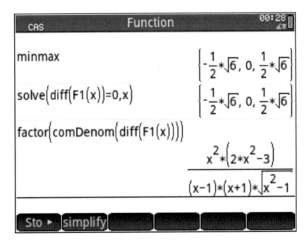

Begin by selecting the **CAS** key on the HP Prime. If the **CAS** view of the screenshot has computations, clear the **history** first. To clear the **history**, press the Clear key. Both HP Prime/ Pro/ Virtual and HP Prime Free need to do this screen.

For **with** press the **Symbol Template**. Key in the command line. Press **Enter**. The result is 0. The HP Prime **CAS** view is likely calculating extraneous answer using the Complex number system coming up with 0 for its result. The HOME view is set not to use complex numbers, thus error for **F1(0).**

Begin by selecting the **CAS** key on the HP Prime. If the **CAS** view of the screenshot has computations, clear the **history** first. To clear the **history**, press the Clear key. Both HP Prime/ Pro/ Virtual and HP Prime Free need to do this screen.

The HP Prime Free will skip entry one. The HP Prime/ Pro/ Virtual will key in **minmax**. For **minmax** press the **Toolbox** key to use **Toolbox > User > CalcSketch > minmax**.

Both HP Prime/ Pro/ Virtual and HP Prime Free will key in entry two and entry three. For **solve** press the **Toolbox** key to use **Toolbox > CAS > Solve > Solve**. For **diff** press the **Toolbox** key to use **Toolbox > CAS > Calculus > Differentiate**. For **factor** press the **Toolbox** key to use **Toolbox > CAS > Algebra > Factor**. For **comDenom** press the **Toolbox** key to use **Toolbox > Catlg > comDenom**.

Now we will use *minmax()* and *solve(equation,var)* to find the *x*-value of the candidates for minimums and maximums. Notice the extraneous solutions in these functions as well. Testing the type I candidates, finding type II candidates and testing them will be covered in our later tutorials. For now we can use graph of the function to see that the local maximum occurs at -√6/2 is and local minimum occurs at √6/2 with the *x*-value of 0 being an erroneous candidate for a minimum or maximum.

The last entry in the screenshot is the result of using the built-in function *diff(f(x))*. The result displayed is the first derivative of the stored function, *f1(x)* = $x^3/\sqrt{(x^2 - 1)}$. This is the equivalent result we get by using the quotient rule to manually work the problem.

The first entry in the screenshot is the result of the library function *minmax()*. The second entry in the screenshot is the result of the built-in function *solve(equation,var)*.

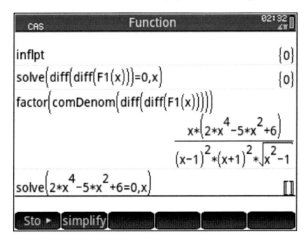

Begin by selecting the **CAS** key on the HP Prime. If the **CAS** view of the screenshot has computations, clear the **history** first. To clear the **history**, press the **Clear** key. Both HP Prime/ Pro/ Virtual and HP Prime Free need to do this screen.

The HP Prime Free will skip entry one. The HP Prime/ Pro/ Virtual will key in **inflpt**. For **inflpt** press the **Toolbox** key to use **Toolbox > User > CalcSketch > inflpt**.

Both HP Prime/ Pro/ Virtual and HP Prime Free will key in entry two, three, and four. For **solve** press the **Toolbox** key to use **Toolbox > CAS > Solve > Solve**. For **diff** press the **Toolbox** key to use **Toolbox > CAS > Calculus > Differentiate**. For **factor** press the **Toolbox** key to use **Toolbox > CAS > Algebra > Factor**. For **comDenom** press the **Toolbox** key to use **Toolbox > Catlg > comDenom**.

Now we will use *inflpt()* and *solve(equation,var)* to find the *x*-value of the candidates for inflections points. Notice the extraneous solutions in these functions as well. Testing the type I candidates, finding type II candidates and testing them will be covered in our later tutorials. Testing the type I candidates, finding type II candidates and testing them will be covered in our later tutorials.

Looking at the first entry and second entry in the previous screenshot bothered us. The function $f1(x)= x^3/\sqrt{(x^2 - 1)}$ is undefined from -1 to 1. The library function *inflpt()* was giving an *x*-value of 0 as a type I candidate for the function changing its concavity. The library function *inflpt()* sets the second derivative equal to zero and solves for *x*. The same for our built-in entry two solution.

By looking at the nested functions of factor, comDenom, and second derivative we see the second derivative as a rational function. Multiplying both side of the rational function by the denominator and setting the resulting numerator to 0 has $x = 0$ as a solution. Since there are no real solutions for the fourth degree polynomial's factor, $x = 0$ is the only solution for the *inflpt()* function.

The original function denominator's restriction of *x* between -1 and 1 does not allow the second derivative at x = 0. Thus the need for us to examine *inflpt()*'s results and the recognize the erroneous *x*-value of 0.

The last tool we like to use when analyzing a graph behavior is the Table of *x*-values. We have one Table page for x-values, functional values, increasing/decreasing values, and concave up/concave down values. We will use the Function Num Setup to set Num Type to Build Your Own.

```
┌─────────────────────────────────────────────┐
│            Function Num Setup        05:18    │
│                                               │
│  Num Start: ┌0.7─────────────────────────┐    │
│             └────────────────────────────┘    │
│  Num Step: 0.1                                │
│                                               │
│                                               │
│  Num Zoom: 2                                  │
│                                               │
│                                               │
│  Num Type: BuildYourOwn              ▼        │
│                                               │
│                                               │
│ Enter table start value                       │
│ ┌Edit─┐ ┌───┐ ┌───┐ ┌───┐ ┌Plot→┐ ┌───┐      │
└─────────────────────────────────────────────┘
```

Press the Num **Setup** key. If necessary, change Num Type: BuildYourOwn. HP Prime Free should do this screen. To set page back to defaults press the **Clear** key.

X	F1	F2	F3
-1.3	-2.64487719	1	-2
-1.22474	-2.59807621	1	-2
-1.2	-2.60505802	-1	-2
-0.99	NaN	NaN	NaN
0	NaN	NaN	NaN
0.99	NaN	NaN	NaN
1.2	2.60505802	-1	2
1.224745	2.59807621	1	2
1.3	2.64487719	1	2
-1.3			

Function Numeric View — 10:55 — Edit | More | Sort | Defn

Press the **Symb** key to see the functions in the **Function Symbolic View** window. Use **the directional pad**. The above screen will appear. **incdec**, or F3, **2*concaveupdown**. HP Prime Free does not have the functions F2 or F3. HP Prime Free will not do columns F2 and F3. The HP Prime Free does not have the **incdec** and **concaveupdown** functions.

We take a look at the functions in a table. This is from the Function Numeric View. The approximate entries two and eight deal with the minimum and maximum. If they were exact values, they should have no sign. The value for the inflection points of 0 from the **CAS** view is erroneous. The table correctly labels it as NaN. We can see from column F3 that the concavity changed following the undefined section of the function, F1.

The table has the same information as given in the graph but for discrete values of x. When it it hard to see the behavior because of resolution and scale issues with the Plot page, using discrete values can be very helpful

We have one Table page for the x-value, function value, increasing/decreasing value, and concave up/concave down value. Our function $f1(x)$ has Type I critical values that we can use for entry two and eight that deal with deal with the relative maximum and minimum. What we normally do in Calculus is come up with neighborhoods based on Type I and Type II critical values and discontinuities. We then pick a representative point for each neighborhood. Since at this point we only wanted to go over the concept we listed both the increasing/decreasing and concave up/concave down function columns with the x-values for the increasing decreasing type Table. In later tutorials we go over how we make and use the two tables. Our only other comment is to repeat what we said earlier, that tables and our one-line functions on Calculator pages are often necessary to come up with results that our HP Prime graph's scale may have a hard time showing or zooming in on.

Exercise 4 Compound Factions

(a) Find the derivative for $f(x)=\dfrac{5}{x}$

(b) Simplify $\dfrac{x^3\frac{1}{2}(4x^2-1)^{-1/2}8x-(4x^2-1)^{1/2}3x^2}{(x^3)^2}$

<u>Solution</u> >>

Apartment Complex Revenue

An owner of 80-unit student apartment complex charges $500 rent per month for each of the units. The owner notices that on the average for each $10 increase that one student will leave and their unit will remain vacant. With all the units full the revenue is 80 x $500 or $40,000. With one vacant it is 79 x $510 or $40,290. For 5 vacant it would be 75 x 550 or $41,250. What would be the maximum revenue? How many would be vacant? What would the rent be for each unit?

Depending on what tools are available to us there are several ways that we can solve this problem. The first method would be to use arithmetic and list the possible revenue for each number of vacancies until we reached the maximum. We could see that after the maximum revenue was reached that the total revenue from additional vacancies would result in less revenue.

Using algebra, after setting up the first few results using the arithmetic model, we could see that if we multiplied the number of rentals, 80 – x, by the rent, 500 + 10x, with x being the number of vacancies we could come up with a formula for the revenue, $R(x) = (80 – x)(500 + 10x)$. Expanding we get $R(x) = -10x^2 + 300x + 40000$. Noticing that this is a parabola we could use complete the square to come up with $R(x) = -10(x – 15)^2 + 42250$. The technique of completing the square will be covered in later tutorials. From the complete the square version of the formula we can see that 15 vacancies will generate $42,250. Then using 500 + 10x with x being 15 we get that the rent would be $650.

The third method would be to use calculus. Here we would use limit theory for differentiation or if past the point of using limits for differentiation we would use the basic differentiation rules and chain-rule to manually differentiate the function. For our function, $R(x) = -10x^2 + 300x + 40000$, we come up with the derivative being $R'(x) = -20x + 300$. Since this is also the equation for finding the slope of the tangent line, we know that at the function maximum or minimum the slope of the tangent line is zero, 0. Setting the derivative, -20x + 300, equal to zero, 0, and solving for x we get 15.

Using our original formula with x equal to 15 we have, $R(15) = [80 – 15][500 + 10(15)] = 42,250$. Looking at the factors and their product, we see that 15 vacancies result in 65 units having a rent of $650 producing $42,250 in revenue. Using the limit definition of the derivative is shown next. Following the limit definition we show how to use our HP Prime CAS and CalcSecTan and CalcSketch calculus libraries functions to work the problem.

Find the derivative for $f(x) = -10x^2 + 300x + 40000$

Substitute $f(x+h)$ and $f(x)$ $\dfrac{f(x+h) - f(x)}{h}$

$$= \frac{f(x+h)}{h} - \frac{f(x)}{h}$$

Expand $\quad = \dfrac{-10(x+h)^2 + 300(x+h) + 40000}{h}$

$$-\frac{-10x^2 + 300x + 40000}{h}$$

Combine $\quad = \dfrac{-10x^2 - 20xh - 10h^2 + 300x + 300h}{h}$

$$+\frac{40000}{h} + \frac{10x^2 - 300x - 40000}{h}$$

Simplify $\quad = \dfrac{-20xh - 10h^2 + 300h}{h}$

$$= -20x - 10h + 300$$

$$f'(x) = \lim_{h \to 0} -20x - 10h + 300 = -20x + 300$$

Due to the length of some of the calculation we split the limit's formula into terms.

HP Prime Family Apartment Complex Revenue

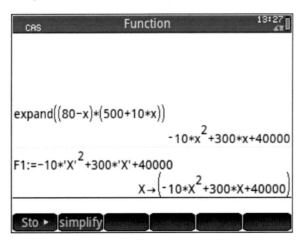

Begin by selecting the **CAS** key on the HP Prime. If the **CAS** view of the screenshot has computations, clear the **history** first. To clear the **history**, press the **Clear** key. Both HP Prime/ Pro/ Virtual and HP Prime Free need to do this screen.

Key in as shown. For **expand** press the **Toolbox** key to use **Toolbox > CAS > Algebra > Expand**. Note the use of the literal capital X in entry two. The single quotes and capital X are necessary for us to enter function F1 into the Function App when using **CAS** view. Lower case does not work for the Function App plus using capital X without quotes will produce a result using the value of capital X rather than its equation.

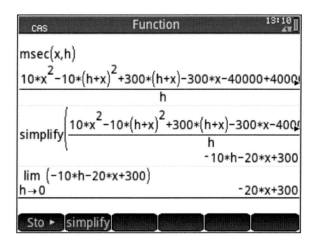

Begin by selecting the **CAS** key on the HP Prime. If the **CAS** view of the screenshot has computations, clear the **history** first. To clear the **history**, press the **Clear** key. HP Prime Free does not have the function **msec**. HP Prime Free will not do this screen.

The HP Prime/ Pro/ Virtual will key in **msec(**x,h**)**. For **msec** press the **Toolbox** key to use **Toolbox > User > CalcSecTan > msec**.

Key in entries two and three. Use the soft **simplify** key. The **lim** command is located by pressing the **symbol template** key.

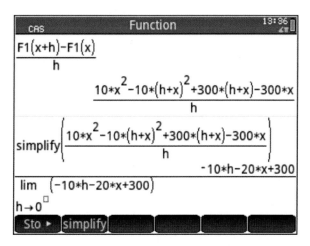

Begin by selecting the **CAS** key on the HP Prime. If the **CAS** view of the screenshot has computations, clear the **history** first. To clear the **history**, press the **Clear** key. Both HP Prime/ Pro/ Virtual and HP Prime Free need to do this screen.

Key in the entries as shown. Key in the command line. Press **Enter**. The **lim** command is located by pressing the **symbol template** key.

This is the technique that the HP Prime Free uses as it does not have **msec**. The first and second entries uses HP Prime calculations to do limit h-> 0 definition of derivative. The HP Prime/ Pro/ Virtual could skip this screen.

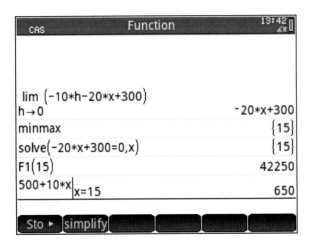

Continuing (after pressing **Enter** to the previous screen, we deleted history area before **lim** h-> 0). Both HP Prime/ Pro/ Virtual and HP Prime Free need to do this screen.

The HP Prime Free will skip screen's entry two. For entry two, the HP Prime/ Pro/ Virtual will key in **minmax**. For **minmax** press the **Toolbox** key to use **Toolbox > User > CalcSketch > minmax**.

Both HP Prime/ Pro/ Virtual and HP Prime Free will key in the remaining entries. For **solve** press the **Toolbox** key to use **Toolbox > CAS > Solve > Solve** The **with** command is located by pressing the **symbol template** key.

Entry three is the technique the HP Prime Free uses as is does not have **minmax**. The HP Prime/ Pro/ Virtual would skip entry two.

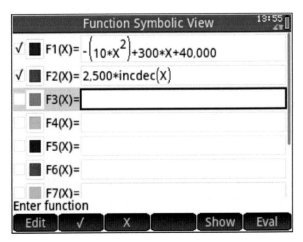

Note: If previous expressions are in F2 and above, use the soft **Edit** key to delete the entry's expression. Press the **Esc** to delete the expression in the edit command line. Press the soft **OK** key to exit the edit command line. Entry one's function F1 has extra parenthesis that were added when we use the CAS view to define it. It emphasis that we are taking the opposite. They are not necessary but will not hurt either.

Press the **Symb** key to see the functions in the **Function Symbolic View** window. The above screen without entry 2 will appear. HP Prime Free does not have the function **incdec**. HP Prime Free will leave entry two blank. The HP Prime Free is done since entry one already has a value.

Prime/ Pro/ Virtual Key in entry two as shown. Press the **Toolbox** key to use **Toolbox > User > CalcSketch > incdec**. Notice the capital X as the parameter in the function. The program function **incdec** uses the function **F1**. The function **incdec** assigns **F0** a value that it uses In its calculations. The values assigned to **F0** are not graphed.

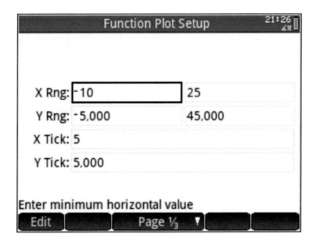

Press the Plot **Setup** key. Page 1/3, change to the default values X Rng: -10, 25; Y Rng: -5000, 45000; X Tick: 5; Y Tick: 5000. Page 2/3, check the Labels box. To set page 1/3 back to defaults press the **Clear** key. HP Prime Free should do this screen.

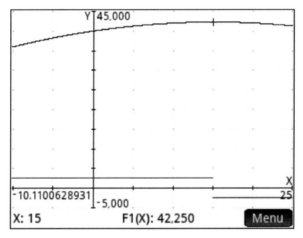

Press the **Plot** key to see a graph of the function. HP Prime Free does not have the red graph F2, **incdec**. HP Prime Free will do this screen. The HP Prime Free plot will only show the original blue graph, F1. We keyed in 15 to set trace to the maximum of 42,250.

We next look at our Library App <u>FcnIncDecConvUpDn</u> and GraphPlus draws the same results. We begin with the FcnIncDecConvUpDn app.

HP Prime/ Pro/ Virtual FcnIncDecConvUpDn Apartment Complex Revenue

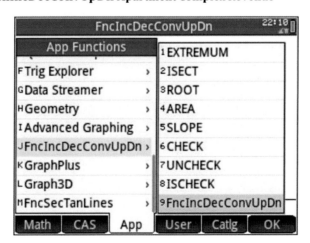

Note: The instructions for this screenshot assume that you have added the CalSketch library and FncIncDecConvUpDn Application Library to your HP Prime/ Pro/ Virtual device. Go to CalSketch for instructions on adding the required library. Go to FncIncDecConvUpDn for instructions on adding this Application Library.

Go to computerlearningservice.com/html/products.html to download the files.

Begin by selecting the **CAS** key or **HOME** key on the HP Prime. If the **CAS** view or **HOME** view of the screenshot has computations, clear the **history** first. To clear the **history**, press the Clear key. HP Prime Free does not have the Application Library **FncIncDecConvUpDn**. HP Prime Free will not do this screen.

Press the **Toolbox** key to use **Toolbox > App > FncIncDecConvUpDn**. Press **Enter** to transfer the result to the command line. Press **Enter** to execute the app from the command line (now shown).

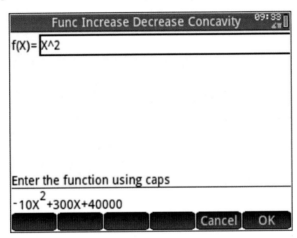

Key in the function as shown. Be sure to use capital X. Press the soft **Edit** key. Use **Esc** to clear the default function, x^2. Key in the new function, $-10X^2+30X+40000$. Notice the Capital X and implied multiplication. Press **Enter** or soft **OK** key to update the field. Press **Enter** or soft **OK** key to see the plot. HP Prime Free will not do this screen.

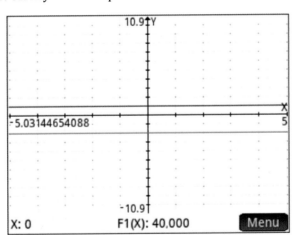

The graphs of the function, secant line, and tangent line are drawn with **FncIncDecConvUpDn** last Plot Settings. The graph of F1 is off the screen. As by examining the screen, last setting is not good. The X-value for the maximum is not on the screen. HP Prime Free will not do this screen.

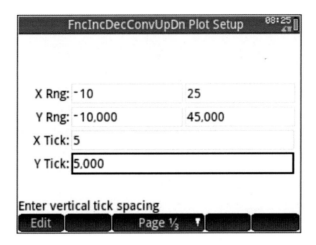

Press the Plot **Setup** key. Page 1/3, change to the default values X Rng: -10, 25; Y Rng: -5000, 45000; X Tick: 5; Y Tick: 5000. Page 2/3, check the Labels box. To set page 1/3 back to defaults press the **Clear** key. HP Prime Free should do this screen.

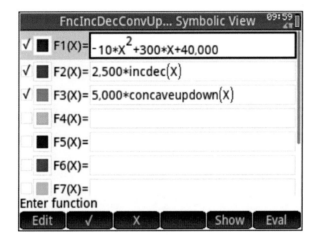

Note: Previous expressions are in F1 and above, use the soft **Edit** key to edit entry two and entry three. Press the soft **OK** key to exit the edit command line.

Press the **Symb** key to see the functions in the **Function Symbolic View** window. The above screen without entry 2 will appear. HP Prime Free will not do this screen.

Prime/ Pro/ Virtual Key edit entry two and entry three to the expressions shown.

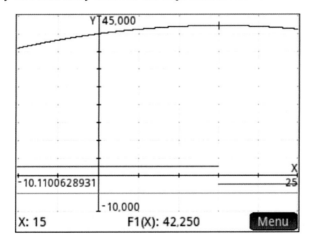

Press the **Plot** key to see a graph of the function. HP The red graph is F2, 2500***incdec**. The green graph is F3,5000***concaveupdown**. F3 is a horizontal line located right above the soft **Menu** key. We keyed in 15 to set trace to the maximum of 42,250. HP Prime Free will not do this screen.

We now look at the GraphPlus app. We will see that it cannot be used to show the graph of the functions with the graph of the increasing/decreasing and concavity functions. However, we can still use it to indicate the maximum value and point to where the maximum value is located. We can use the increasing/decreasing and concavity functions to determine that the maximum value is an absolute maximum for the function.

HP Prime/ Pro/ Virtual Graph Plus Apartment Complex Revenue

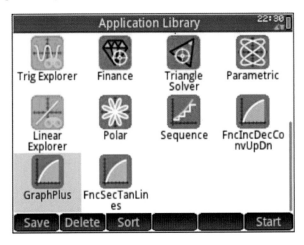

Note: The instructions for this screenshot assume that you have added the GraphPlus Application Library to your HP Prime/ Pro/ Virtual device. Go to GraphPlus for instructions on adding this Application Library.

Go to computerlearningservice.com/html/products.html to download the file.

Press the **Apps** key. Select the **GraphPlus** icon. Press the soft **Start** key.

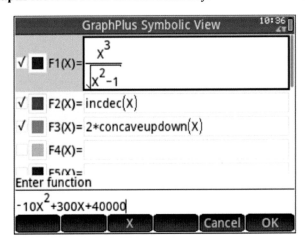

Key in the function as shown. Be sure to use capital X. Press the soft **Edit** key. Key in the function, -10X^2+300x+4000. Press **Enter** or soft **OK** key to update the field. F2 and F3 have our expression in it from a previous use of GraphPlus. Press the **Plot** key. Any value in F2 and F3 will be overwritten with index(X) and 2*concaveupdown(X). We could use the **View** key to reset the App's functions by clearing all functions before we started. As we see in the next screen explanation **View** key reset will not help. HP Prime Free will not do this screen.

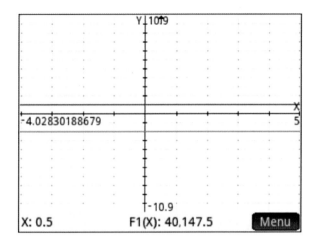

The graphs of the function, secant line, and tangent line are drawn with **GraphPlus** last Plot Settings. As by examining the screen, the last setting is not good. We will change the Plot Settings to help with calculus first and second derivative test but we will not redo the Symb F2 anF3. When we press the Plot key F2 and F3 will be overwritten with index(X) and 2*concaveupdown(X). There is no way to get the 2500*index(X) and 5000*concaveupdown(X) that we need to display the functions F1, F2, and F3 on the same screen. We can still use the app to see if the function's type I critical value is a maximum, minimum, or neither.

The best solution for the Y's range issue of index(X) and 2*concaveupdown(X) being too small is to use the **FncIncDecConvUpDn** Library Application. The **FncIncDecConvUpDn** Library Application was the previous illustration. It allowed us to change F2 and F3 values. HP Prime Free will not do this screen.

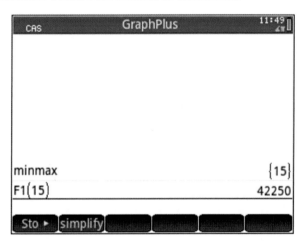

Begin by selecting the **CAS** key on the HP Prime. If the **CAS** view of the screenshot has computations, clear the **history** first. To clear the **history**, press the Clear key. Notice the screen title of GraphPlus.

The HP Prime/ Pro/ Virtual will key in **minmax**. For **minmax** press the **Toolbox** key to use **Toolbox > User > CalcSketch > minmax**. Next key in F1(15). Be sure to use a capital F for F1. HP Prime Free will not do this screen.

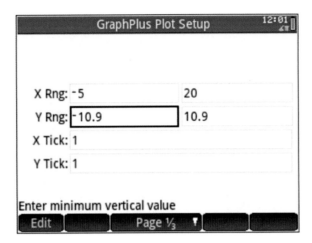

Press the Plot **Setup** key. Page 1/3, change to the default values X Rng: -5, 20; Y Rng: -10.9, 10.9; X Tick: 1; Y Tick: 1. Page 2/3, check the Labels box. To set page 1/3 back to defaults press the **Clear** key. HP Prime Free should do this screen.

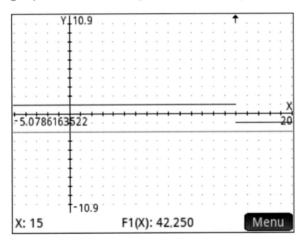

Press the **Plot** key to see a graph of F2 and F3. HP The red graph is F2, **incdec**. The green graph is **concaveupdown**. Because of Y's range the graph of F1 is not shown. Key in 15. See the point (15, 42250) to the left of the soft **Menu** key. Also notice arrow at top op screen indicating this value is above what the screen is showing. HP Prime Free will not do this screen.

The red line, F2, can be used in calculus as the first derivative test. Increasing followed by decreasing, therefore relative maximum. The green line, F3, can be used in calculus as the second derivative test. Negative at F(15),therefore relative maximum. Since to the right of the critical value the function is always increasing and to the left of the critical value the function is always decreasing the relative maximum is an absolute maximum.

We need an appropriate multiplier in order to display our function and our *incdec*(x) function. For the multiplier we picked 2500. We see from all three of the graphs that the function is increasing up to 15 and decreasing after 15. This behavior verifies what we see from the function's graph that an x value of 15 produces a maximum. The maximum revenue of \$42,250, the rent cost of \$650 per unit, with 15 vacancies is shown in the Calculator Scratchpad screenshot.

Final Remark: Be careful using the black box approach with HP Prime CAS built-in functions plus our added library functions to solve problems. We need to add any manual warnings for result shown that could have problems. If we do not know what is actually happening in the box, we can misuse the built-in and our created functions in situations where they do not apply.

In this tutorial we pointed out warnings and how using our HP Prime CAS in these situations can produce erroneous answers. We discussed working the solutions manually as well as with the HP

Prime's **HOME** view and HP Prime's **CAS** view. This way we get an understanding of what is happening and places to look where we can use our tools and places where they fail us.

At this point a function like *minmax*() in our CalcSketch library is not close to being a complete solution. It only includes the *x*-value for Type I candidates and has no ability to find the *x*-value for Type II candidates. It may produce *x*-values candidates that are not in the domain of our function and need to be manually dropped. The Type I *x*-value results it produces are only candidates, they might turn out not even to get elected, that is, be actual minimums or maximums. In our future tutorials or in online and textbook explanations, the understanding that comes from working with the underlying math will help you know how and where to use these black boxes or tools correctly and how to questions there results.

With all that said, *minmax*() is extremely useful now. Function, or kind or functions, does not matter to it. It will come up with the *x*-values for Type I candidates and or possible erroneous *x*-values for Type I candidates. In the case of the previous problem, for the polynomial function *F1*, *minmax*() we do not need to add any warning, therefore no erroneous *x*-valueType I candidates. With us using the CalcSketch library function, *incdec*(), as *F2* in the Function App we were able to verify that the candidate *minmax*() gave us an *x*-value of 15 that produced a maximum of *f1*(15) or \$42,250.

We hope you find this and our future tutorials useful. We have tried our best to be accurate and give you a useful tutorial that helps you increase your math competence. In a work of this magnitude we know there will need to be corrections and revisions. We will try to make the corrections and revisions in a timely manner. We are in the process of setting up Internet support for this endeavor.

Larry Schroeder

Solutions 1.1 - Real Numbers

Exercise 1 Exponential Notation

$$-2^4 = -(2^4) = -16 \text{ opposite of (2 to the 4th power)}$$

This leads us to our next topic, order of operations. Exponential expressions are done before the unary operation of opposite. This is not the same as (negative 2) to the fourth power. That answer would be 16. Order makes a difference.

HP Prime Family Using Exponents

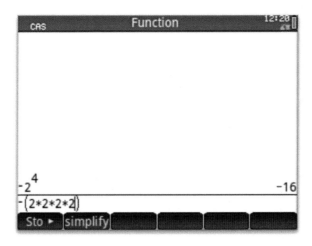

Use the **CAS** view on the HP Prime. Key in the expressions as shown followed by **Enter**. If the **CAS** view has computations, clear the **history** first. To clear the **history**, press the **Clear** key.

The second entry with parenthesis is shown to emphasis that we should do the products first. However, when you press **Enter** the HP Prime will drop the parenthesis and place the negative with the first number. Try it for yourself. The HP Prime is moving the opposite to the first entry of the products. The HP Prime is using the Properties of Negatives.

You could also type (-2) raised to the fourth to see that its answer is 16. As we will see next, precedence can and often does make a difference in our answer. If this exercise had an odd power would doing the wrong order give a wrong answer?

HP Prime Family Additional Explorations

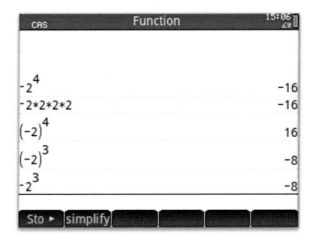

This screen illustrates the questions posed in the previous discussion. We must be careful. The last two entries give the same answer but for different reasons. Entry four illustrates that an odd number of negatives when multiplied results in a negative. The last entry is illustrating the **opposite** of (2 to the any power) is a negative.

As we can see with the screenshot, in the absence of parenthesis, the precedence rule makes a difference. The negative is applied after the number is raised to the exponent.

<< Return

Exercise 2 Order of Operation

Substituting 5 for x	$4+3\cdot(x-1)^2$
Work inside parenthesis	$=4+3\cdot(5-1)^2$
Simplify exponent	$=4+3\cdot(4)^2$
Multiplying	$=4+3\cdot16$
Adding	$=4+48$
	$=52$

HP Prime Family Order of Operations

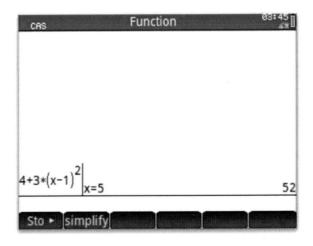

Use the **CAS** view on the HP Prime. Key in the expression as shown followed by **Enter**. Use the **squared** key and **with template**. The **with template** (|) is found by pressing the **fraction/ square root/ absolute value** key. Use the **xt(theta)n** key for the lowercase **x**. If the **CAS** view has computations, clear the **history** first. To clear the **history**, press the **Clear** key.

<< Return

Exercise 3 Repeating Decimal as a Rational Number

Write $x = 0.666\ldots$ as a rational number.

Multiply by 10 because 1 repeating digits
$$10x = 6.666\ldots$$

Subtract x from 10x

$$\begin{array}{r} 10x = 6.666\ldots \\ -x = -0.666\ldots \\ \hline 9x = 6 \end{array}$$

Dividing by 9

$$\frac{9x}{9} = \frac{6}{9} \qquad\qquad x = \frac{6}{9} = \frac{2}{3}$$

HP Prime Family Repeating Decimal Calculations

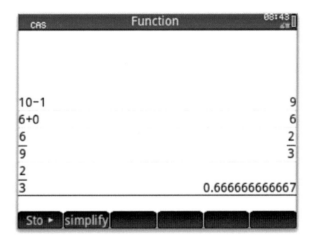

Use the **CAS** view on the HP Prime. Key in the first expressions as shown followed by **Enter**. The second expression was entered as 6-0 followed by **Enter**. (For some reason the HP Prime change it to 6+0). For the third entry, use the **fraction template** from the **fraction/ square root/ absolute value** key. For the fourth entry, use the scroll pad to select the reduced fraction and press **Enter** to copy it to the command line. Use the approximate (the wavy equal sign) key. If the **CAS** view has computations, clear the **history** first. To clear the **history**, press the Clear key.

The **soft** key Copy could have been used to transfer the history item to the command line.

As in the example we could also use the **HOME** view and the **mixed numeral** key from either the **HOME** view or **CAS** view.

<< Return

Solutions 1.2 - Operations and Properties of Real Numbers

Exercise 1 Adding and Subtracting Real Numbers

(a) $-2.1-(-5.3)$
$= -2.1+5.3 = 3.2$

Change subtraction to addition of the opposite. Subtract absolute values, result is positive.

(b) $1\frac{1}{2}+\left(-3\frac{1}{4}\right)=\frac{3}{2}+\left(-\frac{13}{4}\right)$ Switch to improper fractions.

$=\frac{6}{4}+\left(-\frac{13}{4}\right)=-\frac{7}{4}=-1\frac{3}{4}$ Subtract absolute values, result negative.

Alternate Approach

(a) $-2.1-(-5.3)$
$= -2.1+5.3 = 3.2$

Two like signs become a positive sign. Think money, result have $3.2.

(b) $1\frac{1}{2}+\left(-3\frac{1}{4}\right)=\frac{3}{2}+\left(-\frac{13}{4}\right)$ Switch to improper fractions.

$=\frac{6}{4}-\frac{13}{4}=-\frac{7}{4}=-1\frac{3}{4}$ Two unlike signs begome a negative sign. Owe $$1\frac{3}{4}$.

HP Prime Family Adding and Subtracting

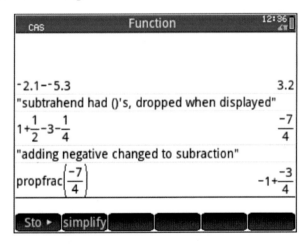

Begin by selecting the **CAS** key on the HP Prime. We used the double quotes " " for comment lines. Erased the copy of each comment caused by pressing **Enter**. First entry was Keyed in with -2.1-(-5.3) with (-5.3) as the subtrahend. Result displayed in the history gave us error when we tried to key it in with the form, -2.1—5.3, which is the result the HP Prime showed as the first entry of the history area. Strange, cannot Keyin result that it showed.

The second fraction entry was Keyed in with "+-3". The "+-3". is displayed in history area as "subtract 3". Notice that the "negative proper fraction" is keyed in with "integer and fraction part both being negative".

The propfrac() function comes from **Toolbox > Catlg > propfrac**.

If the **CAS** view has computations, clear the **history** first. To clear the **history**, press the **Clear** key.

HP Prime uses various approaches to eliminate double signs. Best technique for us to enter double sign problems using the alternate simplified expressions form. Proper fractions will need to have two parts, "integer and fraction" with add for positive mixed numeral and subtract for negative mixed numerals.

We may also use our double signs approach to interpret some of the answers. This would be true for the last solution shown in the history area.

<< Return

Exercise 2 Multiplying and Dividing Real Numbers

(a) $21.1 \cdot (-4.2)$
$= -88.62$

Signs different. Multiply absolute values, 21.1 and 4.2 getting 88.62. The result is negative.

(b) $-\dfrac{2}{7} \div (-5)$

Invert and multiply. Signs the same.

$= -\dfrac{2}{7} \cdot \left(-\dfrac{1}{5}\right)$

Multiplyabsolute absolute values, $\dfrac{2}{7}$ and

$= \dfrac{2}{35}$

$\dfrac{1}{5}$ getting $\dfrac{2}{35}$. The result is positive.

HP Prime Family Multiplying and Dividing

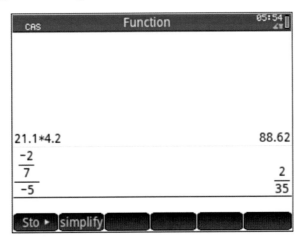

Use the **CAS** view on the HP Prime. Key in the first expressions as shown followed by **Enter**. The second expression use the **Fraction Template** from the **fraction/ square root/ absolute value** key. Use the **Fraction Template** again. We will have a compound fraction. Key in the values using **number keys** and **arrow pad**. Press **Enter**. If the **CAS** view has computations, clear the **history** first. To clear the **history**, press the **Clear** key..

<< Return

Exercise 3 Collecting Like Terms

Simplify: $2\{[5(x-3)+4]-[3(2x-4)+6]\}$

Distributive − expand $2\{[5(x-3)+4]$
$\qquad\qquad\qquad -[3(2x-4)+6]\}$

Combine like terms $= 2\{[5x-15+4]$
$\qquad\qquad\qquad -[6x-12+6]\}$

Replacing with $1,-1$ $= 2\{[5x-11]-[6x-6]\}$

Distributive − expand $= 2\{1[5x-11]-1[6x-6]\}$

Combine like terms $= 2\{5x-11-6x+6\}$

Distributive − expand $= 2\{-x-5\}$
$\qquad\qquad\qquad = -2x-10$

HP Prime Family Collecting Like Terms

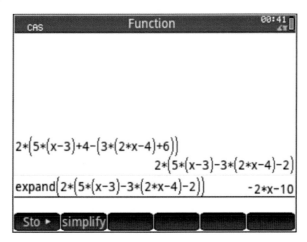

Begin by selecting the **CAS** key on the HP Prime. Key in as shown. Notice that we needed to use **Toolbox** > **CAS** > **Algebra** > **Expand**. Copy the previous solution. Press **Enter**. The soft **simplify** key would also have worked. If the **CAS** view has computations, clear the **history** first. To clear the **history**, press the **Clear** key.

The HP Prime first entry distributive "the subtract" (negative) first. When working manually, we find it better to consistently work from the inside out.

<< Return

Solutions 1.3 Integer Exponents

Exercise 1 Zero and Negative Exponents

If possible, express using positive exponents and simplify.

(a) $-x^0$ for $x = -2.3$ substituting for x $\quad -(-2.3)^0 = -1$

(b) $\dfrac{2^{-4}}{3^{-2}} = \dfrac{3^2}{2^4} = \dfrac{9}{16}$

(c) $\dfrac{x^{-1}}{y^{-2}} = \dfrac{y^2}{x^1} = \dfrac{y^2}{x}$

In part (a) simplifying exponents has a higher priority then the unary operation of opposite. The -2.3 raised to the zero power is 1, and then the opposite of 1 is -1.

HP Prime Family Zero and Negative Exponents

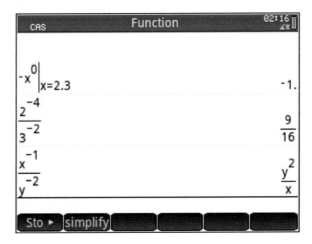

Begin by selecting the **CAS** key on the HP Prime. Key in as shown. The **width** (|) operator and **fraction template** are located using the **fraction / square root / absolute value** key. Entry 3 domain of the result includes y=0, where the domain of the input does not.

If the **CAS** view has computations, clear the **history** first. To clear the **history**, press the **Clear** key

.

HP Prime Family Negative Exponents

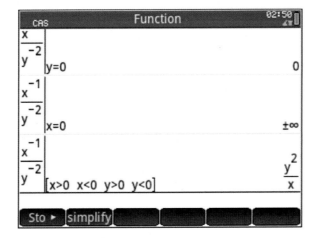

Begin by selecting the **CAS** key on the HP Prime.

Entry one is $x^{-1}/y^{-2}|y=0$. Screenshot cut the numerator's exponent off. Key in rest as shown. The **width** (|) operator and **fraction template** are located using the **fraction / square root / absolute value** key. Using the >< to represent not equal will give an error. Use x>0, x<0, y>0, y<0 as your entry. It will be changed to a row matrix, [x>0 x<0 y>0 y<0] in the history area.

If the **CAS** view has computations, clear the **history** first. To clear the **history**, press the **Clear** key.

Remember from our first screen capture the result is y^2/x with entry three input being x^{-1}/y^{-2}.

For this screenshot's entry one, we use the width operator to specify y=0 which gives us the incorrect answer of "0" to the original entry three result. We have y=0 is in the domain of the result but not in the domain of the input. This is the reason for us to manually figure out incorrect results for division by zero situations. The HP Prime is simplifying first, that is what is allowing the HP Prime to do an illegal substitution of zero in the result.

Entry two results using the width operator to specify x=0 gives us division by zero in the result, thus the HP Prime solution of "undef" which it writes as "plus / minus infinity".

If we specify in the original problem that both x and y cannot be equal to zero, the domain of result and input are the same and no incorrect solutions are possible. The HP Prime however does not allow us to specify not equal to zero for x and y so we use the four inequalities shown.

Note: From this point on we will not supply the manual restrictions, but will assume that the division by zero values are not allowed.

<< Return

Exercise 2 Using the Properties of Exponents

Simplify:

(a) $\left(\dfrac{2^3 \cdot 3}{4^2}\right)^3 = \left(\dfrac{(2^3)^3 \cdot 3^3}{(4^2)^3}\right) = \left(\dfrac{512 \cdot 27}{4096}\right) = \left(\dfrac{13824}{4096}\right) = \dfrac{27}{8}$

(b) $\left(\dfrac{3 \cdot s^{-2}}{t}\right)^2 \cdot \left(\dfrac{t^{-1}}{s^2}\right)^{-3} = \left(\dfrac{9 \cdot s^{-4}}{t^2}\right) \cdot \left(\dfrac{t^3}{s^{-6}}\right)$

$= 9 \cdot s^{-4-(-6)} \cdot t^{3-2} = 9 \cdot s^2 \cdot t$

alternate

(a) $\left(\dfrac{2^3 \cdot 3}{4^2}\right)^3 = \left(\dfrac{8 \cdot 3}{16}\right)^3 = \left(\dfrac{3}{2}\right)^3 = \dfrac{27}{8}$

(b) $\left(\dfrac{3 \cdot s^{-2}}{t}\right)^2 \cdot \left(\dfrac{t^{-1}}{s^2}\right)^{-3} = \left(\dfrac{3}{t \cdot s^2}\right)^2 \cdot \left(\dfrac{1}{s^2 \cdot t}\right)^{-3}$

$= \dfrac{9}{t^2 \cdot s^4} \cdot \left(\dfrac{s^2 \cdot t}{1}\right)^3 = \dfrac{9}{t^2 \cdot s^4} \cdot \dfrac{s^6 \cdot t^3}{1^3} = 9 \cdot s^2 \cdot t$

In part (a) we deliberately used the properties of exponents to assign the outside exponent to all the factors of the denominator and numerator. Seeing that 512 divides evenly into 4096 would allow us to reduce the quotient in step 3. However since we did not reduce the quotient, step 4 would require some work.

The alternate part (a) procedure is the one we should use. Reducing first makes the math much easier.

In part (b) there are no reductions so we must use our exponent properties.

Remember our choices, work with the negative exponents, eliminate the negative exponents, or a combination of both methods. We choose in part (b) to work with the negative exponents and in alternate part (b) to eliminate them.

In part (b) we used the properties of exponents to assign the outside exponent to all the factors of the denominator and numerator for both original factors. Then for both s and t the numerator's exponent was larger than the denominator's exponent so we subtracted the denominator's exponent from the numerator's exponent.

In alternate part (b) we moved negative exponents across the bar in each original factor to make them positive. Then we simplified the first factor and inverted the second factor's quotient to change the negative outside power to a positive outside power. Then for both s and t the numerator's exponent was larger than the denominator's exponent so we subtracted the denominator's exponent from the numerator's exponent.

HP Prime Family Using the Properties of Exponents

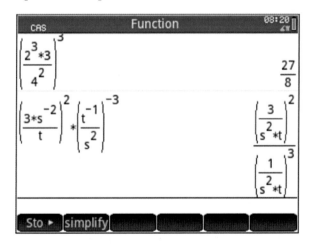

Begin by selecting the **CAS** key on the HP Prime. Key in as shown.

The **fraction template** is located using the **fraction / square root / absolute value** key. We have to use the soft **simplify** key on the last entry to get the final result $9s^2t$. The final result, $9s^2t$, is not shown.

If the **CAS** view of the first screenshot has computations, clear the **history** first. To clear the **history**, press the **Clear** key.

Entry two will not work on the HP Prime **HOME** view since the variables are not assigned values and well use zero as a default. Remember to use capital letters. Division by zero will result in an error message, "Error: infinity result". Entry one will be shown as a decimal. For the HP Prime **CAS** view the domain of the final result, $9s^2t$, means we need to specify that s or t cannot equal zero due to the domain of the original input.

<< Return

Exercise 3 Scientific to Decimal Notation – Decimal to Scientific Notation

Change to decimal notation.

(a) $8.21 \times 10^6 = 8\ 210\ 000$

(b) $4.30 \times 10^{-5} = 0.000\ 043\ 0$

Change to scientific notation.

(c) $0.006\ 25 = 6.25 \times 10^{-3}$

(d) $81\bar{0}\ 000 = 8.10 \times 10^5$

In part (b) we keep the zero and in part (d) we include the zero because in both of these cases the zeros are significant.

HP Prime Family Scientific to Decimal Notation – Decimal to Scientific Notation

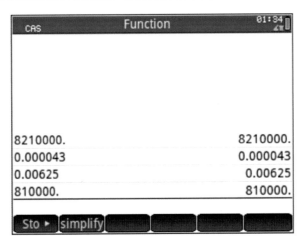

Begin by selecting the **CAS** key on the HP Prime. If the **CAS** view of the screenshot has computations, clear the **history** first. To clear the **history**, press the **Clear** key.

Key in **8.21E6** followed by **Enter**. Upon pressing **enter** the problem was changed to the default notation. We assume we have three significant figures. The first entry is displayed with 7 digits.

For the second entry key in **4.30E-5** followed by **Enter**. Upon pressing **enter** the problem was changed to decimal notation. The HP Prime default notation dropped the significant zero at the end.

For the third entry key in **0.00625**.

Key in entry four, **810000.0**. Note the decimal entry. Exact are not converted to scientific notation in the next screenshot without adding the decimal. There is no way to tell that there are three significant figures.

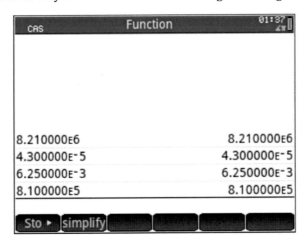

Continuing from previous screen. For the HP Prime/ Pro/ Virtual use the **User EEX** key to set the history area to Scientific. We set the number of digits to our default by having **K_Eex()** call the **first()** subroutine. This is the first time the subroutine is called so Scientific digit is set to a default value of 6. Since all calculation in the history area are decimal, all of the values change.

The HP Prime Free would use the "Home Settings" to set the Number Format to Scientific and decimal digits to 6. The HP Prime scientific notation with a setting of 6 digits has no way to know significant digits. It would be up to us to keep 8.21, 4.30, 6.25, and 8,10 significant digits in our scientific notation answers.

Note: HP Prime/ Pro/ Virtual user need to restore the HP Prime "Home Settings" by pressing the **Apps** key when the HP Prime is in **User** key mode. HP Prime Free user should manually set the "Home Settings" Number Format back to its original settings.

<< Return

Solutions 1.4 – Radicals and Rational Exponents

Exercise 1 Removing Factors from Radicals

(a) Simplify: $\sqrt[4]{x^8 y^8}$

Arrange to 4th power	$\sqrt[4]{x^8 y^8}$
$\sqrt[n]{a^n} = \lvert a \rvert$ n is even	$= \sqrt[4]{(x^2 y^2)^4}$
Absolute value unnecessary	$= \lvert x^2 y^2 \rvert$
	$= x^2 y^2$

(b) Simplify: $3\sqrt[4]{x^3 y} \cdot \sqrt[4]{x^2 y^2}$

$\sqrt[n]{a \cdot b} = \sqrt[n]{a} \cdot \sqrt[n]{b}$	$3\sqrt[4]{x^3 y} \cdot \sqrt[4]{x^2 y^2}$
Exponents	$= 3\sqrt[4]{x^3 y \cdot x^2 y^2}$
$\sqrt[n]{a \cdot b} = \sqrt[n]{a} \cdot \sqrt[n]{b}$	$= 3\sqrt[4]{x^5 y^3}$
$\sqrt[n]{a^n} = \lvert a \rvert$ n is even	$= 3\sqrt[4]{x^4} \cdot \sqrt[4]{x \cdot y^3}$
	$= 3\lvert x \rvert \sqrt[4]{x \cdot y^3}$

(c) Simplify: $\sqrt[3]{\sqrt{128}}$

$\sqrt[m]{\sqrt[n]{a}} = \sqrt[mn]{a}$	$\sqrt[3]{\sqrt{128}}$
Arrange to the 6th power	$= \sqrt[6]{128}$
$\sqrt[n]{a \cdot b} = \sqrt[n]{a} \cdot \sqrt[n]{b}$	$= \sqrt[6]{2 \cdot 64} = \sqrt[6]{2 \cdot 2^6}$
$\sqrt[n]{a^n} = \lvert a \rvert$ n is even	$= \sqrt[6]{2} \cdot \sqrt[6]{2^6}$
Simplify absolute value	$= \lvert 2 \rvert \sqrt[6]{2}$
	$= 2\sqrt[6]{2}$

In part (b) we use the Equivalent Properties of Equalities, Symmetric property to allow us to use the Product Property of Radicals in reverse order to combine, and then use the Product Property of Radicals in forward order to split into two fourth root that can be simplify.

Alternate Approach

(a) Simplify: $\sqrt[4]{x^8 y^8}$

nth Power Removal – even	$\sqrt[4]{x^8 y^8}$
Absolute value unnecessary	$= \left\lvert x^2 y^2 \right\rvert$
	$= x^2 y^2$

(b) Simplify: $3\sqrt[4]{x^3 y} \cdot \sqrt[4]{x^2 y^2}$

$\sqrt[n]{a \cdot b} = \sqrt[n]{a} \cdot \sqrt[n]{b}$	$3\sqrt[4]{x^3 y} \cdot \sqrt[4]{x^2 y^2}$
Exponents	$= 3\sqrt[4]{x^3 y \cdot x^2 y^2}$
nth Power Removal – even	$= 3\sqrt[4]{x^5 y^3}$
	$= 3\lvert x \rvert \sqrt[4]{x \cdot y^3}$

(c) Simplify: $\sqrt[3]{\sqrt{128}}$

$\sqrt[m]{\sqrt[n]{a}} = \sqrt[mn]{a}$	$\sqrt[3]{\sqrt{128}}$
Factor	$= \sqrt[6]{128}$
nth Power Removal – even	$= \sqrt[6]{2^7}$
Simplify absolute value	$= \lvert 2 \rvert \sqrt[6]{2}$
	$= 2\sqrt[6]{2}$

TI-Nspire Family Removing Factors from Radicals– Creating the Exercise File

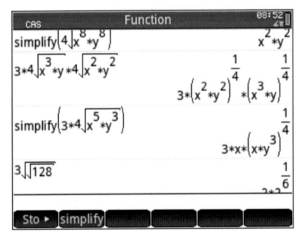

Begin by selecting the **CAS** key on the HP Prime. If the **CAS** view of the screenshot has computations, clear the **history** first. To clear the **history**, press the **Clear** key.

Key in entry one deleted the original radical entry and left the simplified entry so it would fit on one screen. Entry two switched to rational exponent form and use the commutative property. So in entry three we did a hybrid approach. Typed simplify and entered the radical part by manually combining it. The x is missing the absolute value of complete manual approach. Left screen in partial scroll, so that we could see all the solutions.

<< Return

Exercise 2 Using the Properties of Exponents with Rational Numbers

(a) Simplify: $\left(\dfrac{x^{1/3}}{y^{1/3}}\right)^{3/2}$

$\left(\dfrac{a}{b}\right)^n = \dfrac{a^n}{b^n}$ $\qquad \left(\dfrac{x^{1/3}}{y^{1/3}}\right)^{3/2}$

$$= \dfrac{x^{1/2}}{y^{1/2}} = \dfrac{\sqrt{x}}{\sqrt{y}}$$

(b) Simplify: $\left(\dfrac{3x^{1/3}}{y^{2/3}}\right)^2 \cdot \left(\dfrac{2x^{-3/4}}{y^{1/2}}\right)$

$\left(\dfrac{a}{b}\right)^n = \dfrac{a^n}{b^n}$ & negative exponent $\quad \left(\dfrac{3x^{1/3}}{y^{2/3}}\right)^2 \cdot \left(\dfrac{2x^{-3/4}}{y^{1/2}}\right)$

$\dfrac{a^m}{a^n} = \dfrac{1}{a^{n-m}}$ & $a^m \cdot a^n = a^{m+n}$ $\quad = \dfrac{9x^{2/3}}{y^{4/3}} \cdot \dfrac{2}{x^{3/4} y^{1/2}}$

lowest common denominators $\quad = \dfrac{18}{x^{3/4-2/3} \cdot y^{4/3+1/2}}$

simplify $\quad = \dfrac{18}{x^{9/12-8/12} \cdot y^{8/6+3/6}}$

$\qquad = \dfrac{18}{x^{1/12} \cdot y^{11/6}}$

HP Prime Family Using the Properties of Exponents with Rational Numbers

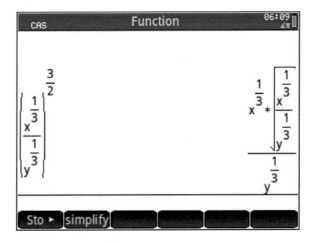

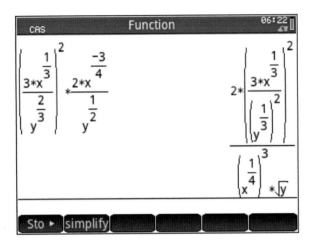

Begin by selecting the **CAS** key on the HP Prime. If the **CAS** view of the screenshot has computations, clear the **history** first. To clear the **history**, press the **Clear** key.

Key in as shown. No useful results. Need to manually work part (a) and part(b).

<< Return

Exercise 3 Rationalizing Denominators

(a) Simplify: $\sqrt{\dfrac{1}{2x \cdot y^3}}$

$\sqrt[n]{\dfrac{a}{b}} = \dfrac{\sqrt[n]{a}}{\sqrt[n]{b}}$ $\sqrt{\dfrac{1}{2x \cdot y^3}}$

Multiply by 1, $\sqrt[n]{a \cdot b} = \sqrt[n]{a} \cdot \sqrt[n]{b}$ $= \dfrac{1}{\sqrt{2x \cdot y^3}} \cdot \dfrac{\sqrt{2x \cdot y}}{\sqrt{2x \cdot y}}$

$\sqrt[n]{a^n} = |a| \ n \text{ is even}$ $= \dfrac{\sqrt{2x \cdot y}}{\sqrt{4x^2 y^4}} = \dfrac{\sqrt{2x \cdot y}}{\sqrt{(2xy^2)^2}}$

Simplify $\left|2x \cdot y^2\right|$ $= \dfrac{\sqrt{2x \cdot y}}{\left|2x \cdot y^2\right|}$

   $= \dfrac{\sqrt{2x \cdot y}}{2|x|\, y^2}$

(b) Simplify: $\sqrt[4]{\dfrac{3x^9 y^2}{8x^2}}$

$\sqrt[n]{\dfrac{a}{b}} = \dfrac{\sqrt[n]{a}}{\sqrt[n]{b}}$ $\sqrt[4]{\dfrac{3x^9 y^2}{8x^2}}$

Multiply by 1, $\sqrt[n]{a \cdot b} = \sqrt[n]{a} \cdot \sqrt[n]{b}$ $= \dfrac{\sqrt[4]{3x^9 y^2}}{\sqrt[4]{8x^2}} \cdot \dfrac{\sqrt[4]{2x^2}}{\sqrt[4]{2x^2}}$

$\sqrt[n]{a^n} = a \ n \text{ is even}$ $= \dfrac{\sqrt[4]{6(x^2)^4 x^3 y^2}}{\sqrt[4]{16x^4}}$

$\dfrac{a^m}{a^n} = a^{m-n}$, Simplify $\left|\dfrac{x^2}{2x}\right|$ $= \dfrac{|x^2|\sqrt[4]{6x^3 y^2}}{|2x|}$

Reduce index of $\sqrt[4]{y^2}$ $= \dfrac{|x|\sqrt[4]{6x^3 y^2}}{2}$

   $= \dfrac{|x|\sqrt{|y|}\sqrt[4]{6x^3}}{2}$

HP Prime Family Rationalizing Denominators

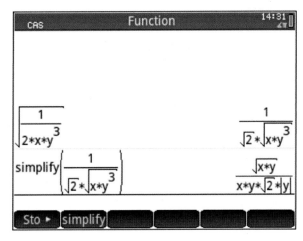

Begin by selecting the **CAS** key on the HP Prime. If the **CAS** view of the screenshot has computations, clear the **history** first. To clear the **history**, press the **Clear** key.

Key in as shown. To finish we need to manually rationalize the square root of 2.

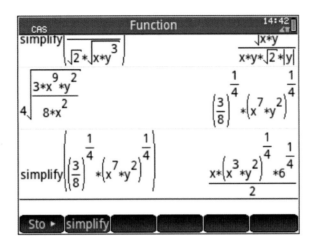

Continuing. To finish put all the 1/4 power back into one radical with index of 4.

The HP Prime did reduce the index as illustrated in the manual form. Not sure about absolute value of x in manual solution but no absolute value in HP Prime solution.

<< Return

Solutions 1.5 – Algebraic Expressions

Exercise 1 Adding and Subtracting Polynomials

(a) Find the sum $(3x^3 - 4x^2 - 5) + (-2x^3 + 3)$

Replacing with 1 $(3x^3 - 4x^2 - 5) + (-2x^3 + 3)$

Distributive − expand $= 1(3x^3 - 4x^2 - 5) + 1(-2x^3 + 3)$

Combine like terms $= 3x^3 - 4x^2 - 5 - 2x^3 + 3$

$= x^3 - 4x^2 - 2$

(b) Find the difference $(5x^2 - 4x - 1) - (x - 2)$

Replacing with 1,−1 $(5x^2 - 4x - 1) - (x - 2)$

Distributive − expand $= 1(5x^2 - 4x - 1) - 1(x - 2)$

Combine like terms $= 5x^2 - 4x - 1 - x + 2$

$= 5x^2 - 5x + 1$

TI-Nspire CAS Adding and Subtracting Polynomials

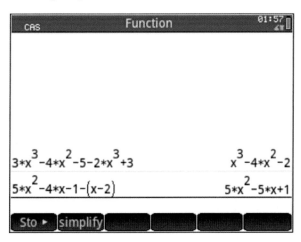

Begin by selecting the **CAS** key on the HP Prime. If the **CAS** view of the screenshot has computations, clear the **history** first. To clear the **history**, press the **Clear** key.

Key in as shown. Both entries were entered with parentheses. The HP Prime CAS dropped all but the subtraction parenthesis.

<< Return

Exercise 2 Multiplying Polynomials

Find the product $(3x^2-1)\cdot(2x^3-x+4)$

Right distributive $(3x^2-1)\cdot(2x^3-x+4)$

Left distributive $= 3x^2\cdot(2x^3-x+4)-1\cdot(2x^3-x+4)$

Collect like terms $= 6x^5-3x^3+12x^2-2x^3+x-4$

$$= 6x^5-5x^3+12x^2+x-4$$

Table form
$$2x^3-x+4$$
$$3x^2-1$$

$$\overline{6x^5-3x^3+12x^2}$$
$$-2x^3 \qquad +x-4$$

$$\overline{}$$

$$6x^5-5x^3+12x^2+x-4$$

When using table form, it is easier to place the polynomial with fewer terms second. The commutative property for multiplication allows us to do this. When performing the multiplication lineup terms with the same degree. Leave spaces if necessary.

HP Prime Family Multiplying Polynomials

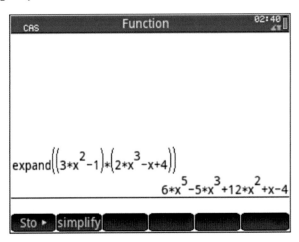

Begin by selecting the **CAS** key on the HP Prime. If the **CAS** view of the screenshot has computations, clear the **history** first. To clear the **history**, press the **Clear** key.

Key in as shown. Press the **Toolbox** key use **Toolbox > CAS > Algebra > Expand** to show the entry as terms. Press **Enter** for the entry. Remember to use multiplication between the factors.

<< Return

Exercise 3 Special Products

(a) Find the product $(\sqrt{x}-3y)(\sqrt{x}+3y)$

The product takes the form $(u+v)(u-v)=u^2-v^2$

Replace u and v $\quad(\sqrt{x}-3y)(\sqrt{x}+3y)$

Simplify $\quad\quad\quad = (\sqrt{x})^2-(3y)^2$

$\quad\quad\quad\quad\quad = x-9y^2$

(b) Find the product $(2x+y-3)(2x+y+3)$

Associative add $\quad(2x+y-3)(2x+y+3)$

The product takes the form $(u+v)(u-v)=u^2-v^2$

Replace u and v $\quad\quad = [(2x+y)-3][(2x+y)+3]$

The first term takes the form $(u+v)^2=u^2+2uv+v^2$

Replace u and v $\quad\quad = (2x+y)^2-3^2$

Simplify $\quad\quad\quad\quad = (2x)^2+2(2x)(y)+y^2-3^2$

$\quad\quad\quad\quad\quad\quad = 4x^2+4xy+y^2-9$

We fist use the associative property for addition to group the $2x + y$ in each factor. This allows us to use the Sum and Difference of a Binomial formula. The first term in this result allows us to use Squares of a Binomial sum formula.

HP Prime Family Special Products

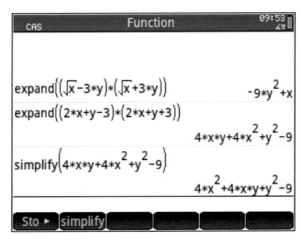

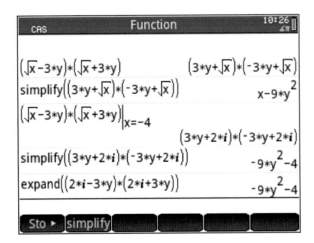

Begin by selecting the **CAS** key on the HP Prime. To clear the **history**, press the Clear key.

First screen. Key in as shown. Press the **Toolbox** key use **Toolbox > CAS > Algebra > Expand** to show the entries as terms. Press **Enter** for both entries. The HP Prime CAS leaves products as factors, thus the need for us to use the **expand** command. We used the Paste key to select a listing of previous entries. Choose the closest version and then edited it for both entries. We used the soft **simplify** key to change result to standard form.

Second screen. The first two entries shows that we could use **simplify** rather than **expand** to display the correct result. Entry three uses the non-real number *i*. We will explain this shortly.

In entry two the domain of the result is larger than the domain of the input. This is about negative values for x are allowed in the result but not the original expression. Same thing applies to entry one in first screen.

Our third entry was where we used the **with** operator "|" to substitute in a number that would exploit the the domain issue. The **with** (|) operator is located in the **template** key. In this situation the **simplify** returned a complex result of -$9y^2$-4. What is happening is the calculator substituted the non-real value of 2*i* for the square root of -4. Later in our tutorials we will introduce imaginary and complex numbers, which involve the use of *i*.

Entry three and four makes use of our knowledge of imaginary and complex numbers. We will learn that the square root of -4 is the same as the square root of 4 times *i*. That is, where *i* is equal to the square root of -1. We will also learn that i^2 is equal to -1. Thus the $4i^2$ in the result becomes -4. Using simplify our HP Prime CAS then switches the terms order so that the answer is in standard form.

Entry five shows what happens in a problem where a complex number is substituted for the negative number in a radical.

What we have is that our HP Prime CAS does not have the statement "Assume all variables represent non-negative real numbers." Our HP Prime CAS having no such restrictions thus the need for us to pay attention to the differences in the domains of the input and results.

<< Return

Solutions 1.6 – Factoring

Exercise 1 Common Factors

(a) Factor the polynomial $-4x-12$

Factor -4	$-4x-12$
Missing factor – Supply value	$=-4(\quad)$
	$=-4(x+3)$

(b) Factor the polynomial $8x^3y-16x^2y^2$

Factor $8x^2y$	$8x^3y-16x^2y^2$
Missing factor – Supply value	$=8x^2y(\quad)$
	$=8x^2y(x-2y)$

For part (a) place the -4 in front of an empty set of parenthesis and think what we need to multiply the -4 by to get our original polynomial, -4x -12. We then use the full distributive property expand or our <u>distributive expand mnemonic</u> to see that x + 3 when multiplied by -4 will produce the original polynomial.

For part (b) factor out $8x^2y$ and follow the same procedure. We see that a missing factor of $x - 2y$ is needed.

HP Prime Family Common Factors

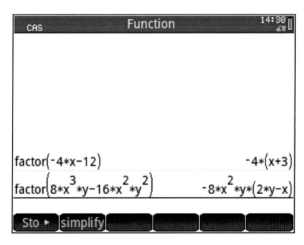

Begin by selecting the **CAS** key on the HP Prime. If the **CAS** view of the screenshot has computations, clear the **history** first. To clear the **history**, press the **Clear** key.

Key in as shown. Press the **Toolbox** key to use **Toolbox > CAS > Algebra > Factor**. Entry one factors a -4. The second entry factor out a negative thus the inside terms reflect this.

<< <u>Return</u>

Exercise 2 Factoring Trinomials

(a) Factor the polynomial $x^2 - 7x + 12$

$|a| \cdot |c| = 1 \cdot 12 = 12$ pairs: 1,12; 2,6; 3,4

$c > 0, b < 0$ add $1 + 12 = 13$; $2 + 6 = 8$; $3 + 4 = 7$

pair is negative $x^2 - 7x + 12$
$$= (x - 3)(x - 4)$$

(b) Factor the polynomial $2x^2 - 6x - 8$

Factor 2 $2x^2 - 6x - 8$
$$= 2(x^2 - 3x - 4)$$

$|a| \cdot |c| = 1 \cdot 4 = 4$ pairs: 1,4; 2,2

$c < 0, b < 0$ subtract $4 - 1 = 3$; $2 - 2 = 0$

largest, negative $2(x^2 - 3x - 4)$
$$= 2(x - 4)(x + 1)$$

In part (b) we factor out the common factor by factoring a 2. We complete the common factor mentally by filling in the blank parenthesis with $x^2 - 3x - 4$. We then use the Factoring Trinomial procedure on $x^2 - 3x - 4$.

HP Prime Family Factoring Trinomials

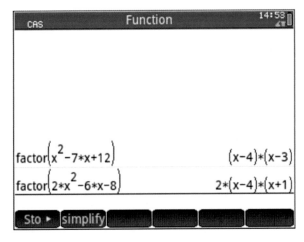

Begin by selecting the **CAS** key on the HP Prime. If the **CAS** view of the screenshot has computations, clear the **history** first. To clear the **history**, press the **Clear** key.

Key in as shown. Press the **Toolbox** key to use **Toolbox > CAS > Algebra > Factor**.

<< Return

Exercise 3 Factor by Grouping

(a) Factor the polynomial $2bx - 2cx + cy - by$

Factor $2x$, $-y$ $2bx - 2cx + cy - by$

Commutative add $= 2x(b{-}c) - y(-c{+}b)$

Factor $b{-}c$ $= 2x(b{-}c) - y(b{-}c)$

                $= (2x - y)(b{-}c)$

(b) Factor the polynomial $8x^2 + 10x - 3$

    $|a| \cdot |c| = 8 \cdot 3 = 24$ pairs: $1,24$; $2,12$; $3,8$; $4,6$

    $c < 0, b > 0$ subtract $24 - 1 = 23$; $12 - 2 = 10$; $8 - 3 = 5$

                         $6 - 4 = 2$

largest positive $8x^2 + 10x - 3$

Factor $4x$, -1 $= 8x^2 + 12x - 2x - 3$

Factor $2x+3$ $= 4x(2x + 3) - 1(2x + 3)$

               $= (4x - 1)(2x + 3)$

In part (a) we use the left distributive property to factor each group. We next use the commutative property to get the terms of the $-y$ factor in the right order. What we are using is that if we keep the sign we can move the terms around. This is a shortcut for the more formal approach of changing "subtraction to addition of the opposite." An alternate approach would have been to move the third and fourth terms first. We then use the right distributive property to factor out the $b - c$.

In part (b) we factor trinomials with $a > 1$ by splitting the middle into two terms. Thus to factor, we need to use grouping or trial and error. If the middle were not any of the difference values, then the trinomial would be prime under integer coefficients.

We extended our mental common factor approach to factor each of the parts. Since the first part common factor produced $2x + 3$ it was necessary to factor out a -1 from the second part to produce $2x + 3$. As we saw in part (a), factor by grouping needs the same expression for both parts. We then use the right distributive property to factor out the $2x + 3$.

HP Prime Family Factor by Grouping

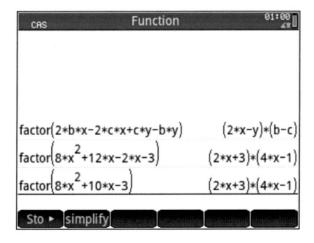

Begin by selecting the **CAS** key on the HP Prime. If the **CAS** view of the screenshot has computations, clear the **history** first. To clear the **history**, press the **Clear** key.

Key in as shown. Press the **Toolbox** key to use **Toolbox > CAS > Algebra > Factor**.

Notice in entry 3 that the HP Prime CAS can work the problem directly. If we forget to place times between the letters in entry one the HP Prime CAS will give us an error message. We will need to edit by adding the times between the letters.

<< Return

Exercise 4 Special Factor Formulas

(a) Factor the polynomial $4x^2 + 20x + 25$

The trinomial takes the form $u^2 + 2uv + v^2 = (u+v)^2$

Replace u and v $4x^2 + 20x + 25$

Change form $= (2x)^2 + 2(2x)(5) + 5^2$

$= (2x+5)^2$

(b) Factor the polynomial $x^6 + 125$

The binomial takes the form

$u^3 + v^3 = (u+v)(u^2 - uv + v^2)$

Replace u and v $x^6 + 125$

Change form $= (x^2)^3 + 5^3$

Simplify $= (x^2+5)[(x^2)^2 - (x^2)5 + 5^2]$

$= (x^2+5)(x^4 - 5x^2 + 25)$

The trinomial in part (b) solution looks like it could be a Perfect Square Trinomial with $u = x^2$. However the middle would have to be -10 x^2 instead of -5 x^2. Using our Factor Trinomial procedure the only other value for the middle that would factor would be -26 x^2. Thus, the trinomial in the second factor of part (b) result is prime.

HP Prime Special Factor Formulas

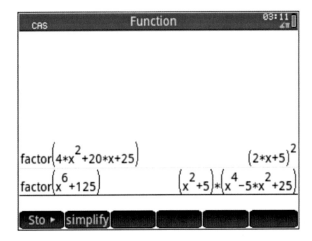

Begin by selecting the **CAS** key on the HP Prime. If the **CAS** view of the screenshot has computations, clear the **history** first. To clear the **history**, press the **Clear** key.

Key in as shown. Press the **Toolbox** key to use **Toolbox > CAS > Algebra > Factor**.

<< Return

Solutions 1.7 – Rational Expressions

Exercise 1 Simplifying Rational Expressions

Simplify the expression $\dfrac{x^2+x-6}{x^2-4}$

Factor x^2-4 $\qquad \dfrac{x^2+x-6}{x^2-4}$

$$= \dfrac{x^2+x-6}{(x-2)(x+2)}$$

Factor x^2+x-6

$|a|\cdot|c|=1\cdot6=6$ pairs: 1,6; 2,3

$c<0,b>0$ subtract $\quad 6-1=5;\ 3-2=1;$

largest, positve $\qquad = \dfrac{(x+3)(x-2)}{(x-2)(x+2)}$

Cancel $\qquad = \dfrac{(x+3)(x-2)}{(x-2)(x+2)}$

$$= \dfrac{x+3}{x+2}$$

HP Prime Family Simplifying Rational Expressions

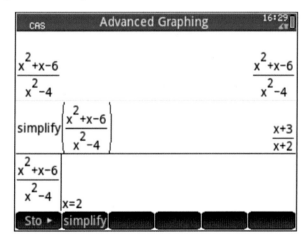

Begin by selecting the **CAS** key on the HP Prime. If the **CAS** view of the screenshot has computations, clear the **history** first. To clear the **history**, press the **Clear** key.

Key in as shown. Use the soft **simplify** key. We will need to press **Enter** to see the edit line result. The **with** (|) operator is located by pressing the **symbol template** key. The x=2 result will be **undef** for the original expression but have a value if used **with** the simplified result. We need to exclude x=-2 from the domain of the original and simplified result.

<< Return

Exercise 2 Multiplying and Dividing Rational Expressions

(a) Multiply $\dfrac{9x^2+6x+4}{3x^2-4x-4} \cdot \dfrac{9x^3-4x}{27x^5-8x^2}$

Factor rationals $\dfrac{9x^2+6x+4}{3x^2-4x-4} \cdot \dfrac{9x^3-4x}{27x^5-8x^2}$

Group, Factor $= \dfrac{9x^2+6x+4}{3x^2-6x+2x-4} \cdot \dfrac{x(9x^2-4)}{x^2(27x^3-8)}$

Factor, Multiply, $= \dfrac{9x^2+6x+4}{3x(x-2)+2(x-2)}$

Cancel $\cdot \dfrac{x(3x-2)(3x+2)}{x^2(3x-2)(9x^2+6x+4)}$

Cancel, Exponents $= \dfrac{x(3x+2)}{x^2(3x+2)(x-2)}$

$= \dfrac{1}{x(x-2)}$

In part (a) the trinomial for the first factor's numerator has an $|a||c|$ of 36. None of 36's pairs added up to 6 so it is prime or irreducible. Note that we handled finding the pairs and adding them mentally.

For the first factor's denominator we used grouping for the trinomial. For the grouping we did the split mentally. Since $|3||-4|$ was 12 and 6 – 2 was the pair making 4. Therefore, we needed -6x and 2x for the split of -4x.

Next we first factored out the common factors for the second factor.

We followed this up with finishing factor by grouping and using the special factor formulas. For the cubic special case formula, we recognized that u and v of the formula were the same as the terms in its first factor. We then used this mentally to write out the cubic second factor.

From here we did the necessary multiplying, canceling, and exponents rules to get our final answer. Notice the prime, irreducible, trinomial cancels with itself.

(b) Divide $\dfrac{x^4-81}{5x^2-9x+4} \div \dfrac{x^2-3x}{5x-4}$

Invert and multiply $\dfrac{x^4-81}{5x^2-9x+4} \div \dfrac{x^2-3x}{5x-4}$

Factor rationals $= \dfrac{x^4-81}{5x^2-9x+4} \cdot \dfrac{5x-4}{x^2-3x}$

Factor, Group $= \dfrac{(x^2-9)(x^2+9)}{5x^2-5x-4x+4} \cdot \dfrac{5x-4}{x(x-3)}$

Factor, Multiply, $= \dfrac{(x-3)(x+3)(x^2+9)}{5x(x-1)-4(x-1)}$

Cancel $\cdot \dfrac{5x-4}{x(x-3)}$

Cancel $= \dfrac{(x+3)(x^2+9)(5x-4)}{x(5x-4)(x-1)}$

$= \dfrac{(x+3)(x^2+9)}{x(x-1)}$

In part (b) we did the traditional invert and multiply. To factor the denominator of the first factor, we again did the regrouping and split of -9x mentally. The rest of the steps are our traditional simplification steps.

HP Prime Family Multiplying and Dividing Rational Expressions

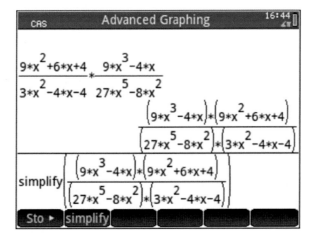

Begin by selecting the **CAS** key on the HP Prime. If the **CAS** view of the screenshot has computations, clear the **history** first. To clear the **history**, press the **Clear** key.

Key in as shown. Use the soft **simplify** key.

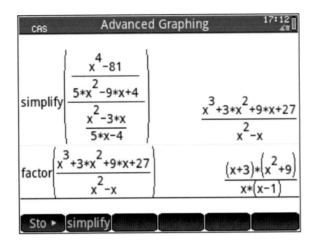

Begin by selecting the **CAS** key on the HP Prime. If the **CAS** view of the screenshot has computations, clear the **history** first. To clear the **history**, press the **Clear** key.

Key in as shown. Press the **Toolbox** key to use **Toolbox > CAS > Algebra > Simplify** and **Toolbox > CAS > Algebra > Factor**.

<< Return

Exercise 3 Adding and Subtracting Rational Expressions

Simplify $\dfrac{4x}{x^2-1}+\dfrac{4}{x-1}-\dfrac{2}{x+1}$

Factor $\dfrac{4x}{x^2-1}+\dfrac{4}{x-1}-\dfrac{2}{x+1}$

Multiply by 1, lcd $=\dfrac{4x}{(x-1)(x+1)}+\dfrac{4}{x-1}-\dfrac{2}{x+1}$

Add, Expand $=\dfrac{4x}{(x-1)(x+1)}+\dfrac{4}{x-1}\cdot\dfrac{(x+1)}{(x+1)}$

$\qquad\qquad -\dfrac{2}{x+1}\cdot\dfrac{(x-1)}{(x-1)}$

Simplify $=\dfrac{4x+4x+4-2x+2}{(x-1)\cdot(x+1)}$

Factor $=\dfrac{6x+6}{(x-1)\cdot(x+1)}$

Cancel $=\dfrac{6(x+1)}{(x-1)\cdot(x+1)}$

$\qquad\qquad =\dfrac{6}{x-1}$

The numerator of the expand step factors into products that can be canceled with a factor in the denominator.

HP Prime Family **Adding and Subtracting Rational Expressions**

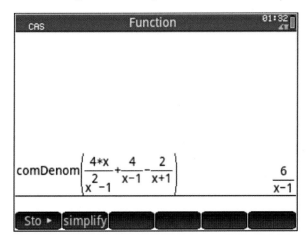

Begin by selecting the **CAS** key on the HP Prime. If the **CAS** view of the screenshot has computations, clear the **history** first. To clear the **history**, press the **Clear** key.

Key in as shown. Press the **Toolbox** key to use **Toolbox > Catlg > comDenom**. The domain of the result may be larger than the domain of the input again applies as the x +1 was canceled. See the manual solution. The domain of the result would include -1 where the domain of the input would not include -1. Due to the nature in using rational expressions of where the domain of result being larger than the domain of the input, we need to be careful in these situations.

<< Return

Exercise 4 **Compound Fractions**

(a) Find the derivative for $f(x) = \dfrac{5}{x}$

Substitute $f(x+h)$ and $f(x)$ $\dfrac{f(x+h) - f(x)}{h}$

Combine quotients, invert $= \dfrac{\dfrac{5}{x+h} - \dfrac{5}{x}}{h}$

Expand, Multiply $= \dfrac{5 \cdot x - 5(x+h)}{x(x+h)} \cdot \dfrac{1}{h}$

Simplify $= \dfrac{5x - 5x - 5h}{xh(x+h)}$

$= \dfrac{-5h}{xh(x+h)} = \dfrac{-5}{x(x+h)}$

$f'(x) = \lim\limits_{h \to 0} \dfrac{-5}{x(x+h)} = \dfrac{-5}{x(x+0)} = \dfrac{-5}{x^2}$

For simplifying the compound fraction we used method 1 to invert and multiply the rational expressions. We then simplified the result. To get the derivative, take the limit as h approaches 0 by substituting in 0 for h.

HP Prime Family Compound Fractions – Part (a)

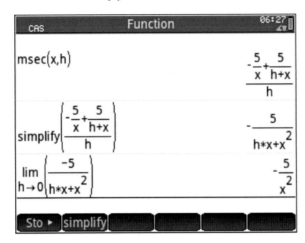

Begin by selecting the **CAS** key on the HP Prime. If the **CAS** view of the screenshot has computations, clear the **history** first. To clear the **history**, press the **Clear** key. HP Prime Free does not have the function **msec**. HP Prime Free will not do this screen. HP Prime Free could use the definition of secant line and built-in simplify function if they wished. This would actually be entry two above with numerator of entry two terms reversed.

Key in as shown. Press the **Toolbox** key to use **Toolbox > User > CalcSecTan > msec**. The program function **msec** uses the function **F1** from the **Function Symbolic View**. Press the soft **simplify** key to simplify the compound fraction. The **lim** command is located by pressing the **symbol template** key.

Go to computerlearningservice.com/html/products.html to download the file CalcSecTan for *msec* in the above screen and *mtan* in the next screen.

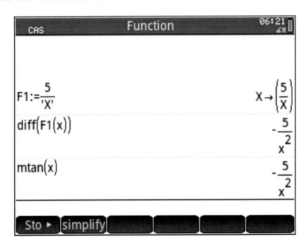

Begin by selecting the **CAS** key on the HP Prime. If the **CAS** view of the screenshot has computations, clear the **history** first. To clear the **history**, press the **Clear** key. Both HP Prime/ Pro/ Virtual and HP Prime Free need to do this screen. HP Prime Free does not have **mtan**. HP Prime Free will not be able to do entry three.

Key in as shown. For **diff()** press the Toolbox key to use **Toolbox > CAS > Calculus > Differentiate**.

(b) Simplify $$\dfrac{x^3\dfrac{1}{2}(4x^2-1)^{-1/2}8x-(4x^2-1)^{1/2}3x^2}{(x^3)^2}$$

Factor gcf $$\dfrac{x^3\dfrac{1}{2}(4x^2-1)^{-1/2}8x-(4x^2-1)^{1/2}3x^2}{(x^3)^2}$$

Expand–Exponents $$=\dfrac{x^2(4x^2-1)^{-1/2}\left[4x^2-3(4x^2-1)\right]}{x^6}$$

Simplify $$=\dfrac{4x^2-12x^2+3}{x^4(4x^2-1)^{1/2}}$$

$$=\dfrac{-8x^2+3}{x^4(4x^2-1)^{1/2}}$$

We use method 3, factor out gcf that includes the negative exponent. The gcf for the numerator is $x^2(4x^2-1)^{-1/2}$. Use the original exponent subtracting the factored out exponent to find the exponent to use inside the parenthesis. The hard one is factoring out -1/2, so for the numerator, we have its second term exponent as $1/2-(-1/2)$, which is an exponent of 1, so the exponent is not needed.

HP Prime Family Compound Fractions – Part (b)

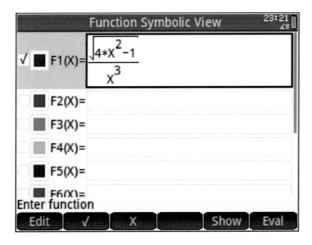

Press the **Apps** key. Highlight the **Function** icon on the Application Library screen. Press the soft **Start** key. Press the soft **Edit** key. The above screen will appear. Enter function as shown. Press the soft **OK**. To erase all functions press the **Clear** key. Both HP Prime/ Pro/ Virtual and HP Prime Free need to do this screen.

Let's look at the derivative of this function, **F1(x)**, from the built-in HP Prime **diff()** command. After using the nested **factor(comDenom(diff()))** command with **F1(x)**, we see that the result it produced is the same as the manual solution shown above.

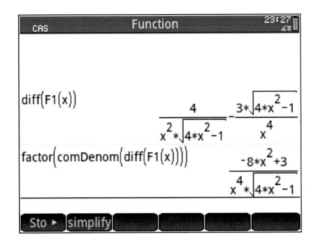

Begin by selecting the **CAS** key on the HP Prime. If the **CAS** view of the screenshot has computations, clear the **history** first. To clear the **history**, press the Clear key. Both HP Prime/ Pro/ Virtual and HP Prime Free need to do this screen.

Key in as shown. For **diff()** press the **Toolbox** key to use **Toolbox > CAS > Calculus > Differentiate**. Press the **Toolbox** key to use **Toolbox > Catlg > comDenom** and **Toolbox > CAS > Algebra > Factor.**

We used HP Prime CAS *factor* and *comDenom* commands to change *diff* answer from terms shown by the derivative's notation result to a rational expression result identical to the manual solution.

We next add the graph of CalcSketch library functions *incdec* and *concaveupddown* to our plot page. The updated Plot page screen is shown below. The functions *incdec* and *concaveupddown* are based on the first derivative and in *concaveupddown* case the second derivative, the derivative of the first derivative.

We take a look at how functions *incdec*(x) and *concaveupdown*(x) help with interpreting function $f1(x)$ graph.

Remember, under the real number system we cannot use the HP Prime CAS original function, derivative operation, basic differentiation rules, or derived functions where the graph of the original function is discontinuous or the limit of the function does not exist.

We may in these situations be able to find a manual result or get a solution from our HP Prime CAS but if the original function is discontinuous or the limit of the function does not exist cases the solution will be erroneous or use complex number system results. Thus, there is the need for us to study discontinuities, limits and definitions, so that we do not attempt to use Algebra, Calculus, and HP Prime where it is not applicable.

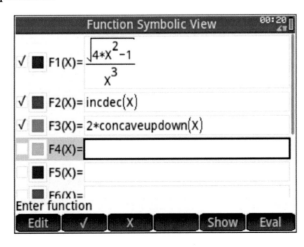

Note: The instructions for this screenshot assume that you have added the CalcSketch library on your HP Prime/ Pro/ Virtual device. Instructions for adding the Calc Sketch ibrary are given following the example's discussion of part (b). If you have not added the CalcSketch library, do so now.

Go to computerlearningservice.com/html/products.html to download the file.

Press the **Symb** key to see the functions in the **Function Symbolic View** window. The above screen will appear. HP Prime Free does not have the function **incdec** or **concaveupdown**. HP Prime Free will not do this screen.

Prime/ Pro/ Virtual Key in as shown. Press the **Toolbox** key to use **Toolbox > User > CalcSketch > incdec** and **Toolbox > User > CalcSketch > concaveupdown**. Notice the capital X as the parameter in both functions. The program function **incdec** and **concaveupdown** uses the function **F1**. The function **incdec** assigns **F0** a value and the function **concaveupdown** assigns **F9** and **F0** a value that they use ln their calculations. The values assigned to **F0** and **F9** are not graphed.

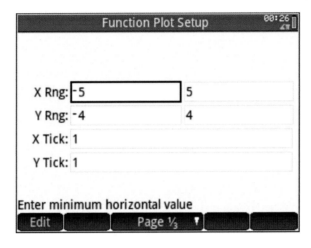

Press the Plot **Setup** key. Page 1/3, change to these values X Rng: --5, 5; Y Rng: -4, 4. Page 2/3, check the Labels box. To set page 1/3 back to defaults press the **Clear** key. HP Prime Free should not do this screen.

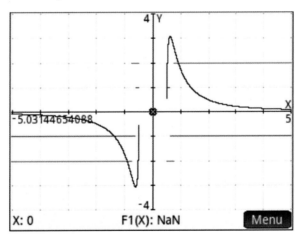

Press the **Plot** key to see a graph of the function. HP Prime Free does not have the red graph F2, **incdec**, or green graph F3, **2*concaveupdown**. HP Prime Free will not do this screen.

We next look at our Library App FcnIncDecConvUpDn and GraphPlus draws the same results. We begin with the FcnIncDecConvUpDn app.

HP Prime/ Pro/ Virtual Graph of Tangent and Secant Line – FcnIncDecConvUpDn Library App

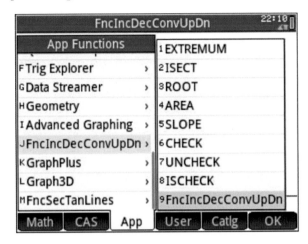

Note: The instructions for this screenshot assume that you have added the CalSketch library and FncIncDecConvUpDn Application Library to your HP Prime/ Pro/ Virtual device. Go to CalSketch for instructions on adding the required library. Go to FncIncDecConvUpDn for instructions on adding this Application Library.

Go to computerlearningservice.com/html/products.html to download the files.

Begin by selecting the **CAS** key or **HOME** key on the HP Prime. If the **CAS** view or **HOME** view of the screenshot has computations, clear the **history** first. To clear the **history**, press the **Clear** key. HP Prime Free does not have the Application Library **FncIncDecConvUpDn**. HP Prime Free will not do this screen.

Press the **Toolbox** key to use **Toolbox > App > FncIncDecConvUpDn**. Press **Enter** to transfer the result to the command line. Press **Enter** to execute the app from the command line (now shown).

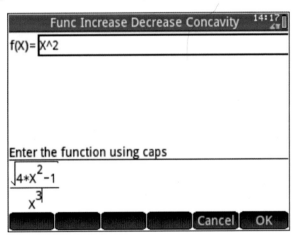

Key in the function as shown. Be sure to use capital X. Press the soft **Edit** key. Use **Esc** to clear the default function, x^2. Key in the new function, $\sqrt{(x^2 -1)}/ x^3$. Notice the Capital X and implied multiplication. Press **Enter** or soft **OK** key to update the field. Press **Enter** or soft **OK** key to see the plot. HP Prime Free will not do this screen.

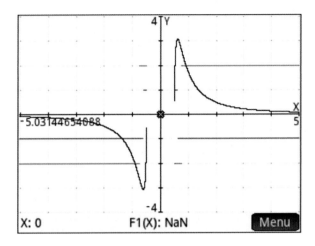

Press the **Plot** key. If necessary press the Plot Setup key. Page 1/3, change to these values X Rng: --5, 5; Y Rng: -4, 4. Page 2/3, check the Labels box. To set page 1/3 back to defaults press the Clear key. Press the **Plot** key again. HP Prime Free should not do this screen.

We now look at the GraphPlus app.

HP Prime/ Pro/ Virtual Graph of Tangent and Secant Line – GraphPlus Library App

Note: The instructions for this screenshot assume that you have added the GraphPlus Application Library to your HP Prime/ Pro/ Virtual device. Go to GraphPlus for instructions on adding this Application Library.

Go to computerlearningservice.com/html/products.html to download the file.

Press the **Apps** key. Select the **GraphPlus** icon. Press the soft **Start** key.

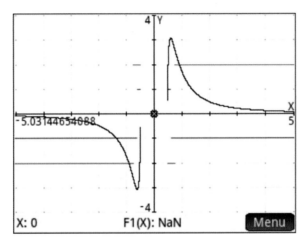

Key in the function as shown. Be sure to use capital X. Press the soft **Edit** key. Key in the function, $\sqrt{(x^2 -1)}/ x^3$. Press **Enter** or soft **OK** key to update the field.

Press the **Plot** key. If necessary press the Plot **Setup** key. Page 1/3, change to these values X Rng: --5, 5; Y Rng: -4, 4. Page 2/3, check the Labels box. To set page 1/3 back to defaults press the **Clear** key. Press the **Plot** key again. HP Prime Free should not do this screen.

Looking at the next two screenshots we see the Library functions *minmax* and *inflpt* values. We can see from the graph and the *incdec* function that the *minmax* candidates in the next screenshot that the *x*-value are where the absolute minimum and maximum of the graph occur.

The *incdec* graph in the above screen is correct. No part of it exists at places where the original function is undefined. By the y-axis label 1 there is a short stretch with a value of 1. It makes the label look like it is negative 1. Right before the absolute maximum at an x-value of $\sqrt{6}/4$ there is another short stretch of 1. Remember 1 means increase and -1 decrease.

Remark: We like to view the HP Prime result with skepticism. As we said before, just because the answer came from the HP Prime does not mean that it is necessarily correct. It is very easy to enter problems incorrectly, use incorrect operations or commands, enter or leave out parentheses that create a problem that was different then what was given, or not pay attention to discontinuities, all these factors can lead us to errors.

Before leaving the graph we note that the *concaveupdwn* graph is also correct. No part of it exists at places where the original function is undefined. Manually doing the second derivative would be involved and error prone due to the many steps and calculations. Our HP Prime can easily perform the second derivative operation. See the screenshot after the next screenshot. Using the nested factor and comDenom command we can put the HP Prime CAS second derivative's result in a very readable form. We need to view the *concaveupdwn* graph with reservations since it is built on the second derivative and we are unsure about its possible faults.

There are two *x*-value results produced by our HP Prime CAS for possible inflections points, shown as exact values in the next screenshot and in the screenshot after that one as decimals. The CalcSketch library function *inflpt* gives us two possible *x*-value results where two of the *x*-value results are candidates which turn out to be actual *x*-value for the inflection points at which the graph changes its concavity. The *concaveupdwn* graph verifies that the two candidates, given by *inflpt*, are actual *x*-value for the inflection points. Note that this is a correct use of the second derivative by the HP Prime CAS as the *inflpt* function is finding results at *x*-values where the function is continuous.

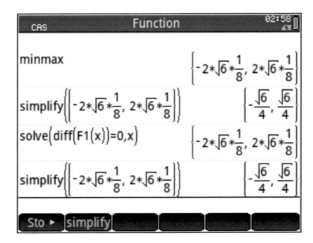

Begin by selecting the **CAS** key on the HP Prime. If the **CAS** view of the screenshot has computations, clear the **history** first. To clear the **history**, press the **Clear** key.

The HP Prime free will only do entry three and four. The HP Prime Free will does not have the first function, **minmax**. For **diff** press the **Toolbox** key to use **Toolbox > CAS > Calculus > Differentiate**. For **solve** press the **Toolbox** key to use **Toolbox > CAS > Solve > Solve**. Press the soft **simplify** key.

HP Prime/ Pro/ Virtual key in the above as shown. For the last two entries follow the HP Prime Free instructions. For **minmax** press the **Toolbox** key to use **Toolbox > User > CalcSketch > minmax**. Press the soft **simplify** key.

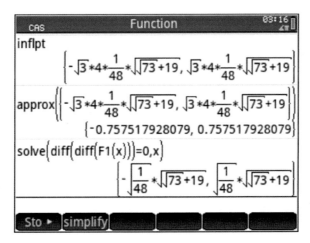

Begin by selecting the **CAS** key on the HP Prime. If the **CAS** view of the screenshot has computations, clear the **history** first. To clear the **history**, press the **Clear** key.

The HP Prime free will only do entry three. The HP Prime Free will does not have the first function, **inflpt**. For **diff** press the **Toolbox** key to use **Toolbox > CAS > Calculus > Differentiate**. For **solve** press the **Toolbox** key to use **Toolbox > CAS > Solve > Solve**. Press the soft **simplify** key.

HP Prime/ Pro/ Virtual key in the above as shown. For the last two entries follow the HP Prime Free instructions. For **inflpt** press the **Toolbox** key to use **Toolbox > User > CalcSketch > inflpt**. Press the soft **simplify** key

In the next screenshot we change the manual calculated inflection point candidates to decimals and look at the second derivative. As we mentioned earlier, we see from the graph of the *concaveupdwn* function that the two results are actual *x*-value for points of inflection. By setting the second derivative's numerator equal to zero and solving for *x*, we arrive at the *x*-value result for the two possible inflection points. This is what the HP Prime can do. Use the solve command of the HP Prime's CAS to set the numerator of the second derivative equal to zero and solve for x. We get the same two answers.

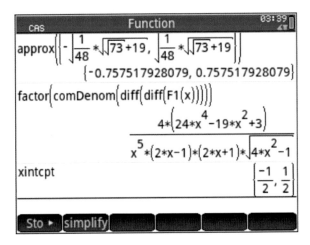

Continuing. Both HP Prime/ Pro/ Virtual and HP Prime Free need to do this screen. The HP Prime Free does not have the **xintcpt** function. HP Prime Free cannot do entry three above.

Key in as shown. Use the approx key, shift Enter. For diff() press the Toolbox key to use Toolbox > CAS > Calculus > Differentiate. Press the **Toolbox** key to use **Toolbox > Catlg > comDenom** and **Toolbox > CAS > Algebra > Factor**.

HP Prime/ Pro/ Virtual for **xintcpt** press the **Toolbox** key to use **Toolbox > User > CalcSketch > xintcpt**

The last tool we like to use when analyzing a graph behavior is the Table of *x*-values. We have one Table page for x-values, functional values, increasing/decreasing values, and concave up/concave down values. We will use the Function Num Setup to set Num Type to Build Your Own.

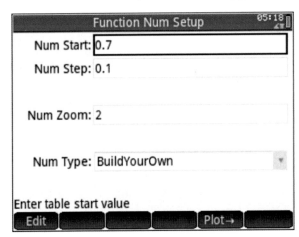

Press the Num **Setup** key. If necessary, change Num Type: BuildYourOwn. HP Prime Free should do this screen. To set page back to defaults press the **Clear** key.

X	F1	F2	F3
-0.8	-2.43945234	-1	-2
-0.61237	-3.07920144	-1	2
-0.6	-3.07094888	1	2
-0.5	0	NaN	NaN
0	NaN	NaN	NaN
0.5	0	NaN	NaN
0.6	3.07094888	1	-2
0.612372	3.07920144	-1	-2
0.8	2.43945234	-1	2
0			

Function Numeric View   02:26

Edit   More   Sort   Defn

Press the **Symb** key to see the functions in the **Function Symbolic View** window. Use **the directional pad**. The above screens will appear. **incdec**, or F3, **2*concaveupdown**. HP Prime Free does not have the functions F2 or F3. HP Prime Free will not do columns F2 and F3. The HP Prime Free does not have the **incdec** and **concaveupdown** functions.

We take a look at the functions in a table. This is from the Function Numeric View. The approximate entries two and eight deal with the minimum and maximum. If they were exact values, they should have no sign. The exact values for the inflection points are not shown. The exact values are very complex, we could have use approximations such as -0.757519 and 0.757519. Instead we picked representative points -0.8 and 0.8. We can see from column F3 that the concavity changed. The last entries to note are entries 4 and 6. These show the y-intercepts. The graph of the functions does not.

The table has the same information as given in the graph but for discrete values of x. When it it hard to see the behavior because of resolution and scale issues with the Plot page, using discrete values can be very helpful.

<< Return

Detailed Index: HP Prime Techniques

Overview

Use the detailed Explanations 1.1 – 1.7 index links to take us to the tutorial's discussions of the concepts.

From the tutorial's discussions we will find manual explanations and solutions, HP Prime screenshots with HP Prime solutions, and self-checking related exercises. Here, we will find the HP Prime's CAS view solution and if a HP Prime's HOME view solution is unique it will also be shown. If there are related Application Library Apps there application to the topic will be shown as well. Programs and Application Library Apps that aid our understanding of the topic and increase our solution efficiency will be created and used.

To learn HP Prime Techniques, use the screenshots, examples, and exercises for the listed concepts to see the HP Prime's CAS view and HP Prime's HOME view features plus related programs and Application Library Apps.

Drawings that add to understanding will also be referenced.

[HP Prime / Pro/ Virtual] – **Brackets** around a topic indicates that the tutorial's discussion of the topic is for all HP Prime devices but the HP Prime Apple, Android, and Windows Free app.

HP Prime Techniques

Explanation 1.1 – Real Numbers / Explanation 1.2 – Operations and Properties of Real Numbers / Explanation 1.3 – Integer Exponents / Explanation 1.4 – Radicals and Rational Exponents / Explanation 1.5 – Algebraic Expressions / Explanation 1.6 – Factoring / Explanation 1.7 – Rational Expressions

Explanation 1.1 – Real Numbers

Using Exponents (Operations with exponents, precedence order negative and exponent such as -2^4)

Order of Operations (Default precedence order +-x/, using fraction template, parenthesis, exponents)

Irrational Numbers (Using approximation to display decimal approximation)

Rational Representation for Repeating Decimal (Technique to represent a decimal number as a rational number, arithmetic operations)

Root on a Number Line (A drawing showing where a radical lies on a number line)

Absolute Value (Using absolute value with a variable to display definition, using the with operator, inequalities operations, absolute value with positive and negative numbers)

Absolute Value and Distance on a Number Line (Using the Solve Library Application – Using the CAS "solve" Function – [Creating an External Backup File] – Internal Backup – Alternate Internal Backup)

Programming Related Information ([Creating the "distrnl" function] – [Running "distrnl" from Program Catalog] – [Running "distrnl" from HOME view] – Delete all user variables - ["dist": #cas one-line "solve" function] – ["dist2": CAS "solve" function using input Notepad++])

Arithmetic Sequences ([Arithmetic Series Notepad++] – [A Collection of Miscellaneous Programs Notepad++] – [Arithmetic Sequence: HP Prime view] – [Evaluating the function results by entering the parameters for the function, enter the parameters as variables to recall the arithmetic nth term and arithmetic sum formula] – Arithmetic Sum using Define)

Pi Approximation (Using a measuring wheel to approximate pi, arithmetic operations)

Explanation 1.2 – Operations and Properties of Real Numbers

Addition and Subtraction Rational Numbers – Addition (Addition with a number line)

Addition and Subtraction Rational Numbers – Subtraction (Subtraction with a number line)

Graph of Function y=f1(x) (Graph of Function F1 using the Function Application Library App)

Gas Air Balloon – Subtract to Add (One of the basis for alternate approach: justification for using subtraction to do addition)

Gas Air Balloon – Add to Subtract (One of the basis for alternate approach: justification for using addition to do subtraction)

Alternate Approach – Add and Subtract (Think money, all 5 possible problem types illustrated)

Adding and Subtracting Real Numbers (Both traditional and alternate approach "think money" shown, adding comments using quotes)

Multiplication of Real Numbers (Like signs: result Positive; Unlike signs: result Negative)

Distributive Property (A drawing using signed numbers to represent the distributive property)

Expand and Factor (HP Prime CAS distributive expand and factor commands)

Division of Two Real Numbers (Like signs: result Positive; Unlike signs: result Negative; Problems involving zero: Undefined, Zero, and Indeterminate)

Multiplying and Dividing Real Numbers (Evaluating signs, examining compound – complex fraction results)

Properties of Fractions (Equivalent fractions – identity true:"1"/ false:"0", reduced form, negative numerator equivalent negative denominator , adding fractions, precedence rule gets us into trouble when not using template or parenthesis for dividing fractions, CAS screenshot - use of comDenom command to add and multiplying by variables, division by zero in denominator – answer incorrect in CAS view, we need to be aware of the domain in original and result that can produce an error in HP Prime results}

Properties of Negatives (able to use variables used to demonstrate – multiplying by -1 same as without, expanding over parenthesis with and without -1; same properties shown – this time with numbers)

Collecting Like Terms (TI-Nspire CAS uses nested parentheses rather than different grouping symbols, may need to use expand command to switch its answer to terms)

Explanation 1.3 – Integer Exponents

Multiply Exponents (Multiply positive exponents – add exponents)

Multiply Exponents (Multiply zero and negative exponents – add exponents)

Positive, Zero, Negative Exponents (Drawing illustrating negative exponents)

Zero, Negative Exponents (Variable raise to zero power using with operator and variable not equal to zero equals 1 – no possible error in this case, variable raised to zero power equal to 1 – need to watch out for $a = 0$, 0^0 is undefined, a^{-n} results in $1/a^n$)

Negative Exponents (Numbers raised to negative power – displayed as fraction, pi to negative power – display as fraction, to display as a decimal need **Shift Enter**, **approx**)

Equivalent Expressions (Fraction as variables times itself is equivalent to numerator and denominator made up of variables times themselves)

Zero, Negative Exponents (Opposite of variable raised to negative power using with to substitute in a value, negative exponents for a constant, negative exponents for a constant in the denominator, need to be aware of domain of input and result difference which result in incorrect answers in exercise, followed by rational constant to negative, additional domain problems and incorrect answers)

Additional Exponential Properties (Use the various properties of exponents to solve problems involving constants and exponents, working with variables, variables in the denominator generate warning)

Scientific Notation - Light Year Calculation (Using HP Prime's E notation for scientific notation, calculating with units of measure)

HP Prime Precision (Identity property with radicals that look impossible – both true and false, decimal representation should why we get both true and false)

Exact Mode, Display Setting, and Appropriate Mode (Displaying very large numbers, Num **Settings** default settings – [scdgts function from our program Key_user sets approximate results in history area to 5 decimal places])

Scientific Notation Program ([Adding Global program that sets number of decimal places with function scdgts] – [with the User key it sets up EEX key to toggle between Standard and Scientific Notation with scdgts function number of decimal places] – use manual Scientific Notation Num **Settings** if necessary)

Constants and Units in Calculations (Add units to our numbers – perform calculation using units – use the Convert function – [apply scdgts to the results] – use manual Scientific Notation Num **Settings** if necessary)

Significant Zeros (How we manually handle significant zeroes and how HP Prime handles significant zeros)

Explanation 1.4 – Radicals and Rational Exponents

Definition of Square Root (Using the solve command to come up with square roots of a number)

Definition of Square Root (Using the Numerical Solve, fSolve, command to come up with a square root of a number, use optional range parameters)

Principal Square Root (Using the square root symbol with a perfect square produces the square root, square root symbol with a negative produce an imaginary, square root symbol with a non-perfect square produces the input with the radical, using the **approx** function, (**wavy lines**) below **Enter** key, produces a decimal)

Principal nth Root (Drawing graph of even and odd function and their inverses)

Illustrations of Principal nth Root (Odd and Even nth roots of positive and negative numbers, even nth root of negative results in a complex number form)

Properties of Radicals (Simplification of exact radicals flawlessly, used for algebraic solutions of radicals that are not exact – switched to rational exponents)

Defining Rational Exponents using Radicals (The Properties of Radicals are often written in rational exponent form, behavior various with property and complexity of the problem, solution may or may not help us see how the Properties of Radicals is manually performed or appear to be very useful)

Removing Factors from Radicals (Works ok with constants and simple radicals, not as useful with complex problems)

Combining Like Radicals (Simplification by collecting like terms, not useful with complex problems)

Rational Exponents (work problems directly when stated with rational exponents or radicals)

Simplifying Using a Table of Powers (Use Spreadsheets Library Application to make a table for manually simplifying, you need to know mentally the powers for values described in the description)

Properties of Exponents with Rational Numbers (Using rational numbers with the properties of exponents, may need to manually work problem)

Reducing the Index (Simplest form requires the index to be reduced if possible, sometimes necessary to change to equivalent problem or work problem manually)

Simplifying Radical Expressions (Add absolute value where inside variable has an odd power)

Simplifying Radical Expressions – Different Indices (Switches result to rational exponent form, pay attention to division by zero in original problem but not result)

Rationalizing Denominator – Numerical Values (Rational radicands with multiple powers of index will turn out to be a rational answer, others will have radical converted to rational exponent form)

Rationalizing the Denominator (HP Prime CAS solution vary from manual solutions, need to work some of the solutions manually)

Explanation 1.5 – Algebraic Expressions

Adding and Subtracting Polynomials (Polynomials represent real numbers, therefore we use real number properties of Section 1.2 to perform the operations on polynomials, HP Prime drops unneeded parenthesis in the input)

Multiplying Polynomials (Multiplying Polynomials make use of the left and right distributive property, using the expand command we show how the FOIL technique works, the third entry shows us multiplying the two binomials directly, the example and exercise show the HP Prime CAS using the expand command for multiplication)

Special Products Formulas (We use the HP Prime CAS to display them, the example use the expand to directly display the results, in the exercise we extend them to using radicals and nested special products)

Explanation 1.6 – Factoring

Simplifying Expressions – Solving Algebraic Equations (Relationship between simplifying complicated expression and factoring – watch out for solutions with division by zero in original expression, finding solutions to algebraic equations by using the solve command and factoring)

Factoring Over a Set of Numbers – (Manual factor – set of integers, HP Prime CAS – set of rational numbers, using multiplication of factors to show factoring over real numbers)

Common Factors – (Factoring out the gcf, factors some results to radicals, the order of HP Prime CAS factors vary from manual factoring)

Factoring Trinomials – (Looking at leading coefficient is not necessary for HP Prime CAS)

Factoring Expressions with Fractional Exponents – (Factor out smallest power of variable – this can be a negative power, displays common factor of negative power as a positive power by displaying in the denominator, had to look at remaining numerator separately)

Algebra from Calculus – Product Rule – (Algebraic expression involving factoring fractions and negative exponents, need to handle numerator separately)

Factor by Grouping – (Factor by grouping – direct for 4-term expressions, direct for trinomials with $a > 1$, with multiple variables in 4-term expressions – HP Prime CAS needs times signs between variables otherwise appears not to factor)

Special Factoring Formulas – (Use the HP Prime CAS to display the formulas, work special formulas and nested special formulas direct)

Explanation 1.7 – Rational Expressions

Domain of Rational Expressions (Function Plot can show vertical discontinuity, the whole in the graph is not obvious – can use CAS view calculations to locate, need to be concerned about whole in original graph)

Simplifying Rational Expressions (Manual solution as mentioned earlier we will leave out restriction – HP Prime CAS we need to be concerned about restriction)

Multiplying and Dividing Rational Expressions (HP Prime CAS solutions concerned we need to concerned about value that are undefined but as we mentioned in Simplifying Rational Expressions we will recognize that they are important but not provide versions that eliminate them, division input gets changed to compound fraction form, for higher exponents it was necessary to use the simplify command – need to manually factor numerators or see in expanded form that they are equivalent)

Adding and Subtracting Rational Numbers (The manual technique for adding and subtracting rational expressions parallels how we add rational numbers, for rational expressions we use prime factorization of polynomials rather than integers, the lcm command was used with the denominators and factor command was used with the first denominator)

Adding and Subtracting Rational Expressions (Manually we parallel the technique for Adding and Subtracting Rational Numbers, with the HP Prime CAS we need to use the comDenom command followed by the factor command to change denominator into factored form, the warning here are not necessary, and then we extend addition and or subtraction to three or more terms)

Slope of Tangent and Secant Lines ([Display $f1(x)$; Use the *CalcSecTan* library to find mtan(a) at x-value of a and msec(a,h) that cuts the graph at x-value of a and h from a, msec(a,h) written as terms] – work results by using the definitions)

Creating the Library for Slopes and Equations of Secant and Tangent Lines ([Source code listing, *CalcSecTan*] – [Directions for creating the *CalcSecTan* library] – [Explanation of *CalcSecTan* five related functions msec, mtan, lineptm, secline, and tanline] – [Program library *CLSLines*; functions: slopeln, lineptm, linept1pt2, and linexy; great utility library] – [Modified *CalcSecTan* library using *CLSLines* function lineptm])

Creating the Application Libraries FncSecTanLines, FncIncDecConvUpDn, and GraphPlus ([Using Notepad++ source code and inherited Function Application Library show steps to create FncSecTanlines] [Use steps to create FncIncDecConvUpDn and GraphPlus from their Notepad++ source code])

Using the Library for Slopes and Equations of Secant and Tangent Lines ([Transferring the results of *CalcSecTan* library functions secline and tanline to Function Application variables $F2$ and $F3$])

Summary of Steps to Create and Use a Program or Library Application ([Seven steps listed])

Compound Fractions – Definition of the Derivative (Define the function $F1$ using the Function Library Application – [use the mtan function from the *CalcSecTan* Library to find the derivative] – find the derivative by built-in HP Prime CAS methods)

Compound Fractions – Quotient Rule (We have reached the point in Calculus where basic differentiation rules are being established and built-in HP Prime CAS first derivative and second derivative function can be used in solution of problems - The screenshot shows where built-in derivative with solve and *CalcSketch* Library functions produce same result; sometimes to have the result displayed as a rational expression rather than terms, we will need to use factor, comDenom with the functions, they are nested in our use for display purposes – [The xintcpt, minmax, inflpt, incdec, and concaveupdwn functions will shortly be added to the *CalcSketch* Library])

Adding Functions that Assist with Graphing and Optimization ([We will use our FncIncDecConvUpDN and GraphPlus Library Applications] – [To the *CalcSketch* Library we add xintcpt, x-intercept, minmax, candidates for minimums and maximums, inflpt, inflection points, concaveupdwn, concave up and concave down, one-line functions] - [Before discussing the *CalcSketch* Library we look at a Plot of the function, $F1$, the incdec function, a graph of the sign of the first derivative, and the concaveupdwn function, a graph of two times the sign of the second derivative])

Using the Graph and Optimization Functions of the *CalcSketch* Library ([Find candidates for minimums and maximums, HP Prime CAS produces an erroneous candidate for an inflection point, explain how our understanding of undefined alerts us to the erroneous candidate and how we identify that it is erroneous] – workout same solutions with built-in functions)

Using Tables to Verify Minimums, Maximums, and Inflection Points ([Normally we have separate table pages for minimums/maximums and inflection points, full discussion of values to use for x for minimums/maximums and inflection points will be covered in later tutorials, tables are necessary to clarify and prevent misinterpretations that can come from looking at graphs with inappropriate scales for intervals containing minimums, maximums, inflection points, wholes, sharp points, and discontinuities])

<u>Apartment Complex Revenue</u> (We discuss how arithmetic, algebra, and calculus can be used to optimize revenue generated by rent at an apartment complex - We then Define $F1$, use expand to change our model form – [Calculate the value for number of vacancies by using minmax from our *CalcSketch* Library] – [Calculate total revenue by finding $F1$ value for this number, and use the with operator to calculate the rent; graph the function and incdec using an appropriate scale and multiplier] – workout same solutions with the built-in functions - [Use FncIncDecConvUpDN Application Library] – [Look at what information GraphPlus can give us])

Works Cited

Barunik, J. (2017). *Can a stochastic cusp catastrophe model explain stock market crashes.* [online] Academia.edu. Available at: http://www.academia.edu/6213772/Can_a_stochastic_cusp_catastrophe_model_explain_stock_market_crashes [Accessed 5 Aug. 2017].

Cengagebrain.com, (2017). *978-0-495-01364-8 Interactive Video Skillbuilder CD-ROM for Stewart/Redlin/Watson's Algebra and Trigonometry, 2nd by Stewart/Redlin/Watson | CengageBrain.* [online] Available at: http://www.cengagebrain.com/shop/isbn/9780495013648 (Search the cengagebrain website or the Cengage catalog for the availability of the *Interactive Video Skillbuilder CD-ROM* for a particular title) [Accessed 5 Aug. 2017].

Education.ti.com, (2017). *The Number System: Middle Grades Math: TI Math Nspired.* [online] Available at: http://education.ti.com/en/timathnspired/us/middle-grades-math/the-number-system [Accessed 5 Aug. 2017].

Education.ti.com, (2017). *Classroom Activities: Hot Air Balloon - Texas Instruments - US.* [online] Available at: http://education.ti.com/en/us/activity/detail?id=A5C9B7396643452D80E04C1E771FB425 [Accessed 5 Aug. 2017].

Education.ti.com, (2017). *Equivalence: Algebra 1: TI Math Nspired.* [online] Available at: http://education.ti.com/en/timathnspired/us/algebra-1/equivalence [Accessed 5 Aug. 2017].

Education.ti.com, (2017). *Expressions and Equations: Middle Grades Math: TI Math Nspired.* [online] Available at: http://education.ti.com/en/timathnspired/us/middle-grades-math/expressions-and-equations [Accessed 5 Aug. 2017].

Education.ti.com, (2017). *Powers Roots and Radical Functions: Algebra 2: TI Math Nspired.* [online] Available at: http://education.ti.com/en/timathnspired/us/algebra-2/powers-roots-and-radical-functions [Accessed 5 Aug. 2017].

Education.ti.com, (2017). *Tutorials by Texas Instruments - US and Canada.* [online] Available at: http://education.ti.com/en/us/pd/online-learning/tutorials [Accessed 5 Aug. 2017].

Groups.google.com, (2017). *Google Groups.* [online] Available at: https://groups.google.com/forum/#!msg/tinspire/sJ3-S4B2XTM/xzi7GOVXudsJ [Accessed 5

Aug. 2017].

Masetti, M. (2017). *The Cosmic Distance Scale*. [online] Heasarc.nasa.gov. Available at: http://heasarc.nasa.gov/docs/cosmic/ [Accessed 5 Aug. 2017].

Piaf, (2017). *Scientific Notation Issues on Ti-Nspire - TI-Basic Developer*. [online] Tibasicdev.wikidot.com. Available at: http://tibasicdev.wikidot.com/forum/t-647506/scientific-notation-issues-on-ti-nspire [Accessed 5 Aug. 2017].

Schroeder, L. and Tan, S. (2014). *978-0-495-18618-2 WebTutor™ Advantage on Blackboard® Instant Access Code for Tan's Calculus for the Managerial, Life, and Social Sciences, 7th Edition by Tan, Soo T. | CengageBrain*. [online] Cengagebrain.com. Available at: http://www.cengagebrain.com/shop/isbn/9780495186182 (Search the cengagebrain website or the Cengage catalog for other titles in the Tan series containing *WebTutor Advantage on WebCT and Blackboard Instant Access Code* for the title's cartridge) {Accessed 16 Oct. 2014].

Wikipedia, (2017). *Carl Friedrich Gauss*. [online] Available at: http://en.wikipedia.org/wiki/Carl_Friedrich_Gauss [Accessed 5 Aug. 2017].

Made in the USA
Las Vegas, NV
02 November 2024

10969197R00171